MODEL AND MINIATURE LOCOMOTIVE CONSTRUCTION

by

Stan Bray

British Library Cataloguing-in Publication-Data: a catalogue record of this book is held
by the British Library.

First Printing 2003

ISBN No. 0-9536523-7-8

Published in Great Britain by:

Camden Miniature Steam Services
Barrow Farm, Rode, Frome, Somerset BA11 6PS
www.camdenmin.co.uk

Camden stock one of the widest selections of engineering, technical and transportation books to be found.
Write to the above address, or see the website, to obtain a copy of their latest Booklist.

Layout and Design by Camden Studios and Andrew Luckhurst, Trowbridge, Wilts.

Printed and Bound by Haven Colourprint, Pembroke Dock.

PLEASE NOTE!
In this book the author and publisher are only passing on knowledge; if you decide to build your
own model locomotive be aware that your safety, and that of others, is your responsibility,
both in the workshop and when running the locomotive.

Contents

Introduction

Building model locomotives is a fascinating hobby and the completion of a model gives a sense of satisfaction that is overwhelming. The type or scale of the model is a matter of personal preference. Some people like to make small models to run on scenic layouts, some want models that will haul passengers but are still small enough to be handled, while others like to make them as large as possible. Most people make their models from published designs, but others will fathom everything out for themselves, probably working from original works drawings. "It takes all sorts to make a world" and there is no doubt that the saying is very true when it comes to making models.

The degree of skill which an individual brings to the hobby also varies considerably. Many are or were skilled engineers, whilst others just have the urge to use tools and machines and learn as they go. Lack of knowledge at the beginning of a project does not mean an inferior end result as many a first time effort finishes as a beautiful piece of work. Everything improves with experience and this particularly applies to machining techniques. Building model locomotives requires such a wide range of skills and interests it is impossible to cover every aspect in a single volume; this book therefore aims in particular to help those whose knowledge is limited, whilst at the same time endeavouring to make suggestions and offer advice whereby the more advanced builder can improve the model under construction and any future projects.

Most builders make their models with the intention of running them, either on a scenic layout or hauling themselves and possibly others on a length of track. We must not forget however the model maker who wants to build a model, test it to ensure it works and then preserve it in the home or possibly at the office as a constant reminder of the hours of pleasure and maybe also frustration the building of it gave. There is nothing wrong in this attitude, the hobby is about doing ones own thing and enjoying it. It is to be hoped this book will help readers to do just that.

Stan Bray
Lincolnshire
March 2003

Acknowledgments

This book would not have been possible without the help of many friends in the model engineering world. The text includes ideas other than my own, which I hope have always been acknowledged. Except where otherwise acknowledged, the drawings and photographs of parts, machining set-ups etc. are my responsibility. The photographs of complete locomotives come from my own and the publisher's collections. Some have been acknowledged, but because of the passage of anno domini, in some cases it has not been possible to recall the photographer or, in a few cases, exact details of the subject. Photographers whose work appears in this book include Rob van Dort, Dr-ing. Erich von Gumpert, Jean Villette, Pierre Bender, Erik Kammeyer, Manfred Knupfer, Kozo Hiraoka, Kimio Hoshino, Angus Davis, Noel Tyler, Bill Moorewood, David Proctor, editor of *Australian Model Engineering*, Andy Luckhurst, Myford Ltd. and Woking Precision Models; to them grateful thanks is tendered. In particular thanks to Eric Kiebom for permission to use not only his photographs, but for supplying many others from his father Jan's archives. To those whose photographs have not been acknowledged, and those whose locomotive has not been identified, our apologies. If any in either category make themselves known to the publisher, every effort will be made to credit them, or describe their locomotive correctly, in future editions of this book.

Chapter 1: History - how the hobby developed

Model locomotives have been constructed since locomotives themselves were first built. Richard Trevithick built the first practical steam locomotives and there is plenty of evidence that he first built models and then transferred the knowledge gained from them to the full size. The Stephensons also built models of many of their locomotives and the railway companies, when they were formed, carried on this practice. Not every prototype was first modelled but many were and frequently models would be placed in glass cases in the booking halls of stations, to be admired by intending passengers; this was of course in the days when there was little or no danger of vandalism or theft. The practice of modelling future prototypes has continued to this day and the latest electric locomotives have been built in model form before going into production. The practice has not been confined to Great Britain, other countries who built their own locomotives carried out the practice and many of these fine examples of craftsmanship are still to be seen today in museums around the world. Often the models would be made by the railway apprentices, giving them a chance to understand how the full sized locomotive worked and improving their engineering expertise at the same time.

It was not long before people who did not actually work on the railways also decided they would like to build models and the hobby as we know it started to blossom. At first it was a rare thing for anyone to attempt to model a steam locomotive and there were several reasons for this - few in those days had the money to buy the required equipment and they probably did not have the time either as working hours were long and hard. Most who went to work before the first world war would expect to work six days a week and a ten hour day would be quite normal. Then there was the question of somewhere in which to work. Only the better off had their own houses, most people lived in a room or two let off in a house, using shared toilet and bathroom facilities so there was hardly room to set up a workshop.

Some however were able to indulge themselves and homemade models began to appear. Many of the early examples were a little primitive, to say the least, and I can well recall seeing one a few years back that had been found after being been lost for many years. It consisted of a boiler on wheels with a cylinder, the method of raising steam being to heat a block of iron until it became bright red and put this under the boiler. The heat transferred to the water and created sufficient steam to allow the model to travel round a small circle of very primitive track. Things did not stay like this all the time, and although many models bore little resemblance to a particular full sized locomotive, others were very fine replicas.

The publication of magazines such as "Model Engineer" and other similar journals increased the interest in making models, and a number of firms started to make parts for would be builders. These developed in such a way that it was possible to go to a range of establishments and purchase completed sections which could be put together to build a model. A number of firms also would supply completed models, a leader amongst these being *Bassett Lowke* who are still in business today, although no longer supplying parts for model locomotive construction.

The availability of materials led to descriptions of how to build models becoming more prevalent in magazines. Life was getting easier for the average working man and the possibility of a cheap lathe discarded by some factory or another became a reality and so the hobby developed. As is still the case, many of those interested in making model locomotives were not engineers by trade and needed to learn how to use the all-essential lathe. This machine became the workhorse of the home workshop. Few had any other machines, or possibly the room for them, even if money to purchase had been available. The result was a great deal of ingenuity coming into being in adapting the machine to carry out all sorts of operations for which it was never really intended. Even now this practice still goes on, although in these more affluent times many people manage to organise well equipped workshops.

A number of people started to produce designs that suited people in their home workshop and amongst these was Henry Greenly. He published designs in many different scales and it is greatly to his credit that many models built to those designs are still running today and some are still being built, even though he passed away many years ago. There also stepped into the arena, if we can call it that, a man who liked to be anonymous. He wrote under the name of LBSC and as he liked to be known by that non-de plume - where he is referred to in this book it will be as LBSC. He had the happy knack of making complicated operations sound easy, as well as producing many excellent designs, which, most importantly of all, worked well and, in this way, greatly encouraged many others to follow his example. His designs are still made today in their hundreds and many of the locomotives that he himself built are still running.

That the hobby owes a very great debt to LBSC, few will deny. Whether or not it would have reached its present popularity without him is debatable. Both during the latter part of his life and since his passing there have been a number of other people who have produced successful designs. Martin Evans for example has produced many different types and

Fig. 1/1 This very fine 5" gauge model was made in 1902 by the late Gordon Tidey, a very famous railway photographer in his day. It was built with the minimum of equipment, no castings were used and such things as wheel spokes were filed out. No drawings being available, trips were made to Brighton to measure up the original. This model was overhauled by the author in 1970, when it was found to be in excellent running order. The copper boiler had been riveted and silver soldered, and was still sound and steam tight. The only slight deterioration was to the platework and tender. Tinplate had been used in their construction and rust had started to set in around the seams, much of which was in treatable condition, although the cab floor and roof, and tender floor had to be replaced.

there are probably now more of his designs to be seen than those of anybody else. The late Don Young also was a prolific designer and has a large following amongst enthusiasts. Several firms who produce castings and supply materials for the hobby have their own designs available for would be builders and there are also a number of individual modellers who have done successful designs. The end result is that there are hundreds of published drawings available for the would be modeller.

Early designs, even by people like Henry Greenly and LBSC were frequently, although not always, freelance models, based on no particular full sized prototype. In recent years this has changed and modern designs are more often likely to be quite close replicas of full sized engines, although some freelance designs still appear from time to time, and these can be very popular, particularly where they are comparatively simple to build and work well. Some people like to customise a model to their own ideas and freelance designs are ideal for this purpose. Another change that has taken place in

recent years is the size of models that are generally built. Prior to World War II very few models were built to scales greater than three quarters of an inch to the foot and a very large proportion were for smaller scales than that. Once again, the reasons were cost and space. There was one other problem that affected most builders and that was size and weight. Most model locomotives are run on club tracks, which in those days were few and far between. The result was that it was necessary to transport models some distance if one wanted to run them. Ownership of motor vehicles was again limited to comparatively few and so locomotives were transported in a variety of ways, many being carried on buses and trains. Others would be placed in specially constructed trailers for pedal cycles and the lucky few might have a motorcycle and sidecar. There was no point, therefore, in building big heavy models and this situation was to remain until the early 1960s.

It is of interest to think about the type of people who like to build model locomotives. As, at least as far as the passenger hauling models are concerned, a workshop is necessary and this will need to include a lathe, we might expect it to be a hobby for practicing or retired engineers. This is not so by any means. It is quite probable that most participants have never been involved in engineering in any form. I would not try to speculate why a person should suddenly want to learn some engineering skills, sometimes at a very late age, in order to build models, but it is a fact that they do. The enthusiasts come from just about every possible trade that one can imagine and we also see more than a few disabled people taking part. There is a tremendous interest overseas which means that wherever one goes, a little searching out can find a like soul to talk to. I have a very good friend in France who is a prolific model maker. I have known him for twenty-five years. I still cannot speak French and he cannot speak English but we understand each other perfectly and can spend time in each other's company in perfect harmony. He, like many others, was not an engineer but learned to use his machines by reading and practicing. The skills required can be gained in this way by anyone, so nobody should be put off by the thought that they do not know how to use a machine.

In this way the hobby has progressed, but there has been one further development that must be mentioned. Whilst at one time all models constructed for passenger carrying work were steam driven, we now see numerous models that work via electric motors or internal combustion engines. It is, therefore, right and proper that some of this book should be devoted to this type of model making as it has now become an integral part of the hobby.

Chapter 2: Scales and Gauges - choosing the size that suits

When railways were first built the designers could not make up their minds what was the best gauge to use. The scale was no bother as it was going to be twelve inches to the foot. In Great Britain we were finally left with our present standard gauge of four feet eight and a half inches. A very odd size indeed and many people have tried to explain why this should have been decided on but nobody is really sure. There are tales that the Romans used to set the wheels of their carts to that size, or that it just happened that George Stephenson set his first railway to it. Whatever the reason in Great Britain it was adopted early in the history of railways and still remains so to this day.

Brunel was convinced that a gauge of seven feet was a far better proposition, the wide wheelbase allowing for higher speeds on curves. He was eventually over ruled, but who is to say that he was not right. The British standard gauge is used on the near parts of the Continent but in Russia they used until recently several different ones including five feet three inches. In South America and South Africa a gauge of three feet six inches is quite common. Of course we don't

know if the Romans colonised those countries and so that may account for things.

Then there were the narrow gauge lines. Laid for economy a whole variety of gauges were in use, not just in this country but all over the world. In this country at least they were built not only for economy but also because there was less need for extensive government legislation as they were classed as light railways.

As a result of all this the poor old modeller is left in quite a quandary. Not only does he or she want to model to a scale that will fit on a particular size track, but there are numerous sizes of those as well. In Great Britain the most common gauges have been '0', '1', 2½", 3½", 5" and 7¼". In general these have been accepted on the Continent but translated to metric figures. The question is:- what is the most suitable size for our particular needs?

We can start by asking what scales we need to match these standards, assuming the construction of standard gauge prototypes. "0" Gauge is nowadays classed as 32mm between the rails, having originally been 1¼". Locomotives are generally constructed at a scale of 7mm to the foot; while there are advocates of changing the gauge, because it is not consistent with that scale, the scale itself is generally accepted. It may seem slightly odd that a metric conversion is used for Imperial measurements, but in fact it makes good sense as trying to work accurately to that size in Imperial figures would result in some pretty complicated fractions of an inch, the alternative being of course to work in decimals. The gauge is really purely scenic, although many years ago there were successful attempts at hauling passengers over short distances, but these could only be classed as gimmicks.

HO gauge "Crampton" built by Francois Laluque - as can be seen from the 20p coin it is hardly large enough for passenger hauling, but is steam operated.

A model of "Green Arrow" in Gauge 1. Large enough to look good and small enough to handle easily, but only suitable for a scenic layout

Gauge "1" track is 45mm between the rails. Models were originally made to the scale of three eighths of an inch to the foot and later to ten millimetres. There has recently been a move to go back to the original figure because the metric scaling does not match the gauge. It is popular as a scenic gauge and there are many fine outdoor layouts.

This model of a narrow gauge train is scaled at 16mm to the foot and runs on 32mm gauge track. One of the Garden Gauges which are now very popular and many models are being built for them.

Possibly the smallest gauge that can be considered really suitable for hauling passengers is 2½"; models are made to a scale of half an inch to the foot so have the advantage of not being too heavy to carry around. Because of their size they are not very powerful but we do see some lovely models in that gauge. At one time it was very popular, and is now enjoying a revival after being overshadowed by the larger gauges. Its early popularity had much to do with the fact that the motor car was only a rich man's toy and the small locomotives could be transported without a car. The gauge is also used for purely scenic layouts and referred to as gauge three.

For many years 3½" was the most popular passenger hauling gauge by far. Models are built to a scale of three quarters of an inch to the foot and even the larger locomotives are not over heavy. Models will pull several people along and there are many fine designs available. It was possible to move models without a motor vehicle and it was not an

Designed by the late LBSC "Tich" is amongst the smallest designs for a 3½" gauge locomotive, and is capable of limited passenger hauling.

uncommon sight to see club members arrive at their track with the locomotive on a trailer behind an ordinary pedal cycle.

Since World War II, 5" gauge has become very popular and there are numerous designs available. Most people now have better equipped workshops in which to make larger models and most designs will haul a number of passengers with comparative ease. Unfortunately when scaling from full size no easy figure for conversion is available. The generally accepted figure is one and a sixteenth inches to the foot, or 27mm. Both are very difficult figures to work to if drawing up ones own plans. If the figure of an inch is used then the gauge should be 4.7". In the United States they have more or less settled for the gauge of 4¾" which is common, and 5" tracks are rare. As a result models in the United States are generally built to a scale of one inch to the foot.

The largest of the gauges for which models are generally built in home workshops is 7¼" which

"Jubilee" - a more powerful passenger hauling locomotive in 3½" gauge, designed by Martin Evans.

gives an approximate scale of one and half inches to the foot. This results in some very hefty models that generally require a special means of transport. There are a number of designs available, some of which are for smaller, more manageable tank engines and these prove to be very popular. Once again there is a variation in the United States with 7½" as the preferred gauge for this size of model.

With 5" gauge it is possible to ride on the tender of a large locomotive such as this "Britannia", built by Mr. Kohishi.

Another 3½" gauge locomotive, this time "Bantam Cock", a tender locomotive designed by LBSC.

If instead of a standard gauge locomotive we take a fancy to building a narrow gauge engine we are faced with a very different set of figures when it comes to scale. Generally speaking narrow gauge modellers use the same track gauges as people who build standard gauge locomotives, thus allowing access to the many society tracks throughout the country. Modelling narrow gauge prototypes means that the model is produced in a larger scale and thus results in a larger model, at least as far as height and

width are concerned. For example let us accept as a loose scale that 5" standard gauge models are one twelfth full size. (Leaving off the odd bit makes it more convenient.) The same gauge in model form but relating to a two foot narrow gauge prototype would work out at a scale of 4.8 or just over a third of full size. This is pretty massive by any standards. Fortunately it is not quite as bad as it may sound, because most (but not all) narrow gauge locomotives were considerably smaller than standard gauge types. This had to be so because the light railways had severe weight restrictions placed on them. This in itself will usually make for a slightly smaller model, but it will still be larger than a model of a standard gauge locomotive to the same gauge. The

A nice medium size 5" gauge model, of a Japanese Railways 3' 6" gauge Class 5500, built by Mr. Kohishi, to Yoichi Niizaki's design.

exception is prototypes for railways such as those in South Africa, where making a model of an express or heavy goods type locomotive, results in a hefty finished article.

What scale or gauge the prospective constructor decides on is a matter of personal choice. A nice little model running on a scenic railway can be very attractive and is something to be very proud of. It will not

An example of the hauling power of a one inch scale model. Tom Stewart driving his Pacific during efficiency trials in Ontario.

pull people along, but to some that does not matter too much, and they are more than happy to take any opportunity to run their models.

A 2½" or 3½" gauge model will not only be easier to handle, but less expensive to build and, with an understanding household authority, could spend the winter being admired on the mantelpiece. A small tank locomotive in 5" gauge may be small enough to treat in this way, but when we get to larger models and particularly narrow gauge ones then it is essential that there is somewhere to keep them and a means of both handling and transporting. It is very unlikely that anyone has a mantelpiece on which to stand a 7¼" gauge, narrow gauge, model.

There is also the question of equipment needed to build a model. A modest workshop will do for a small model, much larger premises as a rule for bigger ones. There are people who have built large models in small workshops, but the question must first be asked. Will I be able to get it out? There are several known examples of parts of workshop walls having to be removed in order to get the finished model out. Certainly if ones workshop is in the loft, the temptation to build big 7¼" gauge models should be resisted.

The question of gauge and scale must then be for the individual to decide. One other thing to be thought about is the wheel standards. By that we mean the distance between the wheels,

flange depths, width across treads etc. If the model is only ever to be used on a continuous track with no pointwork there is little to worry about. As long as the flanges of the wheels are inside the rails and the model will not fall between the gap, one can go ahead and have whatever sizes one might wish.

The modern trend with passenger hauling models, as well as scenic ones, is to run at ground level on railways with a system of turnouts. In order to negotiate these successfully certain measurements will need to be adhered to. Again, if the model is only to run on a personal layout, some licence can be taken with the figures. As long as it satisfies the individual concerned, that is all that matters. Many

Narrow gauge prototypes make larger models than standard gauge ones. John Vincent drives his 5" gauge "Wren" at the track of the Richmond Hills Live Steamers in Toronto.

When you reach 7¼" gauge, locomotives are really beginning to become large. Two engines awaiting the "off" on the Hemsby railway.

people build models to run on club tracks and whilst there are instances of variations in the standards of these, it is worthwhile using the chart on the next page and working to the measurements shown thereon.

In the case of narrow gauge models this may mean altering the format used on the original locomotive as once a model has been completed, altering the wheel standards is a major operation not to be taken on lightly. Better to get it right in the first place.

You do not have to be male to enjoy the hobby. Louise Tabiner takes her father for a trip behind a 5" gauge "Sweet Pea".

Another important factor when thinking about what to build will be the type of locomotive. Most readers will be familiar enough with the various wheel and axle arrangements. All round the world engines are referred to by these classifications, in one form or another. It's true various companies applied other types of classification and in Britain we saw 4-6-2 engines classed as A1-A3 etc. or 5XP or maybe 2F. The most common description of wheel arrangement was devised by the American, Frederic M. Whyte, and is used there and most other countries. Things differ in France and Spain where they refer to the number of axles. A 2-6-2 would be called a 1-3-1 and a 2-8-0 a 1-4-0. Anyone wishing to build a model of a German locomotive might find that it is referred to as a 3/6. The description in this case gives the number of driving or driven axles first, followed by the sum total of the carrying wheels such as bogie and pony trucks. Thus our 3/6 has six driven axles and six carrying wheels. It could therefore be a 4-6-2 but could equally as well be a 2-6-4. Quite confusing, but something that needs to be known if contemplating building a model from that country. A small tank engine of the 0-4-0 arrangement, built to the same gauge as say an express type such as a 4-6-0 will be very much smaller and easier to handle, although nowhere near as powerful. Size of the model is important and should be given a great deal of thought, it is no use building a massive great engine and being unable to either move it around or find a suitable place to store it.

An excellent example of different scales on the same gauge, on the now closed "Rode Woodland Railway" (7¼" gauge) Eric Kieboom shows his father's small standard gauge Dutch 0-4-0 tank to David Underhill on Kerr Stuart 0-6-0 tank 'Earl Haig', based on a 2' gauge prototype.

A similar size to many smaller 7¼" gauge locomotives, and much larger than the Dutch locomotive in the left hand photograph, this 'Lucky 7' to Don Young's design is actually 3½" gauge, the prototype being a large 2' gauge 2-4-4 tank loco used in Maine, U.S.A.

Garden Gauges:

For many years gauges 'O' and '1' have been popular with enthusiasts of scenic garden layouts. Recent years have seen a large increase in specialist gauges to the following standards, specially intended for this type of operation.

Scale 16mm-1 foot Gauge 32mm.	Scale 22.5mm-1 foot Gauge 32mm	Scale 22.5mm-1 foot Gauge 45mm	Scale 22.6mm-1 foot Gauge 2.5 inches

Standard gauge models to a scale of a half inch to the foot, and running on 2½" gauge track, are also sometimes used on scenic layouts.

Wheel Standards:

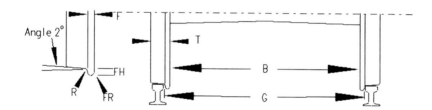

(1) as used in Great Britain and in most countries in Continental Europe

G	B	T	F	FH	FR	R
0=32mm	29mm	2.75mm	1.0mm	1.25mm	0.25mm	0.5mm
1=45mm	40mm	4.5mm	1.5mm	1.5mm	0.25mm	0.5mm
2.½"	2.281"	0.268"	0.093"	0.085"	0.020"	0.035"
3.½"	3.281"	0.375"	0.130"	0.110"	0.030"	0.050"
5.0"	4.687"	0.535"	0.190"	0.140"	0.045"	0.070"
7.¼"	6.800"	0.776"	0.270"	0.203"	0.065"	0.100"

(2) as used in the United States of America

G	B	T	F	FH	FR	R
3.5"	3.281"	0.406"	0.094"	0.094"	0.030"	0.047"
4.75"	4.437"	0.505"	0.125"	0.140"	0.040	0.062"
7.5"	6.870"	0.750"	0.156"	0.187"	0.070"	0.094"

Chapter 3: Frames

Where to start when building a locomotive is something of a moot point. Some people like to make the tender first, if the locomotive has one, on the principle that after completing the engine the tender is still a major constructional item. Others will make a start with the boiler, this being one of the less straightforward parts to build. The vast majority seem to start with the frames, which are comparatively easy and when completed things are beginning to look as though they are moving.

The frames could be described as the chassis of a locomotive as generally everything else will connect either directly or indirectly to them. There are variations in frame design depending on the prototype and anyone wishing to model for example, the 'Rocket', which it is generally agreed was the forerunner of modern steam locomotives, will find it did not have a frame in the generally accepted sense, having a substructure more akin to a wagon than a locomotive. In more modern times the *Leader* Class was another example of a locomotive without a frame in the form that we usually know, having power bogies, rather like a modern diesel engine. In between times there were some other examples. The little *Sentinel* Shunters that became popular with some of the big companies and on industrial railways also had a frame of a different type. Unless one intends to model one of these exceptions it is as well to think in terms of a solid frame acting as the main support for the model.

Plate Frames

British locomotives almost always had what are known as plate frames. These were a pair of heavy, but comparatively thin, plates of considerable depth. Holes were drilled to allow cylinders and various brackets to be bolted on; other items might well be riveted in place and there would be pieces cut out to accept various components. Usually large holes would be made through which a man could crawl to carry out maintenance and these also served to make

the frames lighter. The buffer beams and spacers keep the two frame sections correctly spaced apart, these being either fabricated or cast. Cut out sections are used to hold the horn plates, which act as supports and guides for the axle boxes. Further pieces might be cut out to clear bogie wheels, etc. This system is correct for locomotives from many parts of the world, particularly when they were British built as so many were in the early days of railways.

An example of a typical plate frame, in this case for 7¼" gauge.

Bar Frames

In the United States of America and subsequently in many European and Eastern countries so called bar frames were used. These consist of much thicker

Part of a bar frame. Although originally made from much heavier material for extra support, a great deal is then cut away to reduce weight. In this example an extension is bolted on to support a bogie.

material than the plate type and were sometimes cast; to save weight much of the material is cut away. In model form it is usual to make this type of frame from solid bars of metal rather than use a casting. With bar frames there are no horn blocks provided for the axle boxes, which simply run in wide slots cut out of the frames. In some ways, therefore, making bar frames is no harder than making the plate type as although the initial frame cutting is more difficult, work is saved on the horn blocks.

too flexible and a number of well-known model makers in the smaller gauges use gauge plate. This is a much stronger material and, whilst it is harder to work with, it is much more rigid, particularly when we think of the thin section required. It is not available in sizes for larger scale models, as it is manufactured mainly for making small tools.

Bright mild steel looks good and can give a superb finished result. It has the disadvantage that when cut

Assembled plate frames. The large cut-out at the front is to accommodate the cylinders and the angle piece on the top will support the running boards.

Making frames in this way was not just a case of an engineer fancying doing so. In Britain most tracks were well laid and very even and smooth. In some countries it was not possible for various reasons to lay rails to this standard and the rougher ride created by uneven and sometimes unstable track which caused great strain on the frames. Bar frames are more serviceable in these conditions, with plate frames tending to crack. Even on well-laid railways frames did crack from time to time and locomotives had to be withdrawn from service for repairs. Much depended on the type of locomotive, large engines being more prone to the problem than small tank engines. The situation became quite acute in parts of Scotland at one stage and attempts to introduce larger locomotives to run over track with curves of a tighter radius than normal was deemed to be the cause of the trouble.

Materials

It is most unlikely that we will be tempted to use any material other than mild steel for our frames, it is the most suitable, at least where passenger hauling models are concerned. This is not necessarily the case with smaller gauges such as '0' and '1' where very thin section mild steel can prove to be a little

it tends to twist and warp. This is due to the stresses that are built in when it is rolled being released. It is not difficult to pull it back into shape but it is as well to be prepared for the problem, which becomes more acute if the steel is machined on one edge only. If an oversized piece is used and both edges machined off, the stresses tend to level themselves out a little. On the plus side, bright steel is easy to mark out if a suitable marking out medium is applied to it. Black mild steel at first glance looks nowhere near as good as bright material. It can be cleaned up quite well if one so wishes and it is less likely to twist and warp than the bright stuff - the full sized locomotives never had frames of bright mild steel and what was good enough for them should be suitable for our model. When it is painted it is difficult to tell the difference between bright mild or black steel.

Outside Frames

The majority of locomotives have the wheels running outside the frames but there are exceptions. Some narrow gauge types will have them inside, and are naturally referred to as outside framed locomotives, a number of older type locomotives also were made this way. In most ways frame construction is the same whether the inside or outside type is to be used. They are still spaced and have horn blocks and axle boxes fitted in exactly the same way. There is usually more fine detail on outside frames as most manufacturers left the rivets used in construction proud. One major difference is that when outside frames are used the brake gear has to be fitted inside. Another major difference will be that the cranks on the wheels must come outside

Marking Out.

Before starting to mark out, no matter how this is to be done, it is essential to ensure two straight and true edges on the material being used, at right angles to each other. These will act as the datums from which all measurements are to be taken. It is essential to ensure the ends are square, if not measurements along the length will vary depending on what part

An interesting overhead view of a completed set of outside frames. The centre stay is a plain round bar and working leaf springs are fitted.
The port faces of the cylinders pass through cut-outs in the frames.

the frame, whilst the wheel itself is inside. We achieve this by having extended axles and cranks fitted to these.

Double Frames

At one time there was a fashion for fitting double frames to locomotives. Quite why this came about is difficult to say but in the period when they were made frames were of iron rather than steel and it could well be that this was not strong enough on its own. Sometimes when double frames were used one was made of wood, whether this was the inside or outside one appears to have depended on the designer and to a large extent the country of origin. Most models made with double frames use two steel sections, although no doubt if in search of authenticity wood could be used, particularly if the wooden frame was the outside one. To be correct both frames should have horn blocks and axle boxes but generally in model form they merely have these on the outside frames and clearance slots inside.

Whatever type of frame is being made it is as well if possible to obtain the best quality material one can, as this is going to be the base on which to build. When purchasing the metal for frames try and check it to ensure it is flat and square.

of the material they are taken from. Frequently drawings will show measurements from each other, i.e. from one measurement to the next This is bad practice and can result in quite a large build up of errors. For example if we have a hole at 50mm from an edge and then another hole at 10mm from that, three further holes at say 20mm and another at 10mm, we have six measurements to contend with; say a plus error of 0.5mm is made on each measurement, when we reach the end of our row of holes we will be at least 2.5mm over length or, for those working in imperial measurements, the best part of one eighth of an inch. If we make the same error but taking each of our measurements from a datum, then the final error is still only 0.5mm.

This can best be demonstrated by reference to the drawing of a 4-4-0 tender locomotive frame. The drawing has been simplified to make life easier. Suppose we decide to work from the front of the frame. We have measurements from the front to the bogie wheel centres, then to the centres of the driving wheels. It soon becomes obvious that if we make a plus error of only 0.010" on each one we will finish up requiring a piece of metal longer than we have. If we make a similar minus error there will be an extra piece on the back. Neither of which will do. The drawing shows nice round measurements that are reduced to a minimum number. Imagine what

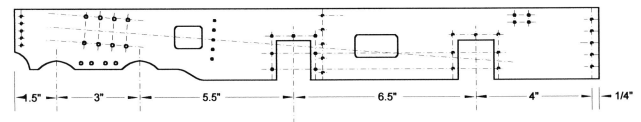

Drawing of a typical plate frame for a 4-4-0 locomotive.

will happen when other measurements are included and wheel centres, etc. are not in nice easy figures but are in tiny fractions, as they possibly will be. By measuring everything from a datum these multiple errors do not occur and any individual mistakes can be fairly easily rectified.

It may also be necessary to trim away an edge of the frame material for other reasons. Frequently the metal we buy in this day and age is sheared from a sheet. This gives a slightly flattened edge that is not suitable and must be removed. If possible it is best to mill the edges square, if not careful filing will be necessary. This at first seems a rather daunting task but it is not all that bad. One thing to be remembered when buying the frame material is that it is no good buying the exact size and then finding there is a need to trim the edges, better to get it oversize. If it is larger by a considerable amount it may be necessary to hacksaw it and all reasonable quality hacksaws allow the user to use the blade sideways which will be the way to use it on the frames. Again if a large milling machine is available life is much easier. The metal can be supported by a couple of angle plates and trimmed to size with a slitting saw. This ensures perfect accuracy as well as saving a great deal of muscle power.

One assumes that the majority of people reading this book will have at least some knowledge of marking out, but a few hints for those with limited knowledge will not come amiss. Firstly let us think of a way that means we have no need whatever to mark the frames out. If a vertical milling machine is available which is big enough to support the frame completely on the table, or if making a small scale model, one has a vertical slide for the lathe with enough cross slide travel to cover the whole frame length, then it is best not to mark out in the accepted sense. Use the machine to set the points needed for drilling, cutting out, etc. With the metal bolted firmly to the table or cross slide and very small centre drill rotating in the machine, the work can be moved by means of the handles. Using the collar graduations, it is easy to get the positions far more accurate than can reasonably be expected by normal marking out

methods. A start can be made on any holes, using the centre drill and lines to be cut can equally be marked out using either very tiny indentations, alternatively the centre drill touching the work very lightly, while rotating will engrave a line. All machines are likely to have backlash on the slides. To prevent this from causing errors, wind the handle in one direction only when measuring. For example if the handle is to be turned to the right, turn it to the left beyond the point where it needs to start, wind it in again and pick up the dial reading while the screw is felt to be under load.

Before marking out commences, particularly on bright mild steel, use some form of marking fluid. Proprietary fluids can be purchased and these are either brushed or sprayed on the metal. They have the disadvantage that when used in situations where oil is allowed to come in contact, the marking medium will frequently be washed away. A more permanent arrangement is to use copper sulphate, which can be bought in crystal or powder form at a chemist. Mix a couple of teaspoons of it in a small quantity of water (a small instant coffee jar is ideal) and allow it to dissolve. It can be painted on the metal and when dry is semi-permanent. A word of warning! If the metal is not clean and grease free the solution will not take. Wiping with rag is not sufficient. It should be given a rub over with fine emery cloth or an abrasive pad such as Scotch Bright. Black mild steel does not usually suffer from the same problem as the scriber marks show up through the black outer skin. Of course if one is marking out using the co-ordinates of a machine, there is no need to use marking fluid.

It is bad practice to mark out with the frames laying flat on a bench. They should be supported against an angle plate and either a Vernier Height Gauge or scribing block used for the marking. If a Vernier Height Gauge is available then it is easy enough to obtain the required measurements. Such tools tend to be scarce in the workshops of model engineers and most people are likely to be using a scribing block. This also infers the use of a ruler and in order to ensure accuracy a simple rule holder that will secure the rule in a vertical position should be made. The point of the scriber can then be set with confidence.

Marking out in this way requires that the frames be put on a flat level surface, ideally a very large surface plate, again not something to be found in many home workshops. If it can be obtained plate glass is a good alternative and it is just possible that a local glass merchant might be able to oblige with a suitable piece, which should be as thick as possible. Failing this good quality chipboard, again as thick as possible, can work out quite well and if it is of the type with a plastic surface so much the better. Pieces of work surfaces used for kitchens are usually quite flat and fairly easy to obtain. It is only necessary to mark one piece of metal, which can then be used as

preference is for screwing the parts together, this allows during cutting and drilling operations for them to be separated if need be. To ensure perfect accuracy when screwing them together, start by drilling the holes in both pieces to tapping size. Open the top one out to clearance size afterwards. Cut the screws to be used to length, so they do not protrude through the lower piece when assembled. The screws need not be of a large diameter and 6BA or 2.5mm will do quite well. Trying to drill the first one clearance size and then the lower one for tapping is fraught with danger and the chances of getting the required accuracy almost nil. Use two or three toolmakers' clamps to hold the frames together during the drilling operation. If rivets are used they should be countersunk and filed flush.

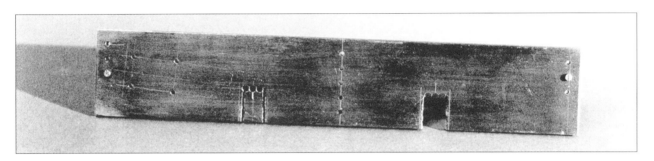

Here we see a simple frame for a narrow gauge 0-4-0 locomotive at the start of its life.
The two plates are bolted together and holes for axle boxes are in the process of being cut.

a pattern for the second side. There will probably be a few holes that differ on each side but this is easily taken care of at a later stage.

When all the lines have been scribed, centre punch for any holes that are to be drilled. Take care over this and use a magnifying glass to make sure the marks are in the right place. Lines that are scribed for the purpose of cutting should also have a series of very light centre punch marks along them, which makes them easier to see when sawing along them.

With marking out completed, drill three or four small holes using places where holes of a similar size will be on the finished frame. These are to be used to hold the second piece of frame material underneath the one that we have marked out, in order that both can be drilled and cut at the same time. It is now time to consider the best ways to put the two pieces together and there are basically two ways to hold them mechanically. They can either be riveted or screwed, the advantage of screwing being that they can be taken apart easily. Riveting will probably make a firmer job. No matter how sharp, drills tend to leave burrs where they break through; they must be removed before going any further. A personal

When all drilling and cutting operations are completed, the rivets can be drilled out and the two pieces separated.

Adhesives

While the generally accepted methods are those referred to above, modern materials allow us an extra option. We can stick the two pieces together, provided the metal is really flat. The best material to use for this purpose is double sided adhesive tape of the type used for holding down carpets. A Cyanoacrylic Adhesive (*Super Glue*) can also be used but again it is necessary to ensure both pieces of metal are perfectly flat. This method is particularly useful when making models for the smaller gauges.

While the two pieces are joined the rest of the holes can be drilled and any cutting and filing done as required. Where there are circular cut outs such as for bogies these will either need to be milled using a rotary table or chain drilled and filed. Chain drilling means drilling a row of holes just far enough from the cut line so that they will nearly but not quite touch it. The holes need to be done in such a way that they just break into each other. For example if we use 4mm holes they should be at 4mm centres so that the periphery of each will touch.

This is not quite so simple in practice as centre punches tend to have a will of their own. Mark out therefore as accurately as possible and assuming the use of 4mm diameter holes start by drilling with a 3mm drill. Open out with a 3.5 and step back and have a look. Almost certainly some holes will be closer to each other than we want. Use a suitable drill to open these so that they break into the next one, or come within a gnat's whisker of so doing. Alternatively use a small file to join them. The accurate ones can be opened with a 4mm drill, but if anything starts to go wrong do not force it. Stop and use a smaller drill or a file.

If you have been really clever and all the holes are perfectly spaced, when you get to the last hole the piece being cut out should drop away. If you are that lucky then you can probably also work miracles. It is more likely some bits will still be held together and these have to be broken or cut away. In days of yore a chisel was recommended, a normal chisel would almost certainly be too large and so it will mean making a special one from silver steel. A much easier idea is to use a sawing wire, which is sometimes known as an *Abrafile*. These are easy to buy and fit a normal hacksaw. They will cut nice neat curves and if it is a small model under construction there is no need for chain drilling as the sawing wire can be used directly to do the cutting.

A Simple Dodge

Even taking the amount of care shown above, getting the line of holes to the exact position required is not at all easy. There is a simple dodge that can be used and which works quite well. Make a centre punch from a piece of round silver steel of the same diameter as the holes to be used for chain drilling. It should be about two and a half inches in length. Take a piece of the same silver steel about half an inch shorter and turn one end down by a tiny fraction. Just about fifteen thousands of an inch or so will do. The length of the machining should be a little more in length than the thickness of the material to be chain drilled. Make sure all burrs are removed and then bind the two

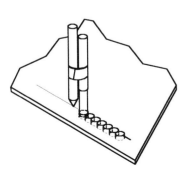

A simple way of ensuring evenly spaced holes when chain drilling.

parts together. I use masking tape for this but no doubt other materials would do as well. The section that has been machined down is set just a little lower than the point of the centre punch. Drill the first hole in the line so the machined section can slide into it, line up the centre punch and tap with a hammer. The spacing must then be right and the device will mark straight lines or curves as one wishes. In theory it should be possible to leave the smaller section in its original size. Experience, however, shows that doing so means a tendency to bind and the small amount machined off just allows easier operation. The only disadvantage of the system is the need to drill one hole and then mark the next, instead of drilling them all after marking out is completed.

Spacers (or Stretchers)

The positioning of spacers is dependent on the model under construction. Published drawings will show positions, but if modifications to the model are being made, then check that the spacers are not going to clash with anything else. If designing your own model the same applies. The spacers must clear valve gear, ash pan and any other bits that are inside the frames. They can be used as a means of holding axle pumps and so do a double job. Most models will need three or four spacers, two of which are accounted for by the buffer and drag beams. We want the others as evenly spaced along the length of the frames as possible, bearing in mind the above.

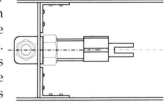

A frame stretcher can also act as a pump stay.

People making models of a prototype should, where possible, place the spacers as they were in full size.

The front end of the bar frames shown earlier, for a locomotive being built by Roger Nicholls. A specially shaped plate has been fitted to support the bogie and the buffer beam is a solid metal bar, temporarily held with Allan Screws.

They should also take the same shape as the originals. On models where one is less concerned with accuracy of appearance, ordinary flat mild steel section, or even round bar can be used as spacers. Usually frame spacers are bolted to the frames, but on small gauge models such as '0' gauge they can be soldered. It is a good idea in the smaller gauges to make simple round spacers that are easy turning exercises, and have the advantage of being easy to place, as this means as little room as possible is required. If designing ones own model, round spacers can be used as a temporary measure; if they are found to be in the way of anything else they are easily shifted.

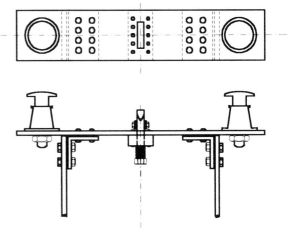

Buffer Beam construction

Additional Holes

As well as the holes required for assembly with spacers, buffer beams, etc. there will be many others on the drawing. The most obvious ones are those for bolting the cylinders in place - often these are on a line at an angle inclined towards whichever wheels will be the drivers. The line of the piston rod centre should meet the centre of the driving axle. Whilst a tiny variation probably will not matter too much it will throw things out of line and should be avoided if at all possible. When marking out it is also as well to think of how the springs will affect the position of the axle boxes (see chapter on springs); the designer of the model will usually have made the line to correspond with axle boxes resting on the keepers, but this might not be what is required.

Other extra holes will include those for brake hangers, reversing stand and valve gear bushes, these are generally straightforward. There is likely to be a hole for a fitting to hold the ash pan in position but this is best left until further progress has been made. The exact position is difficult to assess and it is easier to leave matters until the boiler can be laid on the frames and the correct position found by reference to it.

Buffer Beams

Buffer beams act as the end spacers and, in the case of a tender locomotive the rear one, which does not have any buffers as such, is known as the drag beam. On tender locomotives round rubbing plates were generally fitted and these are referred to in the chapter on tenders and plate work. There are several means of construction of the beams. Some people like to use a piece of angle and mill it to the required shape. Others prefer to use a piece of plate. In most cases small pieces of angle will be riveted to the beams at the correct spacing to take the frames and are bolted to the frames. The buffer beam will carry

a suitable hole or other fixture to hold a coupling and sometimes a lubricator is housed behind the front one. Depending on the amount of detail on the locomotive it may also carry things like brake pipes. These are additions and have no effect on its use as a spacer or a main support for the frames. It is essential to ensure that both buffer beams and the frame spacers are absolutely correct to size. For this reason the beams should be made as a pair, using one length of angle across two beams and then separating afterwards.

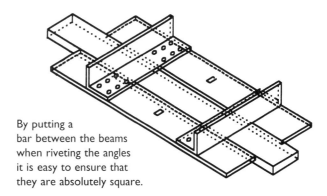

By putting a bar between the beams when riveting the angles it is easy to ensure that they are absolutely square.

One point to watch for is that the angle used is absolutely square. Most angle as purchased is certainly not, unless it has been ground. If it is found to be out of true then it can be machined to get it right. Usually it will only be necessary to machine one edge and this is a job that can be done in the four jaw chuck of the lathe. If anyone would prefer to use a milling machine it is better to bolt the angle to the table on a suitable spacer rather than try to hold it in a vice.

Generally the holes in the buffer and drag beams will be used as a jig for drilling the holes in the supporting angles. Hold both angles to the beams with toolmakers' clamps and check that they are square and the correct distance apart. Accuracy is important in the case of the latter and the measurement should be checked and rechecked with a Vernier Gauge before drilling commences. Check also that they are the same distance from each end. A sixteenth of an inch to one side will hardly notice before the beams are assembled to the frames, but fit them and the end result will be a disaster.

A full-sized example of a buffer beam;
as well as buffers and coupling hook it also supports the steam hose
for train heating and vacuum hoses for train braking.

Once the angles are drilled and thoroughly deburred, and assuming all other holes required in the beams have been made, the parts can be riveted together. Some locomotives would have no trace of rivets showing, they were carefully countersunk and

ground flush, any witness marks were filled before painting. Other companies left the round snap heads of the rivets showing and made a feature of them. If this example is to be followed it is essential that the rivets are carefully placed and holes drilled exactly in line.

To ensure that holes are drilled in line, either mount them on the table of a milling machine, or bolt them to the cross slide of a lathe. Use a nice sharp centre drill to ensure a good start is made for the subsequent drilling operations. Trying to scribe lines and centre punch hole positions will almost invariably result in uneven rows of holes and it is best not to attempt it.

The actual riveting operation can be carried out by supporting a dolly in a vice and closing the rivets with a hammer. Use a ball pein hammer first of all, finishing with a dolly if the rivets are to be left proud. Countersunk rivets are filed flush after they are closed. An ordinary countersink invariably appears to leave a witness mark when rivets are closed. This can be avoided by using a drill twice the diameter of the rivet shank and just sinking it a fraction deeper than the angled section. The rivet will then fill the space completely, when hammered over and it should be possible to file it flush and leave no trace of the countersunk edges.

If snap rivets are used and left as part of the finished appearance, take care that they are the correct size as oversized rivets spoil many models. The only way to be certain they are right for an actual prototype is to

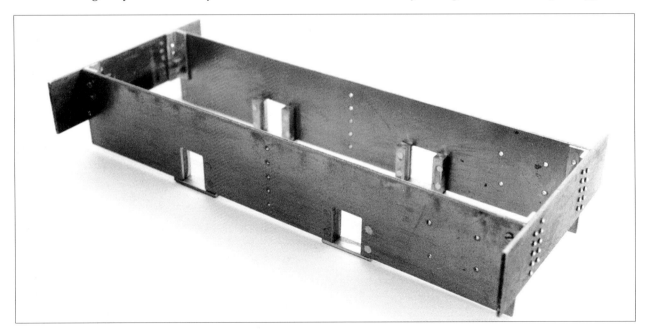

The plate frames shown earlier now fitted with buffer beams. In this case hornblocks are replaced with strips of metal.
The pattern of rivets on the buffer beams is correct to prototype, but the inner ones offer no support and are for cosmetic purposes only.

Another full size buffer beam showing clearly the rivet pattern. The screwed on step on top of the buffer is to assist the crew.

measure the original and that is not a very practical proposition. Think in terms of rivets for heavy work such as buffer beams being around an inch in thickness and use this as a rough guide to get a reasonable size for the model. It is standard engineering practice to use rivets of one and half times the diameter of the metal that is being riveted.

Check with photographs to see how the buffer beams looked on an original. Try and follow the

This very fine example of a locomotive frame by Tony Meek shows exactly how to fit a smokebox door.

pattern of rivets as closely as possible. It may mean that you have to deviate from the drawing of the model by adding extra rivets, in which case almost certainly it will be possible to use smaller ones than those specified, at closer spacings.

Drag Beams

Although the drag beam as used on tender locomotives is similar in some ways to a buffer beam it should be constructed differently. Many drawings will show the same form of construction, but assuming our locomotive is to pull a heavy load, additional strength is needed. This can be obtained by placing

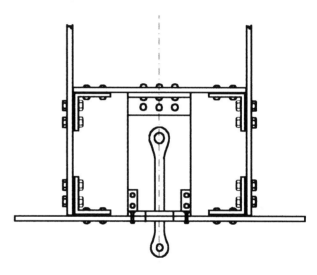

Extra support should be provided
for Drag Beams.

short lengths of angle lengthways and bolting them to the frames giving considerable extra strength. When building the tender this extra strength construction should be repeated as far as is practical on the tender front beam. There is little point in making a nice secure drag beam to a locomotive if there is a danger of pulling out the tender beam. A similar form of construction should be applied to the rear buffer beam on a tank locomotive.

Variations with Bar Frames

It has already been pointed out how the construction of bar frames varies from plate frame. There is also, more often than not, a variation in the fixing of buffer beams as well, and sometimes buffer beams will be bolted directly into the frame. Where rivets are desirable, whether for the sake of appearance or necessity in the construction of a frame, a great deal of care must be taken to get the holes for them a good fit, possibly by reaming them. On a thin plate a rivet will spread and fill a hole, but this does not always happen on thicker material. The result is that the rivet grips only at the two extremities, creating a weakness, hence the need for a particularly good fit.

Assembly

When all the parts are completed the frames can be assembled temporarily with a few screws. There is no point in making a permanent job as they will need to be taken apart from time to time to check the correct fit of other parts. They should also be cleaned and finished by draw filing the edges and deburring where necessary so that everything is as ready as it can be when the time comes for final assembly.

Buffers

Buffers are generally made from stock material and are a simple turning exercise, in fact for an absolute beginner to machining they are the ideal exercise. They are made in two sections, the head and the stock, the latter sometimes, but not often, being machined from a casting. The easiest way to make them is to machine a threaded section on the end of the stocks and pass this through the buffer beam, securing them with a nut behind the beam. This practice was not general in full size but, at the same time, it was not entirely unknown.

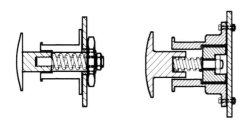

Two ways of making buffers.
The left view shows the easiest method, with the heads secured with a nut behind the beams. The right shows a method that conceals the fitting.

The other way is to make a recess in the rear of the stock and to attach the stem of the head to this, the stocks can be bolted to the buffer beams and the correct number of bolts for the particular prototype used. Even if the idea of making buffers this way does not appeal, dummy bolts should be fitted to make it appear that the buffers are bolted on rather than secured from behind.

Unless a casting is used, steel is the material generally used for buffers. It is always nice to have highly polished heads and it must be agreed that they do look good. It is certainly something not seen in practice, except possibly in a museum or in the

days years ago when the companies used to hold exhibitions and would polish locomotives especially for the show. In that case all sort of unusual bits used to get polished. Mostly the heads were either painted black or just left to rust. In either case a conspicuous round piece would appear in the middle where they were pushed against rolling stock. It may not be generally realised that when passenger or fast goods trains were coupled up, the buffers were always touching each other, the springing of them being sufficient to allow the vehicles to negotiate bends. The exception was the loose couple goods train where a gap was left between each wagon. When the locomotive slowed to a stop the wagons would continue onwards, resulting in the clanging sound of each wagon striking the one in front in succession. It did not stop there as having closed up the buffer springing would then gradually pull them apart again and as the springs reached their maximum tension they would again close up. When it is realised that there might be forty or more wagons in such a train the din created can be imagined. The guard, who always travelled in the rear soon learned to hold on tight to some immovable object, to prevent himself being thrown backwards and forwards. Such happenings are unlikely on our models and so the ring of wear in the centre of the buffers will need to be induced with a bit of fine emery cloth. Not as much fun, but definitely quieter and safer.

Couplings

In the main a locomotive will use either a screw or a three-link coupling. The latter mainly confined to industrial types, the screw is used as a means of closing the stock tight. Both types are fairly easy to make and are more or less filing jobs with a little turning involved, with the addition in the case of the screw link, of some threading operations. They fit as a rule through slots in the buffer beam and generally will be secured with a spring and a nut. The spring should be fairly substantial otherwise the coupling might flop about a bit. Readers in America and other countries and those amongst us who like to model narrow gauge models will find that other types of

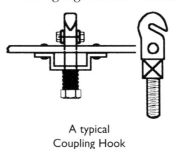

A typical
Coupling Hook

couplings may be called for. Usually these are either an automatic or semi-automatic type and the degree of difficulty in making them depends on how close to the real thing one wishes to get.

Similar couplings have been used on some British express trains since the late nineteen thirties.

Chapter 4: Springs - easing the bumps

A locomotive can be built without any form of suspension and there is no reason why it should not run well providing the track is smooth and even. In the garden gauges many models have no springing whatever and cause no problems. There are probably two reasons for this, firstly the models have short wheel bases which makes them able to follow the rail contours and secondly the small section rail lends itself to being laid evenly. Even so running is improved dramatically if the locomotive axles are sprung, even in these small gauges.

The track for larger gauge models can suffer from a whole variety of problems, it may be very well laid in the first place but because of its weight alone it will be prone to movement. Many ground level tracks are laid on a concrete base and this in some ways will help, even so, the ground the track base is laid on, or in which the supporting pillars of a raised track are set, is in itself quite likely to suffer movement with extremes of weather. If one takes a look at a large concrete area, laid by a professional, it will be seen that it is always laid in sections and that in between each is some form of soft material to take care of the movement. Over a period the sections will become uneven, probably only a fraction of an inch or so difference, but if a track was laid on it would be more than sufficient to cause a derailment. Miniature railways are not usually laid in large sections but even so, suppose that there is a change of height of even a sixteenth of an inch, depending on the size of wheel negotiating it, this could result in a derailment, if the wheelbase of the locomotive was fixed. As one wheel lifted to make contact with the rail, one or more would be lifted clear of the rails. Flanges take care of the problem to some degree and on a privately owned track the owner could have very deep flanged wheels to take care of the unevenness. Take the model to another track somewhere else and it will probably be found that the extra deep flanges will foul the sleepers and they certainly will not negotiate standard pointwork. When springs are fitted they lift or allow the wheels to drop as required and ensure they all stay in contact with the rail, except in the most extreme circumstances. For good running, therefore, good suspension is also needed.

Even very early locomotives had springing, although sometimes it was rather primitive. The very nature of locomotive construction means that it is not possible to spring wheels individually as it is

on a motor car and so the axle boxes are sprung, the springing working as a pair on an axle. Two types of spring are used, coil and leaf and sometimes there is some form of compensating device which usually consists of a bar connecting the springs on one side, so that as one lifts greater pressure is exerted on the other.

Coil Springs

Where driving and coupled wheels are concerned the coil spring was for many years the most popular amongst modellers. In recent years with the

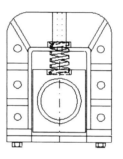 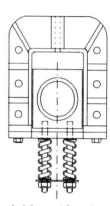

Spring on top of the axlebox, a useful arrangement for small models

Axlebox with springs fitted underneath

Coil springs fitted under an axlebox on a locomotive being built by Tony Meek. It is also worth noting the careful attention paid to detail on the axlebox covers.

improvement of facilities and skills, plus the availability of better materials, leaf springs have come into their own. Not all full sized engines had leaf springs and so even when keeping strictly to prototype some models will still use coil springs. It depends on the size of the model as to how coil springs are fitted. On small scale models it is often the case that one end is recessed in a small hole in the top of the axle box and the other end in either the hornblock, or a bar of metal riveted to the frames; on larger models they are generally located on pegs screwed to the underside of the axle boxes, passing through the keeper plate. The springs are mounted below the keeper and kept in place with nuts, which are also used as a means of adjustment. A similar arrangement is used for bogie and pony trucks. When fitting coil springs it is essential to ensure that the spring ends are ground flush and square and small washers should be put on the ends.

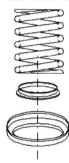

Coil springs should always be seated on washers such as these

Most people probably purchase their coil springs and most commercial drawings specify the size required. The person who likes to make everything will find that suitable spring wire can be obtained from shops dealing in model aircraft. It can be wound round a suitable sized former while rotating the lathe by hand. The wire is kept taunt by being held firmly in a pair of bull nosed pliers, or a similar instrument of torture and pulled hard away from the chuck to keep it at full stretch. For a more refined spring, set the lathe as though to cut a very coarse screw thread and feed the wire through the tool post, keeping it taunt in the same way. As the lathe rotates the wire will move smoothly along the former in nice neat evenly spaced coils. The former needs to be of a smaller diameter than the inside diameter of the spring being wound as when the tension on the wire is released the coils expand slightly.

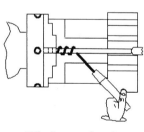

Winding a coil spring in the lathe

Dummy Leaf Springs

For those not wanting to try and make working leaf springs it is possible to cheat a little. Cast springs can be bought and a coil spring set inside and below. The

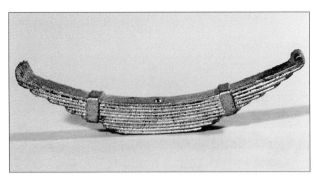

A dummy leaf spring cast from aluminium - used in conjunction with a coil spring it looks quite effective.

action is the same as for a working leaf spring and if you don't tell anyone what you have done it will take quite an expert to find out. If you can't buy the cast springs then suitable dummies are easily made either by fabricating or filing them from solid metal.

Working Leaf Springs

While going to the trouble of making dummy leaf springs it is almost as quick to make working ones, although as usual there is a snag. The springs on most models will be very modest in length and suppose we take a length of spring steel of suitable thickness, which just for the purpose of the exercise is say two inches long and 1/32" thick, possibly 3/8" or even 1/2" wide. Try and flex it and it is to say the least difficult, and yet a set of springs will consist of at least five or six or more pieces, each progressively shorter than the last. The shorter they are the harder it is to bend them. It becomes obvious that with the weight of either a model locomotive or tender, no unevenness in the track will cause the spring to flex and so we might just as well not bother. It is time to start cheating.

Spring Design

We have to start by working out the deflection needed and we do that as follows. Suppose the full sized locomotive had a deflection of three inches, which is a reasonable average, then we need to work out the linear scale of that deflection. This is simple enough just multiply our three inches by the scale being used. For example if the model is one-twelfth scale multiply 3 x 1/12 and we have a deflection of as near as makes no difference 0.25 inches. There is little point in setting about working out the comparison of the model spring strength with the full size but the comparative weights of model and full size will give some idea of what we are looking for. The formula is similar in that the weight of the original is divided by the linear scale cubed, i.e. in the case of a hundred ton locomotive, 100 divided by 12 x12 x12 lbs. It all starts to get very complicated particularly as we then have to involve a formula called *Young's Modulus of Elasticity*. So, dear reader, please just take it that scale springs will on average be at the minimum two thirds stronger than required.

A common way to set about getting the required result is to go for cheating in a big way by making just the top leaf, or possibly the top two, out of spring steel and to use a material with little resistance for the lower ones; if we accept a figure that a scale spring is about two thirds stronger than needed, with a six leaf spring set, two leaves work out about right. We have to take into account the other material, which has some resistance, and so probably a single scale spring is even better. The result is not going to be exact but should be near enough. The material generally chosen as a substitute is *Tufnol* and it needs to be treated before it is used. As sold by the model trade it is in strips that need to be shaped to take up the formation of the proposed spring in order to get the right appearance. It is necessary to heat the material almost to the point of burning it whilst keeping it under pressure to form it. Most people appear to cut it to the required lengths, put it in a round tin of as near the correct diameter to obtain as near the same curvature as possible and then to heat it until it starts to go black. The idea works admirably well and when assembled the difference between that and a proper spring is hard to tell. *Tufnol* also has some springing quality which should be considered when deciding the amount of deflection required.

A development of the idea was used by a friend called Tony Meek, a number of examples of whose excellent workmanship are to be seen in this book, who made a special former consisting of two parts. The material is clamped in this and heated on a hot plate of an electric stove and the end result is not just a curved section but also one that is correctly shaped for the springs.

It is possible to make acceptable springs without the use of spring steel at all. Hard rolled brass is an excellent material as is nickel silver, the latter being particularly easy to work with. Using thinner section metal also helps with the number of leaves and they can be doubled to get the right appearance, when painted it is difficult to tell the difference. Another useful material is the spring steel strip sometimes used for binding wooden crates together. It is not generally thick enough to be used as a single leaf but can be doubled as suggested above and is fairly near the strength required for model work.

Leaf springs are held together as a unit via a buckle in the centre from which an extension presses on the

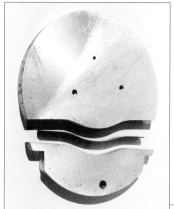

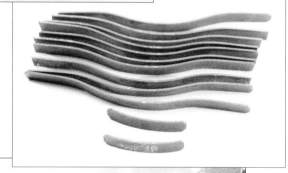

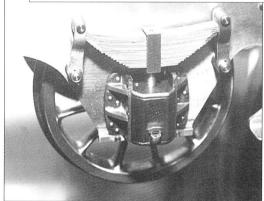

Left: The special tool made by Tony Meek for bending Tufnol used for leaf springs. Below: The Tufnol after treatment in the tool, awaiting trimming to length. Bottom: A complete example of a tender axlebox showing clearly the brackets and hangers required.

axle box; a rod goes through holes in the spring to prevent sideways movement, and retaining brackets at each end. The latter are bolted via an arm to the chassis. The end of the arm is threaded and nuts are used to obtain the correct tension. Generally the arm runs through a guide to prevent it flexing under load. The end brackets are of various types, each company or manufacturer using their own pet scheme. Mostly they take the form of a curved

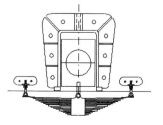
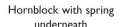

Hornblock with spring
underneath

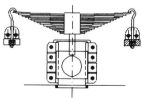

Hornblock with spring
above

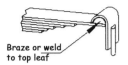

Braze or weld
to top leaf

Just two of the methods
that can be used for
securing the ends
of springs.

section which presses down on the spring but in some cases, particularly in the United States, the arm went through a slot in the top spring and was fixed with a wedge.

Making holes in spring steel is not as difficult as it sounds and holes can be punched in it fairly easily as long as a quick sharp movement is used. A simple tool is required to help line up the spring and also to secure it whilst it is punched, once this is made any number and size of springs can be dealt with. The device consists of a metal block with a recess to accept the spring and a plate to line it up correctly. The punch goes through a hole in the main block and should be kept as short as possible. A quick blow with a hammer does the job, if there is a big difference in the size and shape of the holes being punched it may be necessary to make a couple to cover the different sizes. If the idea of making a tool as described seems daunting the job can be done

by using a punch to the shape of the hole and a block of lead. The spring material is laid on the lead, which has to be hammered flat, the punch is lined up in the correct position and ensuring it is at ninety degrees, it is struck smartly with a fairly large hammer. It must be done in one blow and even then there is the danger of the punch moving, so if a guide can be made it is obviously better.

Coil Springs

Coil springs are fitted as mentioned previously either above or below the axle boxes, and the same formula can be used for obtaining the deflection required. In theory, therefore, if a full sized locomotive had coil springs using material that was one inch diameter, the model built to 1/12th scale will need springs made with wire 1/12th", which works out to around 2mm diameter or 14 SWG. This is not a bad figure but is a little strong for our purposes and it is best to aim at around two thirds of that figure, which will give us roughly a wire of 1/16" or 1.5mm diameter. It is impossible to obtain correct figures but is a reasonable compromise that will work quite well. The number of coils per inch of spring also plays an important part but an average of eight

There are numerous ways of making spring hangers and the drawings above show just two. This photograph of a sprung bogie on a Polish locomotive shows yet another method. It is also worth examining the photograph with reference to the chapter on Bogies as it shows a typical example of the construction methods involved.

works quite well. The outside diameter will depend on the size and scale of the model as well, and can be reduced by scaling directly from the original. As with leaf springs it is all a bit hit and miss and so a reasonable compromise must be looked for. It is worth having in mind the fact that most model locomotives have springing that is far too strong.

Many models run with axle boxes at their lowest point in the hornblocks and this is not correct. The springs are not only there to take care of bumps in the track but also any low points and cannot do that if the axle box is already at its lowest point. Ideally the bottom of the axlebox should be a little way up the hornblocks when in normal position, the spring tension taking care of the position, which should be set when the boiler is full in the case of a steam locomotive.

Balance

Whatever type of springing is used just tightening a nut to get the tension is to say the least a bit hit and miss. If the springs are all differing tensions then while one wheel may lift or drop at an uneven piece of track another may not. This will have the effect of taking the weight off one or more of the coupled wheels causing the engine to lose some adhesion. For good running it is essential that all the springs are at an equal tension with maybe the tiniest bit extra on the drivers. Checking that they are the same is easy and all that is required is a spring balance of the type used at one time for weighing sacks, and nowadays frequently used by amateur fishermen to weigh their catch. It consists of a long bar which is graduated and has a sprung hook protruding from the bottom which moves when a weight is put on it, this makes a pointer register on the scale. Make a simple cradle to fit on the hook, which will go onto the locomotive wheels. Lift the balance and see what weight is required to raise the wheel by the tiniest fraction. Check the amount of lift with a feeler gauge. Check the next wheel and adjust the springs until exactly the same tension gives exactly the same lift, continue until all are the same. The same principle can be used on bogie and pony wheels and on tenders; getting the balance right really does make a difference to the operation of a locomotive.

Springs For Other Purposes

Springs are needed for other purposes on a locomotive, a few examples being safety valves, fire hole door catches and reversing poles or levers. These do not need to be wound from steel spring wire and in some cases such as the safety valve should not be. Stainless steel, bronze or nickel silver

wire will all wind into decent, non-rusting springs, but a slightly thicker section is required than would be the case with spring steel; most designs will specify or suggest the type of spring to be used. Many suppliers of model engineering materials will stock springs that are suitable for our purposes and these frequently will need to be cut to length. With thin springs this can often be done with a pair of wire cutters. Thicker ones can be ground to thin down one of the coils and then snapped to size. All springs should be flat at the top and bottom and if they are self wound or shortened this will have to be done by the modeller. The easiest way to do this is to drill a hole the size of the outside diameter of the spring in a piece of mild steel bar. Slip the spring in it and then take it to the grindstone and grind it flat. Do not try and hold a spring by hand when grinding the end flat, there is every chance of it being snatched and flying away to the darkest corner of the workshop. Worse still there is every chance of serious cuts to the hand. The hole in the bar method of holding the spring is also useful for getting springs to the correct length. Drill the hole and then flatten it with a "D" bit to the exact depth of the spring length required. Simply grind the spring until it is level with the top of the hole and it will not only be the right length but the end will also be square.

A well sprung locomotive on a well laid track. G.M. Cashmore's 5" gauge L.N.W.R. "George the Fifth" on the Colney Heath Track in the 1950s. Note driver's attire, the lack of safety rails, or footboard on the passenger trolley - the latter would cause safety inspectors palpitations in the safety conscious twenty-first century.

To my embarrassment I have no record of the builder of this beautiful fine scale model of an early American 2-6-0, the location or the track gauge, although this looks to be 7¼".
However this photograph is included as the leaf spring on the driving axle can be clearly seen, and that on the front coupled wheel is just visible. This engine has compensated springing and the pivoted bar between the driving and rear coupled axle springs can also be seen.

Based on a Henry Greenly design, the George Smith's 7¼" gauge Southern 'Mogul' was frequently used on roughly laid portable tracks with complete safety, a tribute to the builder's skill in getting the suspension just right.
Here Geoff Asplin speeds along such a track at the Guildford MES clubground, before a permanent 7¼" gauge track was laid there.

Chapter 5: Wheels

A good set of well-finished wheels will not only improve the performance of a model, but can also enhance its appearance. Badly finished wheels on a nice model not only will mean rough riding but also are akin to someone turned out in good quality, clean and smart clothing and wearing dirty, tatty shoes.

Types of Wheels.

A steam locomotive will have varying types of wheels depending of course on the prototype. A simple tank engine (we might even quote "Thomas" as an example) will have only driving and coupled wheels. An express passenger engine could also have bogie and trailing wheels as well. Then if the model has a tender this too will need wheels. Bogie and trailing wheels as well as those of a tender will generally be straightforward to machine and we will come to that part of the story shortly. Most wheels will have spokes, but just occasionally they will be solid, or perhaps solid with some holes in them. This type of wheel was fairly common on the tenders of express locomotives, particularly those of the *London and North Eastern Railway*. Sometimes they would also be used on narrow gauge engines, where frequently even the driving wheels took this form. Large driving and coupled wheels will generally be spoked although there are some locomotives that have wheels of a design that is not spoked.

Non Steam Locomotives

Non steam locomotives of the bogie type will usually have solid wheels, possibly with some small holes in them. Spoked wheels are generally only seen on fixed wheelbase diesel and electric locomotives, including some very early types where wheel arrangements were similar to those of steam engines which included coupled and bogie wheels.

Driving and Coupled Wheels

Driving and coupled wheels look similar to each other but as a rule there are differences in the way they are balanced, which will vary considerably from locomotive to locomotive. Frequently the expression "drivers" or "driving wheels" is used to include all the large wheels on a steam locomotive, but this is not correct. Those names say what they mean, the pistons drive on to the drivers and the others are coupled to those drivers with a coupling rod in order to get better adhesion. The wheels are balanced with weights that in full-sized practice are bolted in position after being carefully checked as to the amount of weight needed. They are there to counterbalance the forces on the cranks of the driving wheels, generated by the reciprocating motion of the pistons. The coupled wheels as opposed to the drivers usually need the weights in a different position in order to function properly. In

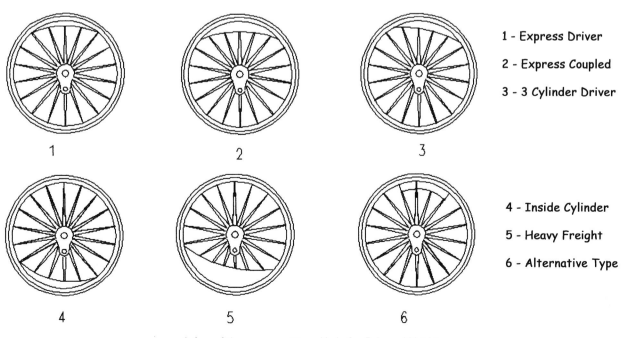

1 - Express Driver

2 - Express Coupled

3 - 3 Cylinder Driver

4 - Inside Cylinder

5 - Heavy Freight

6 - Alternative Type

A few of the many positions likely for Balance Weights.

the case of an inside cylinder engine the driving wheel balance weight will sometimes be as much as ninety or even a hundred and eighty degrees to those on the coupled wheels. Some heavy goods locomotives had large balance weights, while express passenger types generally had smaller ones. Those on driving wheels will often vary in size to the coupled ones and shapes of the weights varied according to the company that built the prototypes.

Most model wheels are bought as castings and have the weights cast in. Frequently suppliers only make one pattern and so, unless one is willing to machine out the weights and re-build them, the modeller is stuck with what is available. This probably matters little as most people who look at the model will not know the difference anyway. Sometimes wheels, when bought as a set, have the weights cast in more or less the right places and should they be purchased in this way care must be taken to ensure that the correct wheel is used in the right place. For anyone wanting to make a model that is as near to scale as possible it will in many cases be necessary to make ones own patterns for the wheel castings. Most people will be happy to compromise but it is a very valid point to look for when buying the castings.

Spokes

Model wheels are almost invariably cast with triangular spokes and for models of many locomotives this is not correct, many full sized locomotives had oval spokes of one form or another, while others had round ones. Casting the correct shape of spoke is difficult and therefore expensive and as far as a supplier is concerned a correctly shaped spoke on a wheel can be something of a liability, particularly as every builder was likely to have used a different shape. Suppliers to the model trade work to very tight budgets, frequently patterns

On the left, the shape of spokes as usually found on cast wheels for models.
On the right the shape more likely to be true to prototype.

for a wheel will be made and less than a dozen sets of those castings sold in a score of years. This means that making true type patterns is generally not a practical proposition and, where possible, a single pattern of the correct size will have to do for several types of model and driving and coupled wheels as well, this is one reason for the use of triangular spokes. It is far easier for both pattern maker and founder if these are used as, when the correct shape is to be moulded, the pattern needs to be split. Rather like wrongly positioned balance weights, for

the average modeller wheels with triangular shaped spokes might be quite satisfactory. When the model is finished and painted, the shape of the spoke is hardly noticeable, and they can be left in that form as it is doubtful if many people would realise that they are wrong. Alternatively it is possible with careful workmanship to re-shape them from the back and to get something like the correct profile. It requires a great deal of work and much will depend on how close to reality an individual wishes to be.

Whatever is decided regarding the shape, it is essential that the spokes on all wheels should be well cleaned with a file, to get them as smooth as possible and to remove all flash. The appearance of wheels is important whether they are to be correct to scale or not. Where spokes and rims are pitted it is worthwhile at this stage filling the holes with a strong filling medium, such as a car body filler. Alternatively it is possible to buy good quality metal filler designed for engineering purposes. This sets almost as hard as the original metal and it is fairly

Start by machining the back of the casting, which can be mounted in either a three or four jaw truck, as long as it runs true. Machine to finished size, remembering to make allowances for any unevenness on the front of the wheel casting. Without removing the casting from the chuck, drill and bore to fit the axle.

easy to use. After filling the holes and letting the filler set, the spokes, rims etc. should be cleaned with a file and emery paper to get as good a finish as practical. Further cleaning work will be necessary before painting but starting at this stage makes life much easier later on.

Machining

Many people have their own ideas on machining wheel castings but for the newcomer to the hobby it is as well to begin with the back. Mount the wheel either in a four jaw chuck, gripping it by the tread, or alternatively mount it on a faceplate. To do this may require packing to be inserted between the faceplate and the spokes, as the boss for the axles and crank will stand proud and if not packed the casting may not lie flat. It might be possible to use a three jaw chuck, but it is necessary to ensure the casting is running as near true as possible. It may also be necessary to use some extra packing material to ensure that it is mounted parallel to either the chuck body or faceplate as frequently castings can vary in width. Check each one with a pair of callipers before mounting and once you are sure it is mounted accurately, face across it until it is smooth, if need be machine the back of the spokes.

When the back is finished, turn the casting round and mount on a mandrel with a backing plate. In the photograph a smallish 3½" gauge driving wheel is being machined on a three jaw chuck. Larger wheels require the use of a four jaw chuck or faceplate; either way drill the backing plate to accept the mandrel after facing it across which ensures the casting will run true. Note that there are no balance weights on the wheel - these will be fitted later in the correct place and to the correct size.

They should be recessed and there are examples of castings, where again to save cost, the pattern maker has made the spokes lie flush with the rim and boss at the back. A few patterns, although not as many now as there were some years ago, have the back filled in completely, in which case it is essential that this metal is machined away until all the spokes can be seen.

Axle Holes

Before each casting is removed from its mounting, drill and bore it for the axle. In theory it should be possible to start with a centre drill, continue with a drill and finish with a reamer. This assumes that everything is going to happen in a perfect manner; unfortunately life is not always like that. The centre drill will start the hole accurately enough but many things can go wrong when it comes to drilling. There are a whole host of reasons why a drill will run out of true - bad sharpening, a slight hard spot in the casting, trying to force the drill too fast, to mention just three. Some improvement can be made if a stub drill is used as there is less of it to flex and wander, but this is still not an ideal solution. If a hole is drilled and is not accurate, a reamer will never bring it back to where it should be and the only real answer to ensure absolute accuracy is to bore the hole. We get used to the idea of only boring either large diameter or long holes, but there is no reason why boring should not apply to smaller ones. A tiny boring bar can be made from silver steel, or an old centre drill ground to the required shape. The actual boring operation will not take long, a smaller hole having, of course, been drilled first to allow the tool access. If you do not fancy your chances of getting all the holes the same diameter by boring, then by all means finish with a reamer. If the undersized hole is true the reamer will follow the line and it too will remain true. Reaming should not really be necessary, as long as the tool is brought to exactly the same dial reading each time the holes should all be the same. The best way to check for the correct finished hole diameter is with a gauge made from a specially machined steel bar of the correct diameter.

The Treads and Flanges

Once all the wheels have been machined on the back a mandrel should be made up on which they can be mounted for machining the outer face, the rims and treads. The form of this mandrel will to some extent depend on the size of wheel. It needs to have a nicely fitting spigot to go in the axle hole and either a tapped hole for a bolt or a threaded end to accept a nut. It should be made of material of sufficient diameter to support the rear of the wheel while it is being machined, alternatively make up a separate back plate for the purpose.

The back of a small bogie wheel being machined; note how it has been necessary to machine a step, to break into the spokes as well as to conform to the correct rear profile of the wheel.

A good way to start the actual machining process is to machine the outer edge of the flange to nearly the correct size. Then machine the rim nearly to size and square - at this point DO NOT try and finish it. Attempting to taper the tread and get it to the correct diameter at this stage is a waste of time, as trying to return the top slide, which will need to be set over for the operation to its original position each time, is near impossible.

The next operation will be to machine the tread diameter, including the taper if required and each wheel can be returned to the mandrel for this. It is

then possible to work purely on top slide settings, instead of having to juggle between those and the cross slide. There are several schools of thought on how useful a tapered tread is on a model, some people believe it to be a waste of time. It may be that this sort of thinking goes back to many years ago when most tracks ran in a straight line and there were no curves to be negotiated. In full sized practice the tread is used to assist the locomotive around corners, in the same manner that a differential gear does on a motor car, and it will do exactly the same for a model. It is worth doing and improves the running quality of the model as well as its appearance. With the tread completed, finish the rim to size and shape, taking care to remove all burrs.

The final operation is to machine the bosses where the crank pin will fit and this can be done with the wheel in a chuck gripped by the flange. Fit pieces of paper or soft metal shims between the chuck jaws and casting to prevent damage. Ensure the wheel is pushed hard against the step in the chuck jaws and then work to dial measurements rather than trying to use a rule. Once a dial setting has been established as a position for a measurement then that must be adhered to, so make sure when doing so that the handles are wound back sufficiently for any backlash in the lead screws to be taken up, in order that the slide is under load when the measurement is noted. It is preferable to write down the markings to which you are working as somebody is always likely to interrupt proceedings and the number forgotten, so make a list of readings for flange diameter and thickness, wheel width and tread minimum and maximum diameters. At the same time as the boss is machined the outer edge of the rim can also be reduced to size.

Crank pin holes must be positioned correctly and at ninety degrees to the back of the wheel, a simple jig should be used to ensure this is so. It need only consist of a bar of metal with two holes, spaced at the distance of the centres of axle and crank pin. Put a piece of round bar in one which will locate as a nice fit in the axle hole and drill through the other into the boss, this will ensure that they are all the same distance apart. Failure to do this will result in binding of the coupling rods.

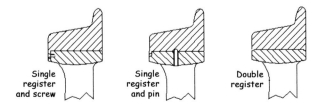

Three methods of securing rims to wheels

Nearer to Prototype

So far we have worked on a the theory of using cast iron wheels as they are, and the vast majority of model wheels are finished in this way. Cast iron is not a very hard-wearing material, in spite of what it does to ones lathe tools, and if a model is to have extensive running it is likely that grooves will be

A small solid wheel being profiled on a mandrel. Made from steel bar which has been bored and then parted off, giving a good solid and hard-wearing wheel.

worn in the treads after a period of time, if that running is on steel rail. In full sized practice steel tyres are fitted to wheels which not only means less wear and greater strength but also allows for replacement tyres to be fitted when wear does occur. It is also useful to do this in model practice, in which case the castings should be machined without flanges and square on the rims, an allowance being made for the tyre thickness. Tyres can be made complete with a flange and fitted to the wheels in a variety of ways. In full-sized practice they were shrunk on. The rim was heated and then when it had expanded it was forced over the casting and subsequently machined true. This idea can be followed in model form and we have the advantage

that not only can we heat the rims but also put the casting in the freezer and get some shrinkage. In this way the parts will fit easily together and provided machining has been accurate will stay that way when they have returned to normal temperature.

There are easier ways that work for the modeller, and which have less chance of upsetting domestic bliss. Modern anaerobic retaining compounds will hold both parts together securely enough and it is easier to spread a bit of adhesive around and push the parts together than to heat bits up and freeze others. Do not forget to follow the manufacturers' instructions on the gap required for the adhesive as this is critical. Alternatively we can make the parts a force fit and just ensure they do not separate by inserting a number of small screws through the rims. Whichever system is used the assembled wheels will need to be machined when completed and this will hide any screws that might have been used. Tyres were never fitted purely by shrinking them in position in full sized practice; although that was the main means of securing them, there was always also some form of registering as a security system and a similar system should be used when building a model.

When machining tender, bogie, or trailing wheels, or wheels for non-steam locomotives, the same principles apply except that there is no need to put in holes for crank pins. Solid type wheels or those with holes in can be made from mild steel blanks if one wishes. If driving wheels for narrow gauge models are machined from steel bar, balance weights will be required and these can be fabricated from mild steel plate and screwed in position. The heads of the screws, which should generally be countersunk, can be filled and smoothed over so, when painted, will not show. Sometimes on these engines the weights are riveted with snap head rivets, a system that is easy enough to duplicate in model form.

Some enthusiasts who want to get everything exact, machine their driving and coupled wheels from solid mild steel bar and mill the spokes out after machining the rims and centre. The process is not as hard as it sounds and the end result is usually a very fine wheel that is likely to be more true to scale and full sized practice than can be obtained with a casting. Because of the greater strength of mild steel, spokes can be made much thinner when made individually in this way than is possible with a casting. Take a look at the prototype and generally it will be found that the spokes have a much more slender appearance than that usually seen on a model.

Keying the wheels to the axles is the safest method and a simple keyway cutter is easily made.

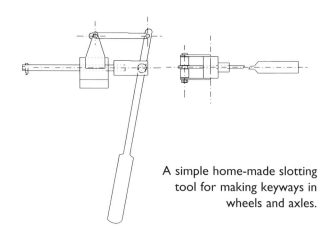

A simple home-made slotting tool for making keyways in wheels and axles.

Although the use of a round key is very common, to be absolutely correct if wheels are to be keyed in position, the key should be square. While the keyway on the axle can be milled, a special tool will be needed for the internal keyway in the wheel. A simple device that will fit the lathe tool post is all that is required and it can easily be made from scrap material.

Driving wheels don't come much bigger than this!
In 3½" gauge, this model of a "Crampton" express locomotive of the French Nord Railway was built by A. Joseph of Paris.

In Great Britain the 8' diameter driving wheels of a Stirling Single ran a Crampton close.
This 5" gauge version by Pat Inwood of York works as well as it looks.

Chapter 6: Axles & Cranks

Materials

It is always as well to use a good quality steel when making axles as, apart from the fact that it will wear better, there is also less likelihood of it twisting and warping. Silver steel is a good material to use and has the advantage of a ground finish. In theory that finish will be smoother in the bore of the axle box and so create less wear. There is a school of thought that this is not necessarily so and that a well machined piece of steel has advantages as the minute grooves that are left actually trap oil and so give better wearing properties - it is doubtful if there is any hard evidence either way and like so many things the final decision must be left to the builder. A personal preference for such items as axles is a good quality high carbon steel and old car half shafts are ideal; although these are not quite so easy to find these days, a visit to a car breaker should result in enough for ones needs and, as only useless ones are needed, they should be obtained at scrap prices. The steel is excellent and a good finish can be obtained.

Although the use of high carbon steel has been stressed it is appreciated that those who are less experienced in machining may find difficulty in using it, if so machine it with a carbide tipped tool, which will help. Anyone building a model that will not have extensive running can make the axles from mild steel, which will do the job quite well enough on a model that is lightly used. The wearing properties may be the least of our worries but the danger of twisting, during and immediately after machining operations, is only too real when bright mild steel is used. One way of preventing distortion is to heat the metal until it is red hot and maintain that heat for about ten minutes, allowing it to cool naturally, another is to leave it in the garden for a few months until it is very rusty after which it does not distort. The use of steel that has been used before such as the car half shaft, also guarantees that it will not distort when machined.

Setting Up

Ordinary axles as used on bogie, pony and tender wheels are quite straightforward to machine, as are those used on a locomotive with outside cylinders. It is simply a case of putting a step at each end to fit in the holes in the wheels. For good running, care should be taken to ensure the step is absolutely true to the outside diameter of the axle. A really accurate

three jaw chuck is about as rare as finding a hoard of gold in the garden, and so it is not advisable to use one for this operation. Machining between centres is generally recommended and the accuracy of the method cannot be doubted. A flat will be required somewhere on the axle so that the lathe carrier can get a grip and, for the first end to be machined, it can be filed where the step is to be machined later. Life becomes more complicated when we turn the axle round to do the other end as it means putting a flat either on the part that has just been machined, which will spoil the fit in the wheel, or alternatively the flat can be put on the outer diameter but then will spoil the surface, possibly at the position needed as a bearing. A way round the situation is to make up a special carrier that has a bolt with a sharp, pointed end as a driver. Instead of filing a flat a small indentation can be made in the axle with a centre drill and the driver located in that, without too much detriment to the finished work. A suitable carrier can be made from an old, large nut. Drill and tap for the screw that will act as a driver and use the same screw to clamp to the work, in other words whereas carriers normally have a driving peg and a securing bolt, in this instance one bolt does both jobs.

Perfect accuracy can be achieved by using the four jaw chuck carefully set for the work to run true, with experience gained by practice it is possible to set work to run more accurately this way than can be achieved even between centres. It is essential that both ends of the axles are centred, which will allow accurate lining up of work for later operations and also can be used for supporting from a tailstock centre

Crank Axles

For a locomotive with inside cylinders a crank axle will be needed, in full-sized practice this would almost certainly have been a massive forging in the early days and a high quality steel casting later on. Model traction engine builders are able to buy forgings and castings for crank shafts ready for machining, but as far as is known no such luxury is available to the model locomotive builder. It will, therefore, be necessary for the axle to be either machined from solid or built up, both methods have advantages and disadvantages.

Machining a crank axle from the solid, if done carefully, gives a very neat and accurate result. The danger of warping is increased with the additional machining involved. Assuming that machining from solid has been decided upon, then the first consideration is the size of bar from which to make the axle; anyone who has never tackled such a job before will be amazed at just how large this can be. Usually square section will be used as it works out the most economical. Both ends need to be accurately marked out and centred for the journals. The axle can then be machined between centres starting with the cranks and finishing with

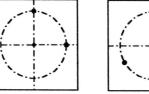

Centres for crankshafts for two and three cylinders.

The metal was supported between centres in much the same way as on a lathe with a method evolved for rotating the work when machining the journals. A good compromise is to mill the gap between the webs and to finish machining on a lathe. It involves making a device to allow both headstock and tailstock centres to be set over in order to get the offset.

Fabrication of a crankshaft is a far easier proposition even if the end result may not be quite as good

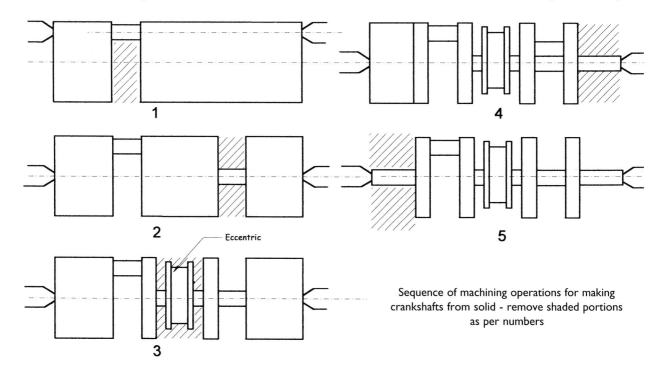

Sequence of machining operations for making crankshafts from solid - remove shaded portions as per numbers

the main axle section, the ends of which will need to be stepped to accept the holes in the wheels. A simple jig can be used on the faceplate to ensure that the offset of the crank journals is correct. This is not really a suitable job for the four jaw chuck, partly because of the difficulty in re-setting accurately and also because large forces are involved and there is a danger of the axle twisting in the jaws while machining operations are taking place. It is a long laborious task but something to be proud of when completed. If the locomotive is to have an axle-driven pump, the eccentric will also have to be machined and this will involve another centre at each end and machining the eccentric before the main axle section.

It is possible to make a crank axle on a milling machine, the method was demonstrated by Ivan Law at the Model Engineer Exhibition and in some ways appears to be easier than working with a lathe.

looking. The webs can be made on the lathe using a simple jig to ensure they are accurate. Round bar is pushed through the holes that have been bored - and they should be bored rather than drilled, the gaps are adjusted and the whole unit brazed or silver soldered together. The unwanted parts are then cut

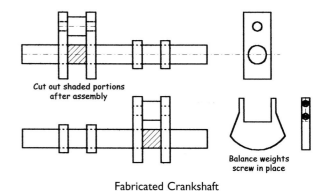

Cut out shaded portions after assembly

Balance weights screw in place

Fabricated Crankshaft

out and the axle cleaned up. An alternative to brazing is to pin the parts together and secure with a retaining compound. This needs to be done with great care, to ensure the correct fit for the parts and prevent them working loose after a period of use; if an eccentric is required it should be fitted before final assembly takes place. Some people, to ensure greater accuracy, machine steps on the journals, which can make locating them in the webs easier and much more accurate. The journals and main axle should be centred so these can be used later for lining up purposes when required.

How the wheel is fitted to the axle is a matter of choice, at one time a force fit was invariably used, nowadays the use of a retaining compound is more usual. If the decision has been made for a force fit, study a table of engineering fits to ensure that the correct tolerances are made. The wheels must be squeezed on to the axles and definitely not hammered into place, it may be possible to do this in the workshop vice. It is essential to take care that the wheels are set square on the axle, as it is possible for a slight angle to occur. If this happens the force used to push the wheel on removes some of the axle material and the result is a wobbly wheel. Care must always be taken not to make the step too large, or the hole too small when using a push fit. Doing so can very easily crack the wheel casting, a mistake which cannot be corrected.

If using a retaining compound, always study the manufacturer's instructions, a minute gap of a couple of thousandths of an inch or so has to be left between wheel bore and axle to allow the compound to work correctly. It is not possible to have both force fit and retaining compound. There is a hidden advantage to the use of a retaining compound which is not often considered. When a force fit is made it relies on matching two parts as accurately as possible, driving them together so that friction keeps them together. No matter how carefully machining is done the finished result is a series of minute grooves. If for any reason the model is kept in a damp place this will allow rust to set in. This can have one of two effects, it will either literally bind the two parts together, or it will break the bond when put under tension. If the latter happens the wheel works loose. This is one of the reasons that retaining compounds are now popular in industry.

It is advisable whichever system is used, to drill a tiny hole that dissects wheel bore and axle and push a steel pin in. It not only acts as a key but also enables one to re-locate the wheel should it be necessary to remove it at any time.

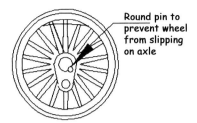

Round pin to prevent wheel from slipping on axle

Where driving and coupled wheels are concerned they will need to be quartered and so many ideas abound on this that a separate chapter has been devoted to the subject. Whatever method of fixing is used. and whether the wheels need to be quartered or not, don't forget to put the axle boxes on before the wheels, unless of course they are of the split type.

Axle Boxes

While dealing with axles it is logical to deal also with axle boxes. Generally they are nothing more complicated than a piece of bronze or cast iron bar with a hole in the middle to accept the axle and a

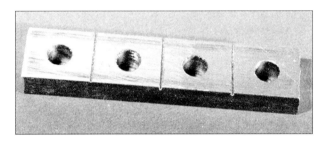

Axlebox strip bored for axles, but with guides still to be machined

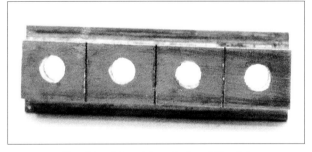

Complete axlebox strip ready for splitting into four individual axleboxes.

tiny one to allow oil to feed in at the top. Mostly there are flanges on one side which, in conjunction with the springs, retains the axle box in the horn-block. Some early designs call for a double sided flange, and sometimes split axle boxes might be specified. The advantage of the latter is obvious in that they can be taken off without having to remove the wheels from the axles, and adjustments for wear can be made.

Machining axle boxes accurately is not difficult. Generally they come as a cast stick and the flanges on them all can be machined at one setting, They should be bored to size on the lathe unless a boring head is available for the milling machine. In order that all the holes are in the same place a jig can be made up and mounted on the faceplate. The first one is adjusted with a wobbler and those that follow are simply clamped in position. Either a groove or a single flange is used to fit them into the horn blocks and this can be done either on a milling machine or a vertical slide.

Horn blocks

Generally these will be castings and the first operation must be to clean the recesses that will mate with the cut out sections in the frames. They are always riveted to the frames and may be made of bronze or cast iron. As usual schools of thought vary on the method of machining them accurately in order to line them up for the axleboxes but careful

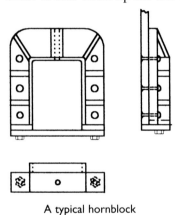

A typical hornblock

work on the milling machine will do as good a job as anything. A good way, if the machine has sufficient room, is to mount the frames with the horn blocks riveted in place, on the milling table and machine straight across, after of course checking thoroughly to see the frames are parallel to the table. Old time model engineers did not have sophisticated machines and so it was usual to file the inner faces and, looking at many of the models that were made, there appears to have been no ill effect on either appearance or running ability.

Sometimes pieces of angle or bar stock will be specified as horn blocks instead of castings, mainly on narrow gauge locomotives. They must be riveted accurately in line with the slots and they should be machined to ensure they are perfectly flat and true after riveting. The same principle is used of setting the frame on the milling table and machining across, in order to line them up for the axleboxes.

Crank Pins

Whether our model locomotive is inside or outside cylindered it will have crank pins, except in the case of a single wheel prototype with inside cylinders, in

which case the driving wheels will be driven directly via a crank axle and there are no coupling rods. In the case of other inside cylinder types, crank pins will be used to connect the driving and coupled wheels to each other. If the model has outside cylinders one pair will be connected directly to the cylinders via the connecting rods and those crank pins will be extended to accept both connecting and coupling rods. This means that the driven wheel needs a pin of more or less double length, in order to accept both rods.

Crank pins should be made of good quality steel and are one of the easiest components to make, the work involved generally consisting of no more than machining a step on a length of bar which is drilled and tapped, or threaded at the other end. It is essential that the step, which will fit in the hole in the wheel, is absolutely accurate and concentric with the body of the pin. The fitting specified at the other end will usually be either a screw or a nut. In full-sized practice this would be an unlikely arrangement, except possibly on a small narrow gauge locomotive. It is far more likely that there would be four or more threaded holes and a plate would be held in place with bolts. If we are modelling in the smaller sizes this is not very practical and a single screw can be used with a mock up of the four bolts to give the correct appearance. It is simple enough to make - a piece of bar of suitable diameter is turned down and threaded to fit the pin, four small tapped holes are made in the outer section and after assembly very short bolts are screwed in to give the correct appearance. The threaded holes can be used for

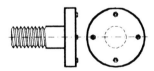

Screw axle pin retainer with false bolts

A full sized example of a fitting on a crank pin, using four bolts.

tightening up purposes by putting screws in two of the holes and a bar using a bar in between as a lever.

In order to ensure the pin is absolutely concentric with the step, and as most three jaw self-centring chucks are far from accurate, they should either be machined between centres or set true in a four jaw chuck. This generally applies only to the machining of the step for locating in the wheel. The end that is to hold the retaining washer or plate can be machined in a three jaw, as if it is slightly off centre it will have no ill effect. The only exception to this is when the retainer is to fit in a recess in the bearing as sometimes happens as, if it is off centre, there is the chance of it binding. As with axles, at one time crank pins were always made as a force fit in the wheel, it is more usual now to use a retaining compound.

The holes for the crank pins must be located accurately and square in the wheel bosses. To be absolutely sure to get this right a drilling jig should be made. This is a simple device and all we need is a piece of flat mild steel bar about 0.75 inches or 8mm thick and anywhere from 0.5 inches or 12mm

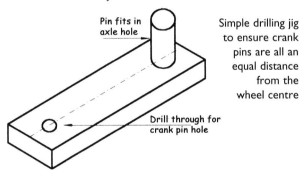

Pin fits in axle hole

Simple drilling jig to ensure crank pins are all an equal distance from the wheel centre

Drill through for crank pin hole

to 0.75 inches and 20mm wide. Drill two holes on a line down the centre on the same centres as the pin will be from the axle centre. Make sure they are square through the bar. One should be about 0.1875 inches or 5mm diameter. The other needs to be somewhat larger. The larger hole is to accept a pin of the same diameter as the axle hole, which is stepped to fit and can be secured with our retainer. Scribe a line down the centre of each wheel boss and then using the jig, drill through for the crank pins. Open out the crank pin holes if required to the right size. Allow plenty of time for the retainer to set before carrying out any further operations.

Quartering Wheels

When the wheels are fitted to the axles they must be accurately quartered. For two or four cylinder models this means they are at ninety degrees to each other, a three cylinder locomotive would normally have them set at one hundred and twenty degrees.

Whilst a degree or two out will neither notice or matter, it is essential that they are all the same. So if one pair are set at eighty seven degrees they must all be set to that angle. Better of course to get it right if possible, there are various ways of so doing and here there is an advantage to fitting the axles with a retaining compound that does not set too quickly, rather than as a drive fit. Some retainers set immediately and these should not be used, as there is not sufficient time to adjust the fitting before they do.

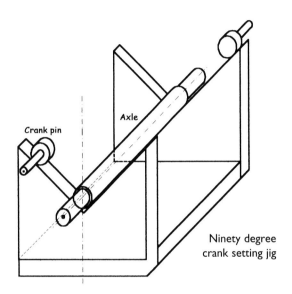

Crank pin

Axle

Ninety degree crank setting jig

There are several ways of quartering accurately. A proper jig can be made up in which the wheel will slide and the pins rest against the edges. It is a fairly foolproof system but somewhat time consuming to make the jig. The easiest way of all is to make up two stepped pins. The larger diameter fits into the axle hole and the smaller one is the same diameter as the crank pin. Fit the crank pin in both wheels and put them half way on the axles. Rest the wheels on a surface plate or the lathe bed and put one stepped pin in the axle hole. Set a square on the surface plate so that it touches both the try pin and the crank pin. Fit a stepped pin in the other side and use parallels to ensure that both pins are at ninety degrees by putting a straight edge along the pins and using a clock gauge to ensure they are absolutely level. The wheels can be pushed on the axles at that stage and once again a retaining compound will be better than a push fit as some adjustment can be made if need be.

Alternatively it is possible to use two blocks machined to size and set the work in the lathe. It is a method that is likely to result in a slight error of the angle, but all will finish the same and more time can be taken over the work. No doubt some people will devise their own methods of quartering. It is all a

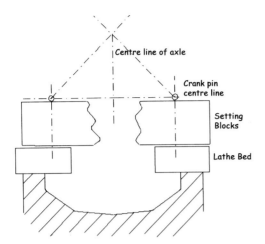

**To find correct height of Block
take angle of cosine of throw
PLUS half Crank Pin diameter
from the Centre Height of lathe**

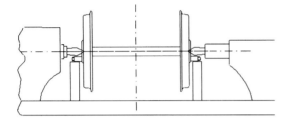

Using two accurately machined blocks
to set cranks at ninety degrees

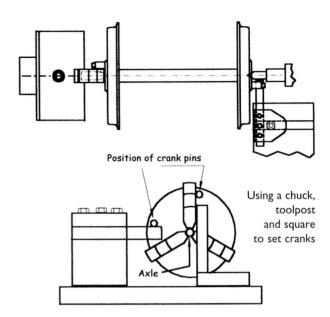

Using a chuck,
toolpost
and square
to set cranks

matter for the individual. Some methods that suit one person may not suit another. It must be stressed however that correct and accurate quartering is essential to the smooth running of a model locomotive, no matter what scale.

The use of a retaining compound for fitting axles is without doubt a chance to use the advantages of modern materials. Even so it is not a good idea to rely entirely on it to hold the wheels in position. There are a variety of reasons why there may be insufficient strength and when running it is possible for the wheel to slip on its axle. This is easily prevented by drilling a hole and pushing home a round pin, which can also be held with the retaining compound and will ensure that wheel movement on the axle is impossible.

There are an awful lot of axles, hornblocks, cranks etc. on this freelance 3½" gauge Mallet articulated locomotive.

Chapter 7: Carrying Wheels - bogies and ponies

What They Do

All the wheels on a locomotive could be described as carrying wheels in as much as they either carry or help to carry the weight. Carrying wheels is a term sometimes applied to the smaller wheels that have their own particular task to do. Many engines only had driving and coupled wheels and did their job perfectly well but where we get an engine that is going to travel at high speed or long distances, it will usually have extra carrying wheels on what are known as bogie or pony trucks. Generally these wheels are considerably smaller than the driving and coupled wheels; on some early locomotives they were mounted directly in the frames often with a little side play but unable to swing or turn as can the bogie or pony truck. Goodness knows how those names originated but a bogie generally has four wheels and on a non steam locomotive it may well have six or even eight. A pony usually has two wheels and is often referred to as a truck. Some very large-boilered locomotives built in countries such as America and Russia had pony trucks with six wheels to help support the weight of the very large fireboxes used.

These wheels are important as a means of spreading the weight and also assist a locomotive to travel round bends. Many railway routes had weight limits and so certain locomotives were barred from their use, often the restrictions related to the weight on a pair of wheels. By fitting extra carrying wheels to spread the load, larger motive power became available to these lines. The spreading of weight is hardly likely to concern the model engineer. Most model tracks are over engineered to the extent that weight is never going to be a problem, the use of the wheels as an aid to steering is another matter.

What Are We Aiming For?

In order to build successful bogie or pony trucks it is as well first of all to know what we are aiming at. As well as acting as load bearers they have two functions, to guide the locomotive round curves and to prevent a pitching action from taking place. To expand the latter comment a little, let us think of a locomotive without bogie or pony wheels. Although the springing on it will be designed so it will run as smoothly as possible, those very springs can also cause it to pitch forward and backward. For example if it is about to start and haul a heavy train the weight of that train will tend to hold the back down. Likewise when it runs into a curve, as well as wanting to carry straight on, the rapid slowing effect of the curve will make it pitch forward. These are not vast movements but they can lead to an oscillating effect. Considering the latter case, the sudden

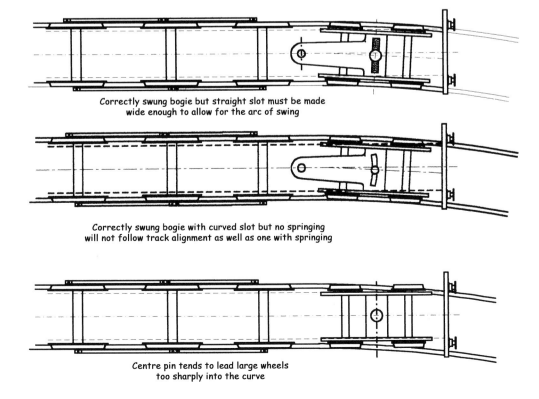

Correctly swung bogie but straight slot must be made
wide enough to allow for the arc of swing

Correctly swung bogie with curved slot but no springing
will not follow track alignment as well as one with springing

Centre pin tends to lead large wheels
too sharply into the curve

slowing having caused the engine to pitch forward, as it takes the strain of the train again, the back will tend to dip down. On a locomotive moving slowly or hauling a light load the effect is negligible, the larger the load and the faster the speed the greater the effect. If one has ever driven locomotives, full-sized or models, and used engines fitted with extra carrying wheels, the difference in performance becomes immediately obvious, when compared to fixed wheelbase types.

On a model it is essential that, as well as being properly made, bogies and ponies are correctly fitted and adjusted. If they are not, there will be no improvement in performance, which may be worse rather than better. The adjustment has to be such that slightly more weight is on the driving and coupled wheels, at the same time the adjustment has to allow the weight of the engine to fall on the carrying wheels in circumstances where the coupled wheels need some assistance. A typical example of this is on a curve, and applies particularly at high speed.

The rigid wheelbase of the coupled wheels will try to force the locomotive straight on, only after it reaches a certain point, almost behind the front wheel contact, will it start to turn. If a bogie is fitted, because of its shorter wheelbase and smaller wheels it will turn much more easily, and will start to pull the locomotive round - at this point temporarily the weight at the front end will be partially taken on the bogie springs, the coupled wheels following the curve without the momentary tendency to continue forward, and pitch downward as the curve slows the engine.

At one time it was possible that an 0-6-0 locomotive would be used in a difficult area such as the Scottish Highlands; these, as traffic increased, were generally neither large or fast enough to cope. Various ways of dealing with the problem were tried, including double heading with two locomotives. That was an expensive answer with the use of a great deal more fuel and an extra crew to pay. To increase speed a larger locomotive, with a more powerful boiler was needed. Because of the lightly laid rail and tight curves, just adding another pair of wheels to the same locomotive type and fitting a larger boiler wasn't possible as the weight on the wheelbase became excessive. In many cases the problem was solved by building an engine with larger wheels for more speed and adding bogies to enable a longer frame to be used which would carry a larger boiler. The end result was the birth of the 4-4-0 type locomotive which for some years became the mainstay of express passenger traffic throughout the world, followed by the 4-4-2 *Atlantic* type which also became popular as an express type the world over. There were to be later developments with a return to six coupled engines, with smaller driving wheels, a pony truck at the front replaced the bogie, the result was more traction whilst not necessarily increasing the length or weight of the wheelbase.

Frequently bogies and ponies are fitted at the rear of a locomotive where they assist in carrying the weight of the heavy firebox that added to the pitching motion already referred to. They also help correct the tendency of the coupled wheels to continue round a non-existent curve when straight track is again reached. The coupled wheels would not actually follow the track of course, the flanges would ensure that, but a nasty jerking motion would be imparted as the engine straightened and the smaller carrying wheels would to some extent compensate for this by guiding the engine along the track. The mathematics and dynamics of the thing is much more complicated than the above explanation which puts it in very simple terms indeed.

Springing

If we take the bogie first, for maximum efficiency we will be looking for three different sets of springs. The axles are sprung to take care of any unevenness in the track, in the same way as driving and coupled wheels. The bogie pivot is sprung so that it will support the weight of the locomotive when need be and there should be side play springing in order to bring the engine into line as quickly and smoothly as possible. The axle springing will often have some form of compensation so that as one wheel tends to lift pressure is brought to bear on the other axle.

On smaller gauge models all this springing becomes virtually an impossibility and it may be necessary to compromise. Frequently with small models there is no springing at all for the wheels, axles just run in bushes rather than having movable axle boxes, working on the principle that the wheelbase is so short that there will always be at least three wheels in contact with the rails. As quite frequently driving and coupled wheels are not sprung either there is little point in it anyway. The side control springing is also sometimes left off. Springs fitted for side control must be very light, so the unit is just allowed to slide free, in these sizes it is acceptable, although not as effective as when controlled. On early toy locomotives, the bogie to frame springing was also dispensed with, the bogie unit being there for appearance only. If any serious running is to be done a spring between the bogie and frame is essential as a minimum requirement. If it is possible to fit side control springing do so, and certainly once we get to 2½" gauge models and over, springing of the bolster and for side control is essential.

Bogie Frames

It is usual to cut frames of bogies and pony trucks from steel plate of the same thickness as used for the main frames. The shape of the spacers will vary considerably with the design of the model and, as a rule, the central spacer, or bolster as it is called, will be the place where the locating pin is fitted; this will usually pass through a slot. The supporting spring rests on top of the spacer and underneath the main frame. Large cup washers should be fitted to both

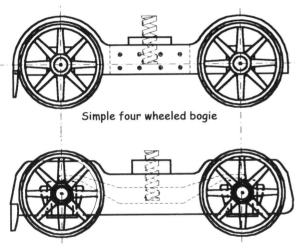

Simple four wheeled bogie

Bogie with compensated springing

save wear and allow ease of movement, the pin should be long enough to allow a small drop below the level of the driving wheels when free. The exact amount cannot be given, as it will vary with gauge and type of model, about three sixteenths of an inch on five inch gauge models is a rough guide, getting progressively smaller or larger as we go up and down in scale.

Axle Boxes

In all models from gauges 3½" upward, axle boxes and hornblocks should be used in the same way as with the main frames. While castings can be used for the axle boxes there is no reason why they should not be machined from a bar of bronze or gunmetal. An alternative to this could be steel bar fitted with bronze bearings. Advice given for machining main axle boxes applies equally to those for other wheels. There is a great deal to be said for fitting ball races; although this was not generally full-sized practice, they last longer and run more freely than plain bearings. Ideally they should be self aligning.

Hornblocks

In many instances cast hornblocks are not used on bogies. It is common practice to rivet a strip of bar or angle along the edges of the cut-outs and allow the axle boxes to run in these. Sometimes coil springs will be fitted over the axle boxes and supported by pieces fitted to the bogie frame. Some Continental locomotives had quite distinctive leaf springs fitted outside the bogie frame but there were just a few examples of the practice in Britain.

Spacers

These are generally bolted on and once again it is worth having a look at full-size practice as frequently the fitting of the bolster and spacers gives a quite distinctive regular pattern on the bogie sides. Sometimes they may be riveted rather than bolted, using angle iron as a joining material. The central bolster must have adequate strength as it is the main support and sometimes castings are used, but it is quite usual to fabricate it. If possible it should be made from a bar which is thick enough to bolt directly into, without the need to fit angle sections. In full-size practice a casting would often have strengthening webs of quite distinctive pattern

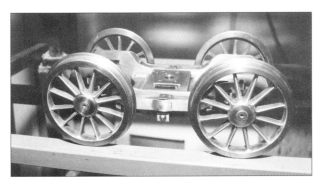

A well made four wheel bogie. The anchor pins for the side control springing can be seen at the side of the frame and flat plate was used to spread the load around the pivot.

The underside of the bogie shows how a large spacer also acts as the pivot, the ends being spaced with small diameter rods. This is true to the prototype.

which can be duplicated when fabricating. However it is essential when fabricating to ensure there is sufficient weight to prevent the bogie from bouncing off the track when in use.

Round bar is often used to make end spacers for bogies on models, it is both easy to use and successful in operation, but much more likely would have been some form of angle, which can be copied by riveting or silver soldering square blocks to the frame ends to accept the bolts which will hold it in position. Sometimes a bogie will be fitted to the locomotive frame with a swinging arm, which is a metal bar bolted at one end to the frames and at the other end to the bogie, to allow extra movement that might not be possible with the more normal type of fitting. It is a useful device where tight radii are to be negotiated.

Pony Trucks

The main difference in construction of a pony truck and a bogie, apart from the number of wheels, is that there is never a central pin for the truck to rotate on. Instead part of the pony frame is brought up to connect to the main frame and the pin is fitted there.

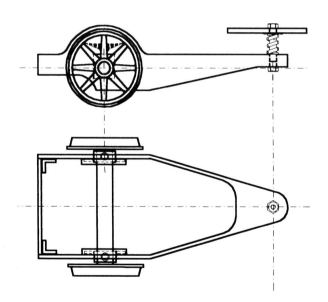

Construction of a typical Pony Truck

As with a bogie, a spring should be put over the pin, although it will be much shorter than that of the bogie.

Although we can put the pony truck anywhere we think fit within reason, the position of the pivot needs to be correct. Failure to get it right does not necessarily mean it is not going to work properly, but

The underside of a pony truck of fabricated construction. This photograph also gives a good view of the linkage used for cab operated drain cocks.

for good smooth operation the swing must be of a radius to suit the wheelbase of the locomotive - if not there are likely to be derailments or, at the very least, rough riding. The formula for finding the correct position is quite easy and applies whether the pony is leading or trailing. It is best explained by reference to the diagram below. Draw a line from the intersection of the pony wheel centre and the point of contact to the rail, at right angles to the rail. The distance from point 'A' to point 'B' should be half the rigid wheelbase of the locomotive. At a position on the rail that is half the rigid wheelbase which we shall call 'C' (and remember this is not necessarily the centre wheel of a six coupled locomotive), draw

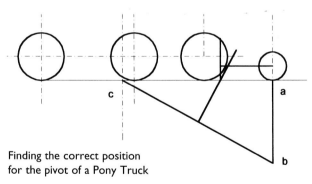

Finding the correct position for the pivot of a Pony Truck

a line to meet 'B'. Halfway along the line 'C' - 'B' draw another line at right angles and, where this meets the rail, another line at right angles to the rail. The correct point for the pony pivot is on that line.

Where two carrying wheels are used under the cab of an engine these are usually set in a truck which allows side play but does not swing in the manner of a bogie. Additional plates are fitted to the frames and the wheels run inside these in ordinary axle boxes and horn blocks, some side play is allowed. Springing is via leaf springs set on the outside of the frame extension. This arrangement was to be seen on many of the larger express locomotives and the support given gave the crew a nice comfortable ride.

Weight Distribution

From what has been discussed so far it becomes apparent that weight distribution is the all-important thing where these carrying wheels are concerned. This must be looked at in the context of weight distribution as a whole. Most weight must rest on the driving wheels followed very closely by the coupled wheels. The front-end carrying wheels carry about five to ten percent less weight than these and the rear end ones a tiny bit less than that.

An International Hobby

One of the great pleasures of having built your own locomotive is taking it to other tracks, in your own or other countries, to run it. Not only can you run your model under varying conditions, you may also make lifelong friendships.

The weight of even a 3½" gauge locomotive means that intercontinental trips are difficult, but visiting tracks around Europe with a model is now very easy and well worth considering.

But t'was not always so - for many years the building of passenger hauling model locomotives was largely confined to the English speaking world; in Europe and elsewhere they were lone model locomotive builders, but clubs as were to be found in Great Britain, the U.S.A. and Canada, and in Australasia just did not exist.

During the 1960s this started changing as some of the "lone hands" started making contact with others in their countries, and tracks began to appear in Germany, Holland and France, opening up the prospect of international visits as, rather remarkably, these were all built to the existing 'imperial' gauges, rather than metric ones.

The author led a contingent of British model engineers with their locomotives to the first international meeting, held in Metz, France, in 1972 and organised largely as a static Exhibition by Jean Villette, where French, German, Belgian and British locomotive builders got together.

Coincidentally, in the Spring of 1973, the publisher took his model traction engine to the *Nienoord* childrens' park in Leek, Holland where Rob van Dort, founder of the Dutch Live Steam group, was responsible for a 7¼" gauge railway. A small event, visited by some Dutch, Belgian and German enthusiasts, was organised, giving rise to an annual event that continues to the present day.

However the first international event where large numbers of visitors ran their locomotives took place in the late summer of 1973, at the track of the *Dampfbahnfreunde Friedrichsruhe* near Öhringen in southern Germany. The *DBF* was a small club led by Manfred Knupfer, and included the Zimmerman brothers who were developing a very successful line of "kit" locomotives and components in 5" gauge. In a very short time an extensive ground level track for 3½", 5" and 7¼" gauges had been built, incorporating a number of circuits, complex point work and severe gradients. The author was again in a contingent of British model locomotive builders who took the long road to this *Dampfbahnparadies* where he met the publisher, who had come with a small Dutch contingent, for the first time. There they both met a considerable number of model engineers with locomotives from all over Germany, and Denmark, as well as visitors from France and Switzerland.

It was a truly wonderful weekend which gave considerable impetus to the establishment of Club tracks in Europe, inspired the publisher to organise the first British *International* meet, at the Guildford Society's track, in July 1974 and vastly increased ferry companies' profits, as model engineers and their locomotives crossed and re-crossed the Channel, visiting new friends.

Thirty years on, club tracks are to be found all over Holland and Germany, with a number in France, Switzerland and Spain, plus at least one each in Italy and Denmark. Japan also has a number of clubs. Many hold annual meets for visitors; details may be found in the model engineering press.

Constructing a model steam engine is immensely satisfying. Running it can be equally satisfying and almost inevitably will lead to enjoyable social contact at your local club. Such contacts can be greatly increased by visiting other clubs, be they national or in other countries, and the author strongly recommends you try such visits and find out just how enjoyable they are for yourself.

The author looks worried as Dutchman Jan Kieboom drives John Dalton's 5" gauge "Halton Tank" out of the station. Jan was inspired to start building his own locomotives, including that on the dustjacket.

The author waits, water can in hand, on the right as, on the left, Rob van Dort from Holland drives the Nienoord Spoorwegen's 7¼" gauge gas fired 4-6-0, based on a "Royal Scot" chassis, into the station. The publisher is also in this shot, pretending to be Dutch.

On the inner circuit, Arnold Kaliwoda from Berlin takes his partially complete 5' gauge model of an East German Railways 01 class Pacific for a test run.

Vagn Hansen from Denmark built his gas fired 7¼" gauge Austrian narrow gauge 0-4-0 from measurements taken from a commercial 'G' scale electric model.

On the 5" gauge tracks Les May raises steam on a 'Butch' 0-6-0 tank, whilst event organiser Manfred Knupfer rushes past, hauling a train of mixed stock with his German 4-6-4 tank locomotive.

And a good time was had by all! Elmar Mayr hauls some happy passengers with his stylised 5" gauge German narrow gauge locomotive.

Öhringen 1973 – the first International Meet

Chapter 8: Cylinders

What is a Cylinder?

The dictionary gives several descriptions for the word cylinder, for example: "A surface traced by a straight line moving in a circle, or other closed curve, round and parallel to a fixed straight line." A bit of a mouthful and perhaps instead of using such a complicated description we could just say a hole, sealed at each end, generally, but not always longer than its own diameter, at least where steam engines are concerned.

Cylinders, of course, are used in most types of engines but the purpose of this chapter is to deal with those designed for steam. All readers will be aware that inside the cylinder there is a piston and when force is applied to the end of this, it moves away from that force. This movement in turn is converted by a crank into a rotary motion. For many years people had not quite fathomed out how to convert the motion of a piston into a rotary one and the only purpose a steam engine could serve was that of a pump. The invention of the crank changed this and once rotary motion had been obtained it was a short step to convert the engine to drive a vehicle, either on the road or on rails.

Steam

The force we are talking about is steam as against petrol or similar fuels used these days. With petrol, diesel or gas the force applied comes from a rapid burning of the fuel, which is created either by some form of spark or by the heat generated from compression. The burning is so rapid as to be almost an explosion. With the steam engine the principle relies on the ability of steam to expand and it is essential to make use of this expansion. The amount that it does expand is quite incredible, and if we took a normal kettle of water and could heat all the water in it until it was steam it would expand to fill an area of something like twenty-five cubic feet, or a whole room. In the case of our locomotive this expansion is curtailed, firstly by the boiler and, when released from that, by the cylinder - it is still expanding and so pushes the piston back. Perhaps it is worth noting here that steam is not the white wet stuff we see coming from the spout of a kettle, but a dry colourless gas. The white cloud is condensed steam and therefore is at a much lower pressure. If we can get the steam into the cylinder via a valve, which we will come to later, and stop any more coming in, then the amount that has been allowed in will by its

expansion create the power needed to drive our model locomotive. This means a cylinder with a good valve system and a well fitting piston that will not allow any of the precious gas to pass by it, and so will get the utmost efficiency from it.

The Valves

In general two types of valves are used in model steam locomotives, slide and piston; full-sized locomotives, particularly in the later years, used some other types and a few dedicated modellers have built models using these. It is proposed to deal only with slide and piston valves and how to make cylinders using them.

Slide Valves

For many years slide valves were virtually the only type used by model makers, mainly because it was considered too difficult to get piston valves steam tight, although piston valves are now quite common as a result of the general all round improvement of skills and equipment. This has in no way diminished the popularity of slide valves, which anyway are more suitable for some models.

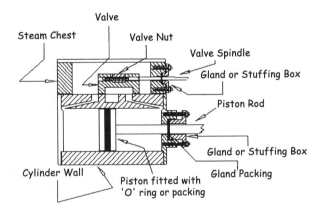

Layout of Slide Valve Cylinder

Basically the slide valve system consists of three holes called ports in a flat surface. In the garden gauges these may be literally holes, while with larger models they will be slots, and they are housed in a closed box known as the steam chest. One port allows steam into the cylinder at one end, the middle one allows it to escape when it has done its work, the third allows steam in at the other end which also, after completing its work, escapes through the middle port. There is only one opening to the steam chest, to which a pipe from the boiler is connected via the regulator, allowing steam to enter the steam chest under controlled conditions; the only means of escape for the steam is through the ports. A valve covers two of these so steam can only get into one and from there via passages it can pass into the cylinder bore. The uncovered or open port lets steam into the front of the cylinder, where it pushes the piston back. By the time the piston has reached the end of its stroke, the valve has moved to the other end of the steam chest, covering the original open port and exposing the one at the opposite end. *(Note that the middle port is covered by the valve at all times.)* The spent steam escapes by going back the way it came in, although the port through which it entered is now closed off from the steam chest by the valve, it can escape as the valve has a recess at the bottom which covers both the first and exhaust ports. It takes the line of least resistance and escapes through the exhaust port and via some piping into the smoke box where it is released up the chimney. The cycle is repeated from the other end, that port being open to the steam at this stage. A very simple arrangement but also very effective, and we can see that, unlike the internal combustion engine, the steam operates at each end of the cylinder, whereas on the internal combustion engine the piston returns from whence it came as a result of energy received from its own momentum and the assistance of a flywheel. The steam still has not entirely completed its work as the draught it creates when escaping also draws up the fire, thus ensuring that a constant supply of steam is maintained.

Materials

In model form the cylinder will be made from a solid block, either a casting or a piece of solid metal, from this the bore of the cylinder and the face on which the valve will slide, known as the port face, will be machined. The cylinder ends are sealed, one with a plain disc and the other with a disc that incorporates a hole for the piston rod and a gland that will prevent steam from leaking, both of these are bolted to the cylinder block and a gasket is fitted to prevent any leaks. Many designs specify using bolts to hold these end covers in place, this is not correct; studs and nuts should always be used for the purpose. These make it easier to fit and replace the covers.

In full-sized practice cylinders were often made in a different form to that used on most models. They were cast in such a way that as little metal as possible was used in their construction. It was not just a case of cost cutting, or reducing weight. The less metal that there is the less the steam will be inclined to condense and the more efficient it will be.

A cylinder casting for a slide valve locomotive with outside cylinders and inside valve gear. Note the end as been blocked up with a piece of hardwood. This is marked off with a centre and used to get the bore in the correct place when setting up.

Adopting this idea is not usually possible with a model and so we have to use cylinders that are not quite as efficient as they might be. A builder wishing to take advantage of a reduced amount of metal can always try and machine away some of the unwanted material.

Full-sized cylinders often take a different form to those on a model and the photograph shows the components for a piston valve cylinder. It is cast in sections and joined together. If you want to fabricate your own cylinders the idea can be used, using tubing. The cylinder is lagged and a sheet bolted round to restore the more familiar appearance. The result is much less heat loss, giving better performance.

Full-sized cylinders were usually made of cast iron or had a cast iron liner, many models use cast iron cylinders and the liner is dispensed with, but a liner is popular for use in cylinders of cast bronze or gunmetal as it is sometimes called, and in the garden gauges brass is frequently used, normally without a liner. The type of material used might depend on what castings are available. Cast iron is easy to machine, particularly with modern carbide tipped tools and comparatively cheap. Some bronzes are also quite easy to machine, others tend to be what we might call sticky. Unfortunately it is not possible to tell what the material will machine like until a start has been made. The sticky type tends to leave very heavy burrs that can be difficult to remove. Brass is very easy to machine and an ideal material for someone working on a very small lathe. A problem with cast iron is its ability to rust and if it is allowed to do so the locomotive will quickly become inefficient. At the end of running it will be necessary to ensure the cylinders are well lubricated, preferably using a heavy water separating type of oil. Never use the light oils that are sprayed from a can. These have other substances mixed with them that will allow the walls of the bore to dry out and encourage corrosion, although they do not have this effect when used as rust prevention agents on tools, etc. As a result of this tendency towards rusting many modellers prefer to use bronze for cylinders even though it is considerably more expensive than cast iron.

Machining

Cylinder castings can sometimes be in quite a rough state when received from the foundry and before starting they must be thoroughly examined. Then it is necessary to decide which is the best place to start as we need a datum or starting point. Some slide valve cylinders have the port face for the valve running parallel to the bore, others might have it at an angle. Check that the datum you decide on will allow these to fall on the correct lines. Check also that the right measurement between port face and bore is going to be obtained. Many bores that are cast in are slightly out of position, and you must be certain that machining will correct this.

While differing designs may call for the relationship between valve face and bore to be at an angle, we can be absolutely certain that the cylinder ends which will hold the end covers will be at ninety degrees to the bore, so that could be a good place to start. How it is machined will depend on the size of the cylinder in relation to the size of the lathe but when set up it must be certain that the end that will be the datum is going to be parallel to the bore. If for any reason the cylinder ends are not suitable for the first machining operation, another useful datum can be the face used for bolting the cylinder to the frames. Whether the ends are to be used or not, it will be essential to machine one before dealing with the bore, so that we have a known flat surface at ninety degrees to it.

Work Holding

When working with a reasonable sized cylinder it may be that the casting can be held in a four-jaw chuck. If the casting is on the large side it might have to be bolted to the faceplate. There are various ways of doing this. Supporting it on an angle plate, whilst resting on the port face usually works well, but packing may be required in certain places to get it accurately in line. This means the use of shims, a good source of which is old food cans. They can be cut to the required size and bent to shape if necessary. Also useful for holding cylinders to the

A cylinder block mounted in a four-jaw chuck. In this case the port face was machined first to provide a datum and is protected from damage with a piece of aluminium sheet. In order to increase the grip, pieces of metal have also been inserted so the grip is on the main casting rather than the thin lip. Holding the pieces in while setting up takes place can be tricky and they were held in place with plasticine while this was done.

faceplate is the so-called Keats Angle Plate, otherwise known as a vee angle plate. In order to prevent damage to the lathe, if using the faceplate for work holding, the casting should be set away from it, using a spacer to ensure it is square.

The casting must be secured by at least two fastenings and if possible three, and the lathe should be run at a slow speed for the initial machining. We are told that in the case of cast iron the outer skin, which is rather hard, should be removed with one pass of the cutter; something that is not always practical and not worth attempting if it means taking a cut that is too deep. The idea comes from the days when lathe operators used carbon steel tools. These days hardly anybody uses them except for special purposes and modern high speed and carbide tipped tools are quite able to stand up to the machining of the outer surface of cast iron.

A Keats Angle Plate, used to hold a cylinder casting. The wooden bung in the end of the cylinder is being used as an aid to setting up accurately, using a wobbler and scribing block.
When nearly right the scribing block is changed for a dial gauge to ensure absolute accuracy.

Casting Faults

Sometimes an iron casting will have what is known as a hard spot in it. This happens at the foundry, usually as a result of a casting being turned out on to a cold floor instead of being allowed to cool slowly. It may be possible for a tipped tool to cut through such a spot but often it is not and it means returning it to the supplier for a replacement. The annoying thing is that a hard spot always seems to show up when most of the work has been done and involves starting again. But if one is found don't mess around with it for too long, far better to return it and request a replacement, than to do several hours more work and still find it needs to be returned.

Blowholes are another problem and can occur on any type of casting, although most commonly in iron. The tool breaks into a hole during machining operations and often that too means getting a replacement. Sometimes it may be possible to salvage the casting. For example if the hole appears in a non vital place, say where the steam chest cover is to be bolted on and not where the valve will travel, it can be filled using one of the proprietary metal fillers available. Make sure it is a good quality one. I have actually repaired the bore in the cylinder of a stationary engine, using one of these and after years of running it is as good as ever, but this is not generally recommended. It is also possible with gunmetal castings to fill blowholes using spelter or brazing rod and this too may salvage many hours of work. The hope is that none of these problems beset us and we can get on with machining the cylinders. Having established a datum the casting can be taken through the necessary machining operations.

Machining the bore is very much like any other operation on the lathe but when it comes to final cuts it is essential to run the tool through several times without changing the setting. Small boring bars are liable to flex under pressure and if the tool is not moved through a number of times one end may well be a smaller diameter than the other. One school of thought is that cylinder bores should be honed, whilst other people prefer to leave them with a good machined finish, working on the theory that the minute grooves will pick up oil and act as a lubricant. The choice is for the reader to make. If the bore is honed, then the hone must be run at a very slow speed and must not be allowed to come out of

Boring a casting held in the Keats Angle Plate. Several passes are required on the final cut to ensure that the bore is parallel.

the bore at any time while it is rotating. This causes a bell mouthing effect and leads to lack of efficiency. Use either a wheel brace or battery powered hand drill with a very slow speed for honing. Under no circumstances rotate the hone at fast speeds, and ensure that plenty of oil is used. A thin neat cutting oil is best but if not a thin lubricating oil will do, thick oils will clog the hone and must be avoided.

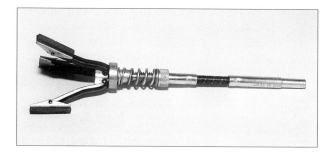

A commercially made hone which is used to smooth the bore. The stones need to be well oiled and the hone rotated slowly while passing up and down the bore. It must under no circumstance come out of the bore during the operation or there will be a bell mouthing effect.

Boring Between Centres

If the casting cannot be mounted on the headstock in any way because of its size, all is far from lost; it can be machined while mounted on the top slide, using tools rotating in the headstock. The photographs show quite clearly how this is accomplished and the results can be very good indeed. A decent fly cutter that works from the faceplate is needed to machine the port face and ends and it is a good idea to use a weight to counterbalance the cutter. A boring bar driven by a dog from either the faceplate or a driving plate and set between centres makes a wonderful job and guarantees a parallel bore. Some people fight shy of boring in this way because they believe there is a difficulty in adjusting the bar. It is really quite easy, using shims of known sizes to make the adjustment.

Larger cylinders can be mounted on the cross slide and bored between centres. The cutter in the boring bar is adjusted by checking its protrusion with shims. Although the system looks complicated it is highly accurate.

Whichever way the boring is done make sure it is accurate and also that the bore is parallel. It might be possible to measure it throughout its length with a

A piece of bar of known diameter is used to check that the bore is both to size and parallel.

pair of inside callipers, but that is a bit hit and miss. The callipers only need to be accidentally pulled over to an angle and the reading will be false. The best way is to get a bar of metal of the correct diameter over its length, machine one to size if necessary before starting on the cylinder, and push this into the bore, making sure that it is clean and free of swarf first. It should be a push fit requiring a little pressure and definitely without shake. Using this it is possible to check the bore over its whole length and also to ensure that both or all the cylinders are the same size.

The Port Face

A good flat and smooth port face is essential and there are a number of ways of achieving this. It can be done on a milling machine, using either an end mill or fly-cutter, or as already suggested it can be fly- cut while resting on the lathe saddle, alternatively

The port face can be machined on a milling machine using an end mill (slot drill) or a fly-cutter. The latter rotated slowly will give the best finish.

it can be faced off while mounted on the lathe, either on the faceplate or in a four-jaw chuck.

Steam Ports

The most common way in this day and age to make the steam ports is by end milling. Drawings frequently show them as square ended but this is not necessary and the groove cut by an end mill is quite good enough. If a square ended recess is desired it will be necessary to either use a very small side and face cutter or to make up a special cutter that will cut

The port face can also be machined on the lathe saddle, providing the ends of the block have first been machined square. To ensure the face is square to the mandrel it may be necessary to use an intermediate piece of metal as shown.

A simple fly-cutter used on the faceplate to machine the port face of the cylinder. It is a very accurate system and no more difficult working this way than on a milling machine.

all three ports at a single go. In the past, before model makers had easy access to such things as end mills and machines in which to use them, this was quite common, but few people now take the trouble to do it that way. Using either a side and face cutter, or the special three gang one, leaves a semi circular recess and this can make life a little tricky when trying to line up the steam passages, so using an end mill is really the best option.

Steam Passages

The steam gets from the ports to the bore via the steam passages and at first attempt the drilling of these can appear quite daunting, but with a little care it is not such a difficult operation as it first appears. Start by either filing or milling a nice angle on the end of the cylinder bore, next carefully measure the depth of the inlet ports and scribe a line on the

A finished port face showing the ports that have been made using a slot drill.

outside of the cylinder casting, to mark their position. If milling of the ports has been done correctly this should be exactly parallel to the port face. Scribe a line centrally to the port and at right angles to the port face. Where this crosses the first line is the place where the steam passages need to break through. Mark the side of the cylinder block in line with the centre of the flat that has been made at the end on the bore and then scribe a line from that to the intersection just mentioned; that line is at the angle the passages must take.

Drilling the steam passages is the trickiest operation and whichever way the block is supported the holes must be started with a centre drill.

An adjustable angle plate used for drilling the passages. A square is set up against a line scribed on the outside of the block in order to line things up properly.

Set the cylinder up on the drilling machine so that if a square is put on the table the edge will be parallel to the angled line. There are several ways of doing this. A vice that will set at an angle is an obvious one. Failing that suitable packing on which to rest the normal machine vice will do. If this is used it is essential to mark the point where the vice fits on the packing in order to return to the right position for subsequent operations. Sometimes a casting is too big for a normal machine vice and it will be necessary to hold it at the required angle with packing to support the end. Again it is essential to mark the point on the casting where it meets the packing and also to keep a very firm grip to prevent it moving while drilling is taking place. An adjustable angle plate can be of assistance here if available and once set to the required angle, that setting will do for drilling all the required holes.

Start operations with a small centre drill and ensure that it goes in at the required angle. When a start has been made, commence drilling, but only for a very short distance. Check by eye with the square that the drill is running parallel to the angled mark on the casting, if so go a bit further and so on until it breaks through into the steam port, take it easy and all will be well. There will usually be three or four holes to be drilled and it is almost certain that they will not end up in a perfect line in the port. This does not matter as long as they all break through into it. If disaster strikes all need not be lost. Tap the renegade hole and fill it with a threaded length of bronze. It is then possible to start again and this time to get it right. It is not possible to carry out this little dodge more than once, but it might save a valuable casting, not to mention all the work that has already been done. Many drawings will specify that the steam passages should be slots, it is difficult to do and probably of no advantage anyway and there is also the problem of obtaining a milling cutter of suitable

Using a vee block to machine the passages. This takes a bit of setting up in order to get things lined up properly. The metal bar under the angle plate was stuck down with double-sided adhesive tape. The set up was moved slowly into position and, when right, a strip of metal stuck down in the same way butted against the end of the vee block. This stopped it moving away when drilling started, and provided a ready set-up for both the other end of this cylinder, and the ends of the second cylinder as well.

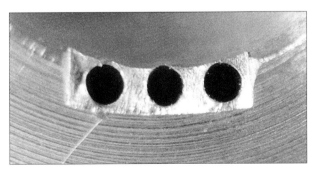

An ultra close-up view of the holes for the steam passages on the cylinder end. A flat is filed first, but it is unlikely to be accurate enough for drilling purposes and so the centre drill is started at right angles to the flat before lining the block up. The drill will pick up in the centre drill holes but wander into position along the scribed line once it is going. If in doubt start with a small drill and open out gradually to the required size.

*The chances of breaking out into the ports at exactly the
same centres that the holes were started at is pretty remote.
As long as all holes reach the ports there is nothing to worry about.
Another ultra close-up view shows how all three have made it into
the port in spite of a little variation.*

length. The passage to the exhaust port is easy
enough as usually little more than a straight hole,
tapped at one end to accept the exhaust pipe, is
required.

Steam Chest

Generally speaking the steam chest is pretty
straightforward and the outside edges can be

*A typical steam chest casting.
Piston valve cylinders have no separate steam chest of course and so,
in many ways, a great deal of machining is saved.*

*Machining the face of the steam chest which is held in
a four-jaw chuck.*

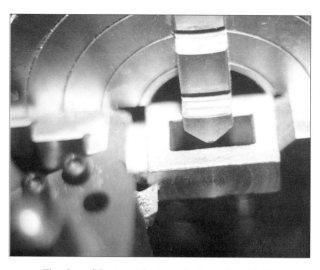

*The edges of the steam chest can also be machined in the
four jaw chuck but use a piece of shim to protect
the already machined surfaces.*

machined square either on the lathe, using the four-
jaw chuck or in a milling machine. The edges to meet
the cover and port face can be dealt with in a similar
fashion. The hole that is to accept the valve rod
should be set accurately using either a clock gauge,
or a wobbler in conjunction with a surface gauge.
There are two types of gland, the screw-in type or
the oval bolt down version. The holes for either type
must be drilled and the hole finished flat to accept
packing, the ideal tool for this being a 'D' Bit.
Covers for the steam chest are generally in the form
of flat plates, just one or two odd designs having
some form of embellishment. They can be machined
flat in either a lathe or milling machine. The holes for
the studs should be drilled through the covers first
of all and then transferred to the steam chest and
finally to the cylinder block. One way of keeping
them in place during the drilling operations is to
stick them together with double-sided adhesive

*The hole for the valve stem and gland needs to be
accurately lined up, using a clock gauge.*

Finish the gland passage with a D" Bit in order to get it flat to accept the gland packing.

A finished steam chest with an oval gland.

tape. Use a tapping size drill and open out the cover and steam chest to clearance size after drilling the block, which can then be tapped.

When all operations are finished put a sheet of fine emery or similar abrasive paper on a known flat surface and rub the port face on it in a figure of eight motion, repeat the operation on the steam chest and covers to ensure a nice flat mating surface on them

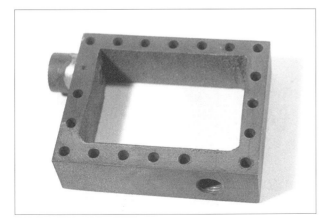

A finished steam chest with a round screw in type of gland. The hole in the front is for the main steam pipe.

Cylinder cover castings may come in pairs. The left one is the rear cover, which will be machined for both the piston rod gland and to fit the slide bars.

all; this operation will also remove any burrs.

The end covers are usually a straightforward turning job. The first operation should be to machine the inner face and step that goes into the cylinder bore. It is usual to have a spigot left on the casting which allows it to be held in the chuck for this operation. The tricky part is holding the covers

Some cylinder covers will include a spigot to aid machining.

square by their comparatively thin edges for subsequent operations. It is generally necessary to put a spacer behind and push it against the body of the chuck. The outside edges on the front cover can be difficult. It is not too bad on the rear one as there should be the boss for the gland on which to get a grip. If holding it proves too difficult, here is a little dodge that might help. Take a piece of plate about a quarter of an inch thick and just a little larger than the cover and rub it and the cover smooth and flat, using fine emery cloth on a flat surface. Stick the cover to the piece of plate using double sided sticky tape, making sure to push it home hard. The plate, complete with cover, can be put in a four-jaw chuck and the cover adjusted to run true and machined. The tape will hold it quite securely and much larger objects than a cylinder cover can be machined in this way with perfect safety.

A cover being machined while held by the cast on spigot; the photograph demonstrates how useful it is if this type of cover casting can be obtained.

A centre punch mounted in the tool post is used to mark the position of the holes.

The rear cover needs some extra work to make the gland whether it be a bolt on type or screw in. Full-sized practice almost always meant a bolt on gland cover as screw in types would not have been practical and it looks better if full-sized practice is followed. Those who prefer to make the screw type should drill and tap the boss without changing the setting in order to ensure absolutely concentricity. When it comes to fitting up the packing for the gland it can be either graphited string, an 'O' ring or a PTFE washer. Some of the bolt on gland covers are oval shaped and the easiest way to deal with these is to file them to shape. Take a piece of hard wood and drill a hole that will be a tight fit for the round section of the cover. Push the cover into the hole and then use a wood screw to secure it. It is now possible to mark out and file the cover and providing care is taken the end result will be as good as any attempt at machining.

Marking out of the holes for bolting on the covers can also be done without changing the setting in the

lathe. How this is done will depend on the equipment each individual has. It is quite easy to make up a system whereby the lathe change wheels can be used for indexing but on many modern machines with gear boxes there are no change wheels. In this case the chuck jaws can be used to index six holes easily enough. Simply put a block of either wood or metal on the lathe bed and rest one chuck jaw on it and spot the first hole. Rotate the chuck until the next jaw rests on the block and repeat the operation and continue with the third jaw. Unfortunately three is all we will get with that block but it is not difficult to use dividers to get intermediate marks by resting one leg on each adjacent jaw and scribing intersecting lines. Some readers will have a tool post drilling attachment that will make life very easy. For those without, a centre punch can be mounted in the tool post, by fitting it in a hole in a piece of square bar held in the toolpost. We have two alternatives: either cross drill the holder and fit a screw to hold the punch in position, or leave the punch floating. Assuming the former, wind the

A simple method of indexing for drilling the cylinder covers. The detent is fitted to a bracket mounted on the change wheel arms but any suitable point will do. It is essential that it is pushed right home and the mandrel does not move during operations.

In order to allow free passage of the steam from the steam passages into the bore, file a small flat on the lip of the locating flange of the cover.

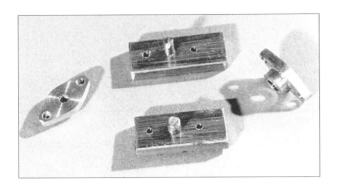

Where oval flanges are used little jigs like these make filing them to shape easy.

saddle in smartly and the punch will make the necessary indent on the cover, but make sure you only have one go as experience shows that there is often a discrepancy if multi marks are made. If the punch has been left loose it can be gently tapped with a hammer to make the marks.

Drilling should be done in the same way as for the steam chest, using the cover as a jig for the threaded holes in the cylinder block. It is worth making a small tapping guide to ensure the tap goes in nice and square. It is all too easy for it to lean at an angle and if that does not result in a broken tap it will mean studs protruding at an angle, which is most undesirable. The guide is only a piece of round bar turned square at the end and with a hole which is a good running fit for the tap. It can make all the difference to the finished product.

When it comes to fitting the steam chest and covers, gaskets will be needed, an easy way to get a good sealing gasket is to wrap PTFE tape round the studs joining each one to the next. A typical example would be one turn round a stud, finishing on the outside, run the tape to the inside of the next stud and wrap one turn round it. From the inside take it to the outside of the next one and a turn round and continue until a double circuit has been completed. When the nuts are tightened down the tape compresses and forms a perfect gasket. The extra little bit round the studs works its way into the holes and fills any slight gap.

Gaskets can also be made from brown paper or special gasket material of various kinds. In this case the material has to be cut to size, the hole positions marked and punched out. A useful punch for this sort of work is the type sold for punching leather that has a number of heads that rotate. It is also possible to make a small punch which will do the job and after locating the position it is tapped with a hammer, ideally while the material is on a block of hardwood.

On most covers which match to the slide bars, flats will have to be machined for the bars to locate on and they will be fixed with screws to those faces. Care must be taken to ensure that the flats are at an identical distance from the centre and that they are at ninety degrees to the cover ends. It may be as well to do this before drilling for the securing studs. Put the cover in the machine vice and mill the first flat, making sure it is accurately located. Put a parallel between the vice jaw and that flat to ensure that the next milling operation cuts absolutely parallel to the first.

Many published drawings show only six or eight bolts holding cylinder covers in place. This is wrong, most cylinders covers would be held on with studs spaced at approximately two and a half times their diameter and, as a result, most locomotives would have at least twenty securing points. If aiming at a true scale model, efforts should be made to establish how many studs are required, but if the correct number are to be fitted a more sophisticated dividing system than the chuck jaws will be needed. A point to remember if aiming for correct appearance is that the protrusion of the stud beyond the nut when tightened down would be about one and half threads. Some companies fitted covers over the front covers of the cylinders, which effectively hid the studs and nuts. Suitable covers can be made from discs of thin mild steel which can be formed over the end of a bar of metal of a suitable size.

The Valve

The machining of the valve should be quite straight-forward, and no complications should arise. There are a variety of methods of securing the valve to the valve rod - whichever is used some form of adjustment is necessary and this usually takes the form of a screw. Another idea is a buckle that encloses the valve and again is fitted with a screw adjuster. As a rule the valve is left to float free vertically and the pressure of the steam in the steam chest keeps it tight on the port face. A number of methods have

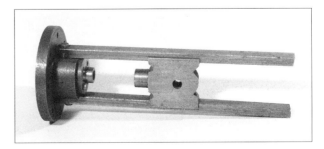

Flats on the covers are used as securing points for the slide bars as demonstrated in this photograph. The gland in this instance is round and fitted with studs and nuts.

The cavity in the slide valve may be cast in and only need cleaning up. If not it can be formed with an end mill or slot drill.

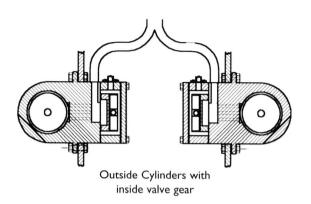

Outside Cylinders with inside valve gear

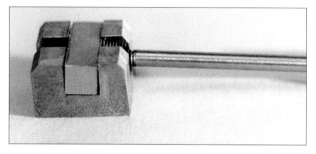

A finished slide valve, fitted to the spindle with a nut, which must be a good fit to avoid movement during working.

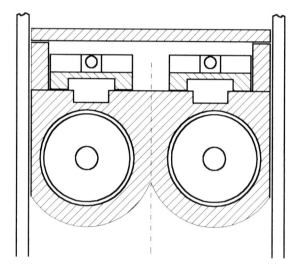

been devised to give slide valves extra sealing properties by mechanically holding them in position but as a rule these refinements are not necessary.

Valve Positions

There are numerous positions in which slide valves are used. If the cylinders are outside the frames then there are two variations. If the valve gear is also outside the frames then almost certainly the valves will be above the block. If the valve gear is inside the frames and the cylinders outside, the valves will either be above the block, and worked via a rocker gear, or at the side of it and worked direct. In this case it is necessary to cut a hole in the frames to accept part of the cylinder block. Where inside cylinders are employed there are a number of variations for the position of the valves, as shown in the following sketches.

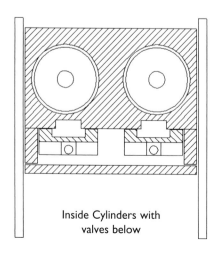

Inside Cylinders with valves below

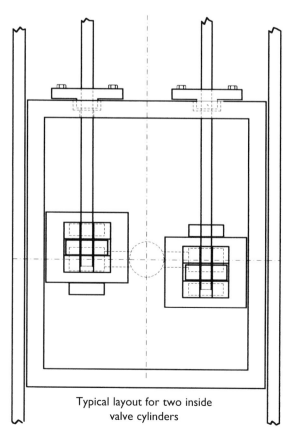

Typical layout for two inside valve cylinders

57

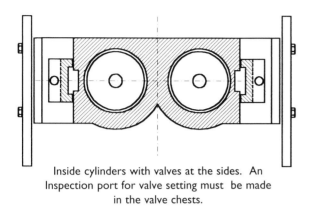

Inside cylinders with valves at the sides. An Inspection port for valve setting must be made in the valve chests.

Inspection plate for valve setting
(Alternatively may be below valves)

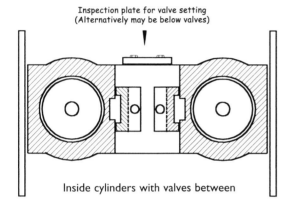

Inside cylinders with valves between

Piston Valves

The general description of machining cylinder blocks, end covers etc. applies equally well to the construction of piston valve cylinders. The steam chest is in the form of a small cylinder which will be integral with the casting - this means boring another hole parallel to the cylinder bore, ensuring it is exactly that. At this point life gets a little more complicated. The valve, or bobbin as it is generally known, passes over the port leading to the cylinder end and the steam is admitted from inside and exhausted outside. The ports are opened and closed by the valve movement. This is the exact opposite of a slide valve that has the steam enter the port ahead of the valve. Readers wishing to make small scale models can make use of this. As working in such small areas is difficult, a locomotive can be reversed by changing the flow of steam from inside admission to outside. While quite useful in the smaller sizes, larger models should always rely on the valve gear for reversing.

Liners

Looking at the drawings it soon becomes obvious that making the steam ports so they are correctly spaced inside the valve cylinder is very awkward indeed. It is possible to drill through the casing and right into the valve chamber, sealing the outer hole afterwards but it still leaves some fairly complicated

work to be done to get the exhaust out, which now comes from outside the valve ends and, as you now have two exhausts from each valve chest, rather than the single one with the slide valve, it is necessary to join them up. It is most important to have a free flowing exhaust and so, to make everything work smoothly, the usual practice is to fit a liner which has the ports milled in it. It also means that the valve can have larger and better flowing exhaust. The liner is generally a push fit into the bore but there is no

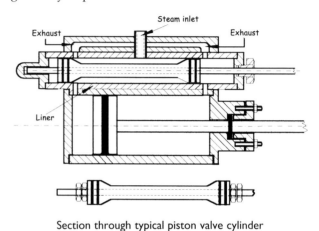

Section through typical piston valve cylinder and detail of valve bobbin.

reason why it should not be secured with a retaining compound. It is usual to make it of bronze, both for ease of machining and to prevent rust forming. Where piston valves are used on garden gauge models, the valve system is simplified and ports drilled direct into the bore.

The Valve or Bobbin

The biggest difficulty with piston valves on models is to get them steam tight. The bobbin can be seen in the drawing to consist of two piston like ends, joined by a central section, and the problem of lack of tightness is because generally the piston areas have to be short, and so the slightest discrepancy in diameter will allow steam to leak. Attempts which have been fairly successful have been made to solve the problem by fitting Teflon valves or rings. It is more usual to lap the valve in and make the piston sections as long as is practical. It is a good idea for the bobbin to be made as a separate unit to the valve spindle, to allow for adjustment of its position on the spindle. While it may require a little more care to make piston valves when compared with slide valves, there is no doubt that, well made, they are a great deal more efficient.

Other Valve Types

As previously stated, it is not proposed to expand on the various other types of valves, such as rotary cam and poppet as it is thought that any one tackling such a project will be well able to sort the machining out for themselves. At the time of writing there are no known drawings of model locomotives with these types of valve, although they were used on locomotives towards the end of the days of steam in Britain and fairly extensively for many years in France and North America. A number of modellers have used them where appropriate and they appear to work very well.

Pistons

As we are dealing with cylinders it is natural also to give thought to the piston and piston rods that will be used in them. These are amongst the least complicated of the items needed for the locomotive. The actual piston may be machined from a casting supplied with the cylinder set or from a piece of solid bar. It is usual for the material to be the same as that used for the cylinder. Piston rods should be made of stainless steel. The most important thing to remember is that piston and rod must be machined in such a manner that they are absolutely concentric with each other.

A piston, in this instance to be fitted with an "O" ring.

Assuming the piston rod is to be screwed into the piston a personal preference is to start with the rod and set it accurately in a four-jaw independent chuck. Machine the rod to the size required for the thread and remember that it is going to have to be a good and tight thread, not a sloppy one. Next run the die along it and, to ensure that it will go right home, put a very slight undercut on the rod. Some people are content to just thread the rod into the piston and leave it at that but, for security, it is better to put a slight counterbore in the end of the piston and fit a locknut.

Although greater accuracy is always possible with the four-jaw chuck, the piston itself can be dealt with in a three-jaw and the required accuracy maintained. The machining of the outside diameter, the grooves for packing or piston rings and the thread for the rod, must all be machined at the one setting, which

will ensure they are concentric. There is a school of thought that the final finish should be obtained by mounting the piston on the rod, which is held in the chuck for the final machining. It does not take too much thought to realise that if the rod, when returned to the chuck, does not run true the whole assembly is thrown out. Also it is very bad practice to hold a small diameter section whilst machining a larger one as there is every danger of the work seizing when the pressure of the tool is brought against the outer diameter, causing scoring of the piston rod.

Packing

The type of packing used in the piston is mainly a matter of personal choice. At one time it was inevitably graphited string rammed hard into one or two grooves. An update on that is to use PTFE tape, but it is necessary to be very careful when doing so, to ensure it does not unravel itself. It should be wrapped as tightly as possible into the groove ensuring the whole area is filled up. The loose end must be forced down the side of the groove, for at least half its circumference, with a tiny screwdriver and then using either the screwdriver or a thumbnail spread the PTFE over the top of the tuck. The material expands with heat and so there should be no danger of it unwrapping.

Piston Rings

The use of piston rings is now very popular, particularly where cast iron cylinders are concerned. They can be purchased in standard sizes but are quite easy to make. Thin rings of cast iron are parted off, including a couple of spares to take care of mishaps. The rings are laid on a piece of metal plate on the bench and with a chisel, or even a modelling

A nice example of a finished cylinder block.
Outwardly it appears to have piston valves, but it could well be a slide valve type cleverly disguised.

We expect to see cylinders at the ends of locomotives. This very unusual model, built by Don Allison,
is of a German prototype with a double-ended cylinder in the middle - some tricky steam passages make this possible.

knife if the rings are thin enough, a split is made at an angle of about forty-five degrees. It is during this operation that the spares might be required. The secret is not to make the rings too thick either in section or width. 'O' rings have also proved popular in recent years and if these are fitted, care must be taken to ensure that the ring can expand. Correct depth and width of the slot can be obtained from suppliers and manufacturers and their figures should be adhered to; failure to do so will inevitably result in flats appearing on the rings after a short period of time.

Yet another modern idea is to make piston rings from Teflon. They are made in exactly the same way as the cast iron types but a lot of time needs to be spent in removing all the burrs and ragged edges that build up very quickly during machining. The gap in the rings should be made with a small saw to allow for the expansion of the material; this expansion is actually one of its advantages. Another advantage of the use of Teflon for piston rings is that less lubrication is required and the fact that the material expands with heat ensures a good steam - tight fit to the pistons.

Built correctly with three cylinders, the Gresley conjugated drive to the centre cylinder of this 5" gauge A4 class 4-6-2
can be seen in front of the outside cylinder.

Whilst hardly a design suitable for the novice, Ken Swan's "Bridget" 0-4-2 tank design in 7¼" gauge makes an attractive, powerful, but still reasonably light locomotive for this gauge. Although freelance, the design is based on industrial practice, hence the unusual sloping steam chest. This excellent example of the design was built by Don Brook of Huddersfield.

Jean Villette

As mentioned earlier, Jean Villette organised the Metz Exhibition where, for the first time, model engineers from a number of countries got together with their locomotives.

A man of boundless enthusiasm, especially where railways and model engineering were concerned, Jean had been writing articles for French model railway magazines, on miniature railways and locomotives, since the mid 50s, and eventually published his own magazine on the subject. He was widely travelled, often with his 7¼" gauge Decauville 0-4-0 tank "Elda"(above), named after his wife. His design for this locomotive and many others, together his magazine, and the national club he established, were significant factors in the growth of model engineering in France.

Chapter 9: Valve Gears

Multiplicity of Designs

Probably the thing that fascinates people most about a steam locomotive is the valve gear, which at first glance seems highly complicated, although most are generally quite simple. The making of valves and parts for valve gears are dealt with in the next chapter; here we take a look at how some of the various valve gears developed and their uses on models.

There are numerous valve gear designs - frequently various locomotive builders would use their own which they obviously thought to be particularly efficient. As one would expect, valve gears improved as time went on and it is doubtful whether the ultimate efficiency was ever obtained. It is not possible to give details about all of these as that would take a complete volume in itself, particularly as there were many variations of individual designs - the most popular are discussed and this should assist generally in their construction. Readers wanting more details will find plenty of published information available about individual valve gear types. If for any reason the idea of working out ones own measurements does not appeal it is worth considering using the valve gear from a well tried published design and making minor adjustments to measurements as required so that it will fit the model.

Good Design

The valve gear ensures that the valves let the steam in and out of the cylinders at the required time. It follows that a well designed and well made valve gear on a locomotive will improve its performance. It will also improve its efficiency, making it more economical in operation. Generally speaking the latter is of little consequence to anyone operating their model, as the quantities of coal and water used during an afternoon or so are hardly likely to break the bank, or cause a major disaster to the environment. Efficiency in other ways certainly is,

as good designing can be one of the means of increasing hauling power, which in turn means better starting and easier operation. Of course the valve gear alone does not do all this; a good boiler and a well designed smoke box all play their part alongside good springing and weight distribution and so we must strive to get all these things as near right as possible.

The History

Long before there were steam locomotives there were steam engines. They were used at first to pump water from mines and later to drive machinery of various sorts. The very early ones were a far cry from even the earliest locomotives. They did not even work on the same principle, relying on atmospheric pressure to operate the cylinder, steam being just a means of creating a vacuum to allow this to happen. As it was realised that more power could be obtained by allowing the steam to actually do the work, so a means of getting it into the cylinder at the right time and allowing it out again were being sought. Actually getting it out can be very simple - drill a large hole in the cylinder just at the end of the piston stroke and as the piston comes back so the steam will escape. This may sound over-simplified but the idea was used on stationary steam engines, which were called *Uniflow*; steam entry, however, still needs to be controlled by some form of tap or valve.

Walschaerts Valve gear on a French Compound Locomotive. The inside cylinders have separate valve gear. Note the use of cotters on the connecting rod and the overall neat, almost flimsy appearance of the various components.

Technology Takes Over

Getting the steam in at the right time was also not too difficult. Labour was very cheap, so they had a man, or more likely a young boy or girl, stand there and open a tap at the right time and in went the steam just when it was needed. It must have been the most boring job ever thought of, and we can only speculate as to how many times the person let his or her thoughts wander and there was nothing to force the piston back. Movement of the piston was mainly dominated by a large flywheel, the momentum of which took it past both front and back dead centres - on a locomotive this function is taken on by the driving wheels. Perhaps the valve operator may have had time to realise the mistake and let in some steam just in time to keep the engine going. There is little doubt that some of the operators did find the job very boring and at some time or another a metal rod or piece of wood was lashed up so that the movement of the piston rod would open and close the tap. When this actually happened we do not know, but it was the earliest form of valve gear.

Automatic Operation

Although there are exceptions with which this book is not really concerned, generally speaking it is a waste of time letting steam in to the cylinder in the same cycle as the stroke of the piston. The valve needs to open a fraction before the piston gets to the end of its stroke, which means it is not possible to connect the valve directly to the big end crank. Another crank of some sort or another is needed and this can be a disc on the crankshaft which, if bored off centre, will rotate out of sequence with it. Put a strap round that and connect it to the valve and we have a means of operation which, by adjusting the position of the disc, can adjust the time when the valve opens and closes. The disc is known as the eccentric and it was not very long before the idea was taken up by engine builders.

Developments

Only after the discovery of the use of eccentric was it possible to build successful locomotives, as it is hardly feasible to have someone standing on the running board opening and closing a tap. The use of an eccentric is not the end of the story or anywhere near it; a single eccentric directly connected to a valve can only operate that valve at a given point, which means the locomotive would only go one way, but use two set at different angles from the crank and both forward and reverse are possible. Now the design of valve gears was being thought about seriously and things were never to be the

same as, for the rest of the period of the life of steam locomotives, designers were going to try and improve the valve gear.

Slip Eccentric

Possibly the simplest type of reversible valve gear is the slip eccentric. In its basic form it can only be reversed by giving the model a little push in the opposite direction to which it had been travelling. It consists of an eccentric for each cylinder running loose on an axle, immediately next to it is a stop collar, which is fixed to the axle and catches on a peg in the eccentric. The collar drives the eccentric one way and when it is rotated half a turn backwards by pushing the model, the collar catches the other side of the peg and drives it backwards. One set is needed for each valve, but frequently in small gauges, models have only a single inside cylinder,

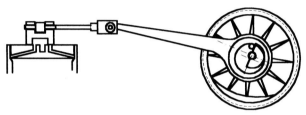

Slip Eccentric Valve Gear

relying on the momentum of the wheels to act like a flywheel, and keep things going. Various ideas have been used to make the gear reversible by adding a lever that will rotate the eccentric, some of which work quite well.

A well designed valve gear will allow the entry of steam to be cut off at various points. By doing this the expansive properties of the steam is used to its greatest effect.

The slip eccentric gear does not allow any change in the position of cut off, but on small models this is of no consequence.

Using an Expansion Link

If we take a strip of metal, put a curved slot in it with the same radius as it is from the axle, connect it to the eccentric by a rod and pivot it centrally, we have an expansion link. This is used in the more advanced gears. A block, called the die block, slides in a slot, curved to the same radius as the link and is connected to the valve rod. If the die block is pulled to the top of the slot the locomotive will travel in one direction - take it to the bottom and the effect is the same as with the slip eccentric gear and the engine goes the other way. Which way it does go depends on the setting of the eccentrics that are usually adjusted so that when the link is at the top, the engine goes forward. The die block is connected to a lever in the cab and moving this alters the position, so we do not have to push the model to change direction, merely alter the lever. The single eccentric gear shown below works on this principle. Although it still does not allow a variable steam cut-off, it is one step of advancement from the slip eccentric. Because only a single eccentric is used it is not very efficient and is not at all suitable for passenger hauling models.

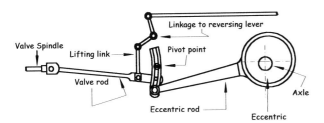

Simple reversing valve gear using a single Eccentric

Hackworth Valve Gear

There were several types of valve gear which used a single eccentric in full sized practice, and these are generally known as radial gears. As far as modellers are concerned the *Hackworth* Gear is far and away the most popular of these. It was invented by the famous locomotive designer, John Hackworth, around 1859, so it is one of the earliest of locomotive gears and it is particularly popular with builders of narrow gauge models. It is a comparatively easy gear to build and although it does not have the sophisticated control of steam of some of the gears to be described later, it is very efficient. It is best used on models with outside cylinders as the design means that parts of it ride quite high above the top of the frames. If used inside it is likely to foul the boiler unless that is pitched very high and setting up the eccentrics also becomes rather difficult.

Hackworth Valve gear in use on a narrow gauge locomotive. This particular example, which is true to prototype, differs from most in that the rods acting as links are round rather than flat, a practice more generally used on marine engines. It can also be seen how high the valve gear is and why it is difficult to use as an inside gear because of boiler clearance.

Two Eccentrics

So far the gears we have talked of use a single eccentric to get the required movement. If instead we use two and connect one to each end of the expansion link, it is possible to get a better degree of adjustment. One needs to be in a position to drive the model forward and the other to drive it backwards. Moving our die block from one end to the other takes the valve drive from a different eccentric, making things much more controllable. It is also now possible to start to move the die block in steps along the expansion link and vary the point at which the steam is cut off. This system was used by a number of designers who had their own ideas as to how the parts should be joined together and the result was a whole host of different valve gears.

Stephenson's Valve Gear

As the name indicates this valve gear was designed by the famous firm of *Robert Stephenson* and is

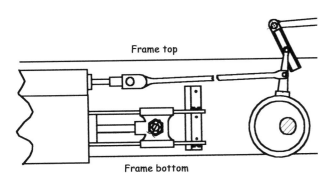

Hackworth valve gear

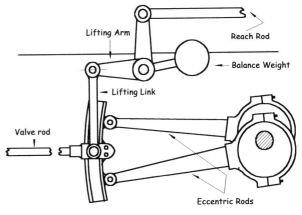

Stephenson's valve gear

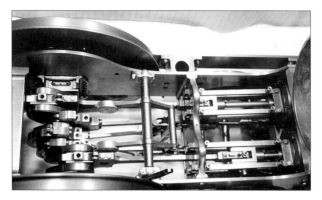

Stephenson's Valve gear for an inside cylinder locomotive under construction. Note the provision made in the eccentrics for oil caps to be screwed in.

Simple basic Walschaerts Valve Gear. Well made and neat, it enhances the appearance of the locomotive.

known as a link motion. One of the most popular valve gears ever designed, it was used in all countries where steam locomotives were to be found. It follows the same basic pattern of two eccentrics pushing the lower and upper half of an expansion link. The die block is lifted or lowered as required. Various designs of expansion link and minor variations occur in the linkages, making variations in the valve gear itself. It is mainly used for inside valve gear working on inside cylinders, but there have been notable examples of it as an outside gear with outside cylinder locomotives.

Another fine example of Walschaerts Gear in model form. It differs from the previous photograph but is still true to the prototype.

Walschaerts Valve Gear.

Walschaerts valve gear in later years became more popular than Stephensons. There were a number of reasons for this, one being ease of access for maintenance and the more common use of outside cylinders; some people also considered it more efficient than the valve gears then in use. To those not used to making such things it may at first appear to be very complicated, in fact quite the contrary is true. Designed by Belgium Locomotive Engineer *M. Egide Walschaerts*, it was to be found on many locomotives built from the early 1900s on. It was actually invented as early as 1844 and it is difficult to know why it took so long to achieve popularity, at least as far as Great Britain was concerned. It is suitable for use on outside cylinders but can also be

Walschaerts Valve gear was used all over the world. This is a full sized Polish Locomotive to a German design; note the hefty support bracket, made from steel channel.

used as an inside valve gear, it is also suitable for slide or piston valves. With slide valves the return crank is set to give an angle of ninety degrees in advance, for piston valves it is retarded by the same amount. As with all valve gears there were variations in design particularly in the expansion link and support brackets.

Baker Valve Gear

As Walschaerts gear eventually became a firm favourite with British designers so did the Baker gear with those of North America and a number of other countries. It was invented by *Abner Baker*, an American, in 1905 and that is possibly the reason it

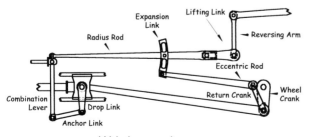

Walschaerts valve gear.
As drawn it is suitable for piston valves; for slide valves the return crank follows the wheel crank.

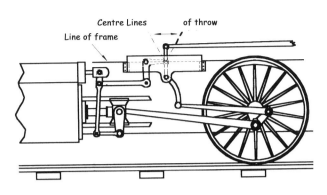

Baker Valve Gear

Poppet and Rotary Cam Valve Gears are not often seen on models, probably because of the large number of tiny parts that are required. This fine example is for a model of the LNER Locomotive "Cock of the North".

found favour there. Unlike most popular valve gears there is no expansion link; adjustments and reversing being controlled by a bell crank. A feature of this valve gear is the heavy bracket used to support it. It relies on a series of links to operate the gear and for this reason care must be taken when making the pins for the various links and the holes into which they fit. If they are too loose there will be loss of motion in the gear and efficiency will be lost.

Other Types of Gear

The gears described have proved the most popular and long lasting and it is for that reason that they have been mentioned in detail. Readers wishing to build models of older prototypes may find they use a valve gear of unusual design. Generally speaking it should be possible to find out some details of how it worked by reference to a specialist museum, such as the *Science Museum* in London, or the *National Railway Museum* in York, as well as from a regional museums, particularly one in an area formerly involved in locomotive building. If they do not have details it is quite probable that help will be given on where to obtain the required information. Readers with access to the Internet can find information relating to all types of valve gear.

Poppet and Rotary Cam Gears.

In latter years a number of designers used gears working on either the rotary cam or poppet principle, the latter in many ways similar to the valves on a motor car. There are a number of different types and they give excellent steam distribution but are not generally popular with modellers, due to the large number of tiny parts that are required. The gears operate in a variety of ways, but still mostly use a system of levers and eccentrics. Some have oscillating cams and other rotary, the action of which opens and closes the valves. Sometimes gears are part of the set up, particularly where linear motion is changed to rotary motion. No doubt, had

the development of steam locomotives continued, they would have become more popular on models; as it is, only a few dedicated modellers appear to be willing to experiment with their manufacture.

Multiple Cylinder Engines.

Many designers built locomotives with more than two cylinders and this sometimes posed problems with valve gears. Sometimes a set was used for each cylinder and some odd arrangements resulted. It is not unknown for a locomotive to have one type operating the outside cylinders and an entirely different one operating the inside ones. Compounding, where the exhaust steam from one pair of high pressure cylinders was used to drive a larger, low pressure cylinder or cylinders, sometimes resulted in some pretty odd valve gear arrangements in the early days. There is even an instance where the inside cylinder of a class of compounds used slip eccentrics, which resulted in difficulties in starting the engine.

As well as using different types of valve gears for each cylinder, designers might also use some form of rocking arrangement, the valve on one cylinder operating another via a system of levers and pivots. Possibly the best known example of this was the conjugated design of *Sir Nigel Gresley* who liked to build three cylinder engines. The valve on the inside cylinder was operated by a rather clever arrangement of levers connected to both outside cylinders, using a fixed pivot two thirds of the way along its length. The whole arrangement was bolted to a special bracket across the frames. It gave the locomotive an unusual sound that was instantly recognisable and when modelled this sound is also apparent. The idea of rockers was also employed on four cylinder engines, almost certainly with the intention of easing maintenance. The inclusion of

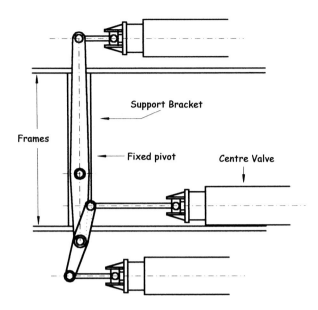

Sir Nigel Gresley's conjugated valve gear
for three cylinder locomotives.

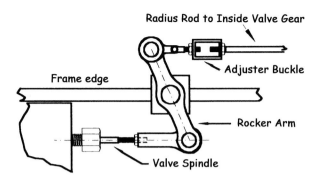

Arrangement of rocker to transfer inside motion
to outside valve chest.

some form of adjustment and extra pivots to allow
the various components to swing in line generally
meant heavy wear on those pivots which in the end
defeated the idea of cutting down on maintenance,
although it was easier to change the bearings in
those than on a full set of valve gear.

Inside Gear Outside Valves

The use of rockers is not confined to multiple
cylinder engines as they are also used to transfer the
motion from inside the frames to the cylinders
outside. The idea was often used in full sized practice
and is popular with model makers particularly where
slip eccentric valve gear is used. It is simple enough
to do, requiring just a pivot and a lever to make the
transfer.

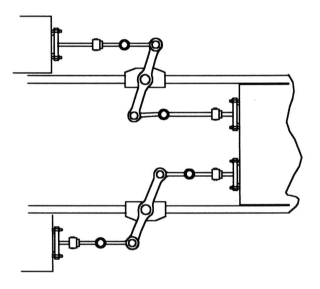

A method of using two rocking levers to operate
the inside cylinders of a four cylinder locomotive
with outside valve gear.

Heinz Muller's exquisite 5" gauge model of the German Crampton "Badenia" uses an outside form of Stephenson's valve gear.

Chapter 10: Making Valve Gears
(good distribution = good running)

Eccentrics and Straps

Reading the preceding chapter on valve gear types it is obvious that basically any valve gear is going to rely on some form of eccentric for its operation. There is nothing complicated about an eccentric and indeed the term can be applied to anything that is not running concentrically. The eccentric is purely used as a means of converting rotary motion to reciprocal and, by positioning it correctly, to open and close valves at the correct moment in relation to the movement of the piston in the cylinder.

Valve gear eccentrics take two forms. The round type as used on slip eccentric, Stephenson's etc., and the plain type used with Walschaerts and similar gears. The latter are pretty straightforward, consisting of little more than a flat bar; it isn't, of course, quite that straightforward as it is necessary to set the eccentric at the correct angle in relation to the piston rod, as well as connecting it to the rest of the valve gear.

Probably the easiest way of making a round type of eccentric is to first machine the groove for the strap and the ideal tool for this is a parting tool. Carefully mark out the distance off centre that the hole must be, set the eccentric in a four-jaw chuck and use a wobbler to ensure that the mark for the hole is central. It can be bored at that setting and it is best to bore it rather than drill and ream. Eccentrics should be made of steel or cast iron and can be secured with

The eccentric which is being made from mild steel bar, is being started off by machining the groove, using a squared off parting tool held in a rear tool post.

The position of the hole has been marked and centre punched, a wobbler and clock gauge is used to set it running centrally in the four jaw chuck.

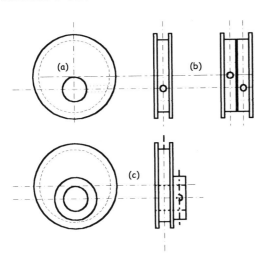

(a) Shows an eccentric held in place by a grub screw
(b) When two eccentrics are side by side, the mating ribs can be dispensed with, the straps preventing each other from riding off.
(c) In this case a boss has been machined on the eccentric, making it easier to secure.

With the material in position, drilling can be started. A centre drill is used as a beginning, followed by a drill and a reamer; this being a part that is not going to rotate on a shaft, a good fit is needed. A better alternative to reaming is to use a small boring bar and accurately bore the hole to size.

*A nice example of finished eccentrics made in the
way suggested in this chapter.*

*Some eccentrics are fitted with a boss as an aid
to holding them in position, this can be machined
at the same setting as the drilling or boring operation.*

a grub screw while adjustments to the valves are made and then pinned to prevent them slipping.

Eccentric straps are bolted round the eccentrics and are usually made from castings but can be

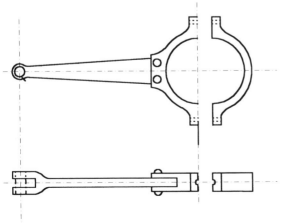

A common method of making Eccentric Straps and Rods

manufactured from solid bar. Start by drilling and tapping through the casting for the screws that will ultimately hold the two halves together, don't at this stage put in the screws. Instead cut the casting in two. It is best to use a slitting saw, which will give an accurate cut. Screw the two halves together and

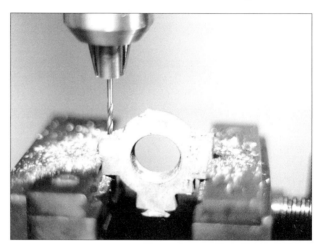

*Start by cleaning the flash off the castings for the eccentric
straps with a file then, after careful marking out, drill the holes for the
bolts that will hold the two halves together, use a tapping sized drill.
Open out the hole for half its distance with a clearance drill
and then tap the remainder.*

*Split the strap in half, either with a hack saw or
better still, as shown here, with a slitting saw.
Clean off any burrs and bolt the two parts together.*

*An example of a casting that has been drilled, tapped and split and
one waiting to be dealt with.*

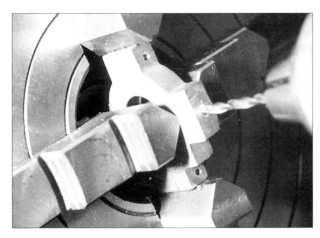

*If the strap is to be screwed to the rod, as is often
the way with small gauge models, now is the time to drill and tap it
using the four-jaw chuck for accuracy.
The hole can also be used as a means of lining up a rod on a strap
where a flange and bolts are used to fix the rod to the end.*

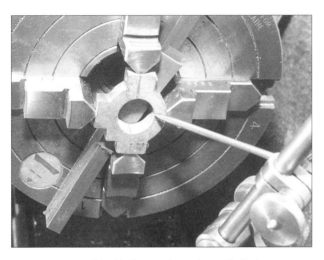

*Use a scribing block to set the casting up for boring.
Note that a packing piece has been put behind it in order to keep it
square while setting takes place.*

*The casting can now be bored to size. Care must be taken to get the
bore accurate, as trying to remount it accurately is an almost
impossible task.*

*Once bored the only remaining task is to machine the
sides for both a good finish and a good fit between the lips of the
eccentric. It is possible to do this by remounting it in the four jaw
chuck, but a better arrangement is to machine a bar to a
tiny fraction over the diameter of the strap bore.
With the casting mounted on the bar, machining the sides is easy.*

An example of two types of eccentric with straps to fit.

*It may be necessary to machine either a groove or a slot
with which to secure the rod, although some designs call for it
to be mounted via a bar and bolts on the end.*

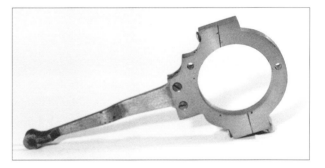

*In this example the rod is screwed in a slot in the strap and then
secured with countersunk screws, although rivets would be more
correct. It is interesting to note the two holes in the strap that appear
to be for no particular purpose. They are actually clearance holes for
bolts and four straps had been bolted together for boring. The
advantages being both a saving in time and the ability to ensure all
the bores are the same. The holes can either be tapped and a piece
of brass rod screwed in, or a piece can be soldered in place.
Either way when cleaned up they will not notice.*

Even small gauge models can be built with correct valve gear. Shown here are an eccentric and strap compared with a 5p piece, the parts being for a gauge '0' model.

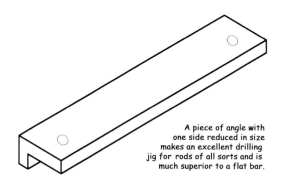

A piece of angle with one side reduced in size makes an excellent drilling jig for rods of all sorts and is much superior to a flat bar.

machine the hole to the correct size using either the four-jaw chuck or the faceplate. It is possible to screw several straps together and machine them all at a single setting, thus ensuring that all the holes are identical. The operation will mean drilling and tapping through the side of them. The holes can either be left or filled afterwards with small lengths of brass bar fitted in position with a retaining compound.

The Various Rods

From the drawings of the various types of valve gear it is obvious that most consist of a number of rods acting as links and the pins to join them together. We can add to that coupling and connecting rods as all these parts will require similar methods of construction. Sometimes there will be expansion links and die blocks, in addition to the eccentrics and eccentric straps. A formidable sounding list, but nowhere near as daunting as all that.

Materials

Most parts for valve gears can be made of mild steel, but the piston and valve rods should be stainless steel. Where practical all holes that will accept pins and act as bearing surfaces should be bushed with bronze. In the smaller scales bushing may not be practical and in that case the bearing holes should be case hardened. The pins can be made of either mild steel or silver steel, both of which wear quite well. There have been some excellent examples of small ball races being used instead of plain bearings and, whilst not generally full sized practice, the idea makes sense.

Construction of the many and various small rods will follow basically the same pattern for all except the return crank on Walschaerts Gear. It is essential that care is taken to drill and ream the holes for the pins accurately and as matched pairs. For this reason a small jig is advised. It does not have to be elaborate. A simple piece of flat bar with two correctly

spaced holes will do, the holes should be of a smaller diameter than will ultimately be needed in the rods. A good alternative to a piece of bar is a length of angle which will allow the metal to butt up to the edges and make errors in alignment less likely.

Using suitable sized pieces of mild steel, but longer than will be required, mark out the shape of the rods, centre punch and drill one of the holes in each. The holes should be smaller than will be required and match the holes in the jig, they must also be a size for which a suitable piece of steel to act as a peg is available. Pass a peg through the jig and the rod, carefully lining the other end with the jig, clamp the two together and drill through. Repeat the operation on each rod, they must be identical and can be opened out and reamed to the correct size after shaping is completed.

Shaping

Shaping of the straight sections can either be done with a file or on the milling machine, using the drilling jig as a means of supporting and holding the work during operations. Many of the rods will also need to be thinned along their length and in most cases this is best left until the ends have been finished. There may be some instances where it is desirable to do otherwise but generally speaking the more metal there is on the rods to give support during the rounding off operations the better.

Rounding the Ends

If a rotary table is available and the rods are not too small the obvious thing is to mill the rounded ends to shape. Make up a pin with a centre in it and slide it into the bearing hole. Use a pointer in the milling machine to ensure that it is centrally under the quill. Clamp the rod tightly on to the rotary table and move the milling table sufficiently to start operations. Take care to make a note of the dial readings on the final cut, so that they can be used for subsequent operations and repeat the operation for each end of each rod.

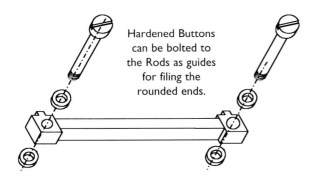

Hardened Buttons can be bolted to the Rods as guides for filing the rounded ends.

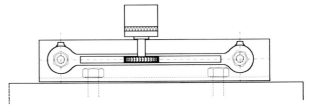

Rods can be fluted by bolting them to a piece of Angle and using a Side and Face Cutter.

If the ends cannot be milled it will be necessary to resort to filing; a well tried method is to make a couple of buttons from silver steel, harden them and use these as guides for filing the rods to shape. If possible when using this method file both rods to shape at once as it is easier to get them both the same if done together.

Finishing

Whether filed or milled it will be necessary to finish the ends with emery cloth, which can be done in a vice and, if strips of material are pulled lengthways round the curve, the result can be very good. An alternative is to use either the milling or drilling machine with a piece of round mild steel to which is stuck emery cloth. The part itself is used as a lever to move it round the tool after being screwed to a heavy metal plate with a spacer, the plate held tight in a machine vice or bolted to the table. If anyone has a vertical sanding machine this is an ideal tool for the purpose. Make up a small plate with a pin in it the size of the bearing holes and clamp to the table. The rod is simply slipped over this and pulled round until the required shape is reached. It is even possible to get the reverse curve by fitting a simple homemade attachment to the machine. The belt is invariably supported by a plate along which it runs. Change this for a round bar and cut a belt lengthways to the required size, it will now roll round the bar and inside curves can easily be generated.

Do not be tempted to pull the rod on a pivot against a milling cutter. There is every likelihood of the cutter snatching the work and causing a very nasty accident.

Fluting

If the rods require fluting it can be done with a small milling cutter either on a milling machine or a vertical slide. End milling in some instances gives the wrong profile and a small side and face cutter is the best tool. If one of suitable size is not available, either a number of cuts with a small slitting saw or a home

made cutter will have to be used. Such a tool is only really a fly cutter in disguise, the single tool having been ground to the shape required for the groove. Where the flutes are both rounded at the ends and tapered out of the groove it may be possible to grind an end mill to an angle to obtain the required profile.

When making the type of groove requiring a side and face cutter, it will probably be possible to hold the work in a vice if a vertical slide is used, which is not usually possible on a vertical milling machine, and so the component should be bolted to an angle plate. It does not have to be anything other than a piece of angle iron, pressed into service for the job. In some ways this has advantages as the angle iron can be drilled and tapped to hold the work, while with an angle plate we have to make use of whatever slots and holes are available. Whichever method is used the cutter is unlikely to leave a smooth finish which will have to be obtained by using a piece of hardwood, cut to shape and covered in grinding paste, which is rubbed along the groove until a nice smooth finish is obtained.

A neat example of Walschaerts Valve gear on a 5" gauge model. Note the careful attention to detail and the cross head used to support the valve spindle.

In full sized practice most rods that were fluted had the grooves on both sides. This was to save weight and for balance, not for appearance. In the case of a model the fluting is for the opposite reason, weight and balance are generally of little consequence in the scales we are talking about, and so fluting can be carried out on one side only

Forked Rods

Some rods have forked ends and there are two ways of making these. Firstly by using a piece of metal of full thickness and making the slot with a slitting saw or milling cutter and then reducing the rest of the rod to the required thickness. Alternatively silver solder a piece on, which means making a spacer to exactly the correct thickness, to locate the parts. This gives a nice square end to the slot, but care must be taken to ensure the spacer is not also silver soldered. To prevent this happening, before assembly, cover the spacer in typing fluid (the white stuff used for correcting mistakes).

Expansion Links

Shaping expansion links can either be carried out using a rotary table on a milling machine, filing by hand, or as an alternative by making up a special device that will give the required curve, using the vertical slide on the lathe.

To use the rotary table, bolt a length of metal to it with a suitable spacer made from scrap metal underneath. Set the milling cutter precisely in line with it and then move the table the exact distance required to obtain the radius by referring to the graduations. That gives the exact place for the slot to be cut and it should be possible to use the same setting for the second link. Further movement of the table will give the other required radii. If the links are going to be filed, it is as well to indulge in a little chain drilling first, but do not use a drill of a full diameter. Use a

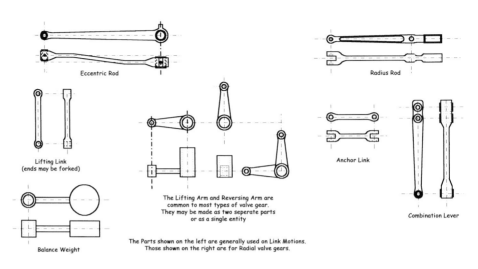

The Lifting Arm and Reversing Arm are common to most types of valve gear. They may be made as two seperate parts or as a single entity

The Parts shown on the left are generally used on Link Motions. Those shown on the right are for Radial valve gears.

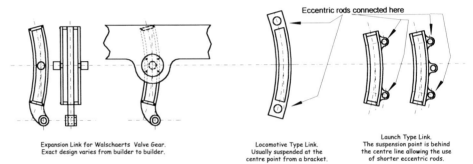

Expansion Link for Walschaerts Valve Gear. Exact design varies from builder to builder.

Locomotive Type Link. Usually suspended at the centre point from a bracket.

Launch Type Link. The suspension point is behind the centre line allowing the use of shorter eccentric rods.

Expansion Link design and construction

A simple home made device for milling expansion links on a lathe, using the vertical slide to generate the required radius.

smaller size and then if there is a slight error in alignment it can be corrected with the file. The home made device for a vertical slide is used in exactly the same way as a rotary table and has much to commend it as control of the work is very easy using that method. The drawing should be self-explanatory and give sufficient information for anyone wanting to make it.

Materials

Expansion links should be made of gauge plate and hardened by heating the metal to a bright red (the colour of a boiled carrot) and quenching in vegetable oil. An alternative is to make them of mild steel, which is then case hardened. It is necessary in this case to have some idea of the type of steel in use, as some free cutting versions will not case harden very well - a recommended quality is EN32.

The shape of expansion links varies according to the

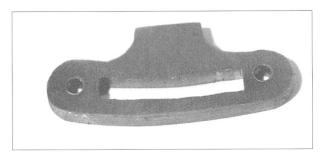

A expansion link for Stephensons Valve gear.

type of valve gear they are for. For instance with Stephensons Gear the link is often supported either top or bottom and raised or lowered with the die block remaining in position. With Walschaerts Gear it is supported centrally and sometimes made in a number of separate pieces. The expansion link remains in position and alterations are made by

An example of hand filed parts for an expansion link for Walschaerts Valve gear.

lifting and lowering the die block. Other valve gears operate on similar principles where they have an expansion link.

Die Blocks

The die block should be made of the same material as the link and also hardened, or alternatively they can be made of bronze. Bronze is not correct according to full-sized practice but it is unlikely to be noticed and has good wearing properties. Shaping the die block can be difficult if the expansion link has been made by using a rotary table, it should be possible to machine the die block by adjusting the settings. Make a long length of the correct radius and then cut it to length after it has been drilled. If the link and die block are filed to shape, getting the die block to match can be a frustrating operation. No matter how one tries there always seem to be gaps between the surfaces when they are put together. For the builder who is more concerned with building a running model than correct appearance, now is the time to really cheat. Make the die block of round material and allow it to run in the slot, like a roller, in fact try a small ball race, hours of work can be saved in this way.

Expansion Link Brackets

In the case of Walschaerts and some other gears the expansion link is held in place with a bracket. This may be quite a small piece bolted to the frames or in some cases a hefty girder. Almost invariably it will involve small angle sections for bolting the bracket to the frames. Castings are available, but expansion brackets are not difficult to fabricate. When doing so it is essential to ensure that the bearings for the pins are lined up truly so that the expansion link will be parallel to the frames and, secondly, that it is positioned absolutely correctly on the frames to ensure that the link is in the proper position.

Larger Rods

When we come to larger items such as coupling and connecting rods, construction is carried out in much the same way except that sometimes the bearings will differ. Many models have plain rounded ends to both types of rod, which is not always correct, although it does make life easier to make them in this way. Most prototypes had some sort of adjustable bearing and there is no reason why these should not be faithfully copied. They have the advantage that any wear can be taken up quite easily. Once again paying attention to full-sized locomotives will pay dividends, and little extra effort is required to get a finished component which, at the

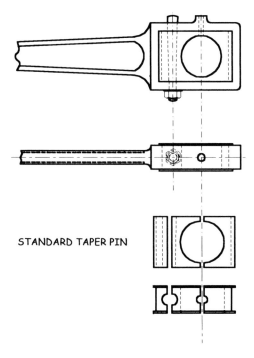

STANDARD TAPER PIN

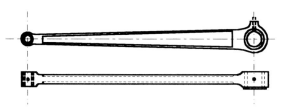

Most Rods have some form of adjustment.
This drawing shows construction using a Wedge and Cotter.

PLAIN TYPE OF BEARING
Whilst not strictly to prototype, a plain bearing connecting rod
is easy to make and works well when accurately machined.

very least, resembles the original even if it does not follow it faithfully. Having said that, if one wishes to make a model and is not too bothered about appearance, then ordinary rounded rod ends and plain bearings will be quite satisfactory.

Connecting Rods

Connecting rods bearings were frequently fitted with wedges and cotters, and on some narrow gauge engines the rod was virtually the same as we find on a traction engine. Although it is unlikely to be necessary on a model, the big end bearings of these frequently required to be adjusted to take up wear. The main thrust from the cylinders is sent along the connecting rod, to turn the driving wheels via a crank, and so the pressures involved are enormous and wear inevitable.

Coupling Rods

The coupling rods are used to couple the driving wheels together. Actually with very few exceptions there are only two driving wheels, the others are known as coupled wheels, but in general terms they all tend to be referred to as drivers. In the case of a four-coupled engine the coupling rods will probably take the same form as the connecting rods, except they will not be tapered. Constructional methods will therefore be exactly the same. If there are more than four coupled wheels a joint is necessary to allow the rods to flex as the wheels rise and fall on the springs. One section fits a pair of wheels and is extended slightly beyond the bearing. The second rod comes from the next pair of wheels and a forked joint allows the two to overlap. A pin goes through a hole in each and joins them together.

In theory it is quite simple, but getting the holes to line up can be a bit of a nightmare. Careful and exact measurement is by far the best method, but not

The late Eric Brown built models with an eye to getting everything as correct as possible. Here we see an example of connecting and coupling rods on an American locomotive, correctly fitted with cotters and wedges. As well as looking correct it also means that there is adjustment for wear if required.

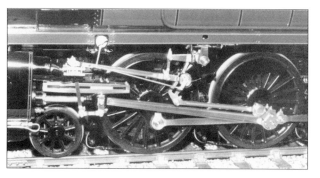

It would be difficult to build valve gear more accurately than this very fine example on a 5" gauge model of a 'Britannia' and anyone building a model would do well to aim at this sort of standard. The thin rod operates a lubricator and once again a cross head is there to support the valve spindle.

everyone finds that easy. The alternative is to make the section with two bearings first, including the fork but not the holes. Make the other section next but do not fit bearing bushes. Put extensions on the coupling rod pins to accept the holes in the rods and slide them on. It should now be possible to mark off the positions for the tongue and the holes. Make the tongue, either by milling or filing after drilling the pin hole undersize. Slip the rods back in position and mark through the holes to the original rods so that the exact position for drilling is known; drilling through in that position will result in perfectly lined up holes.

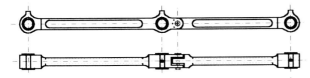

Construction of Knuckle Joint Coupling Rod of a Six Coupled Locomotive.
There must be one such joint for each pair of wheels exceeding four in number.

In the chapter dealing with crank pins a simple jig is described that will ensure they are all in the right place and quartering can be perfectly accurate as well, so any problems are going to come from the measurement between the axle bearing centres.

Spacing the Bearings

One of the best ways to get the correct measurement is to use a large pair of dividers and put the points in the axle centre holes. Providing the centres are not too large and have a nice pointed recess that will accept the divider points this can work quite well. There is always the possibility that the centres are not true, especially if the axles have been made in a three-jaw chuck and that puts things back to square one. Yet another idea is to put lengths of steel, the same diameters as the axles, through the axle holes in the assembled frames and measure the overall distance across them with a vernier gauge or a micrometer. Take the diameter of one axle away from the measurement and that is the exact distance between wheel centres.

Special Tooling

Not every one has a large enough Vernier Gauge, let alone micrometer, and a simple tool can be made from three pieces of mild steel and a couple of screws. Each piece has a hole the size of the bearing in it, the centre one has a slot either side, while the outer ones have holes drilled and tapped in them. The three pieces are put on the respective axles and the screws passed through the slots and tightened up when the correct position is found. This can then

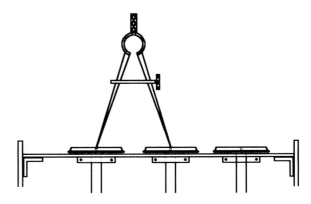

Using a pair of large Dividers to
check spacings for Connecting Rod bushes.

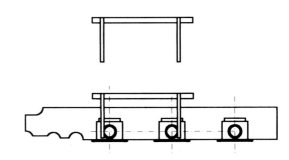

The distance required for location of bearings in Coupling Rods
may be determined by measuring the distance over a pair of axles
and then subtracting one axle diameter.
This can be done with Calipers, a Vernier or a Micrometer if large
enough ones are available. If not a device as shown above can be made.

be used to drill through the coupling rods giving the exact spacing. If there are more than six wheels repeat the operation for the next pair.

Cheating Again

If, even after all these efforts, the measurement is still a tiny bit out - something which happens all too often, in spite of every effort having been made to get things right - don't worry, there is still plenty of opportunity to retrieve the situation. Make up the bearing bushes, first turning the lip so they will fit nicely in the rod. Before drilling the hole slip a piece of shim, about five thou. thick between the metal and one chuck jaw and then bore the hole. The result will be a bearing bush that is ten thou. off centre. The bush for the other end can be made quite accurately. Put the rod on the crank pins after fitting the accurate bush. Put the second bush on the other pin and rotate it until it fits nicely into the hole in the rod. Secure it with a retaining compound after checking that the wheels will rotate without the rod binding. You now have a perfectly fitting coupling rod with a slightly off-centre bearing bush, but this will not affect the running of the locomotive in any way. Although a five thou. off-set has been suggested, this is an extreme figure, and it is much more likely that a shim of no more than two thou. will be needed to do the job.

Bushes

In general bearing bushes should be made of bronze and are a straightforward turning exercise, even allowing for the preceding little dodge. At one time they were always made as a press fit in the holes in which they were to locate, now proprietary retaining compounds is more likely to be used to secure them.

A nice example of spindle joints by Roger Nicholls.
Note particularly the care taken to round off the fork edges.

There is no harm in this, it is used to secure bearings in full sized industry, so must be strong enough for a model. Whilst it has been suggested that bearings are reamed this is not necessarily such a good idea.

Just occasionally split bushes may be needed. These are possibly best made as pairs. Soft solder two half round sections of brass together and bore them to size, without changing the set up use a squared off parting tool to make the grooves and then part off.

The finished bearings bushes, one having been heated to separate the parts.

Lifting Links for Stephensons Valve Gear, made by Roger Nicholls, another excellent example of what can be achieved if care is taken. Readers should not ponder too much on the angle of the reversing rod as it was put that way as a means of suspending the valve gear while the photograph was taken.

A reamed hole rotating on a shaft will be stiff and this stiffness is multiplied by the number of bearings making it very difficult in the end to get anything to move. The ideal way is to bore the bearings rather than drill and ream and to refer to a table of fits for the correct clearance in a particular size.

Where a six or more coupled locomotive is concerned knuckle joints are fitted on the coupling rods to allow for the movement of the axles against the springs; these are generally closer to the crank pins than shown in the drawing in which the distance was accentuated in order to gain clarity. Once again getting the spacings right will require very careful measurement and although some people do mark the joint position from the parts. tiny errors are still likely; again the eccentric bush can be used to correct any slight discrepancy that may occur.

In general, securing coupling rods in place is quite straightforward. Sometimes a large hexagon nut might be specified, it is unlikely to be correct and can spoil the appearance of the locomotive, at other times a number of bolts are spaced round the edge of a plate. Where a locomotive has outside cylinders there is frequently difficulty in finding the necessary space for a securing device and so the bearing bush is shortened and the hole in the rod counter bored. It is then held with a plate and bolts. Some model designs use a countersink on the rod and a countersunk screw; it will certainly hold the rod secure and is an easy answer, but does not look right as the slot is unsightly. If it is thought too difficult to try and follow full-size practice a dodge that can be used is to use a recessed tiny Allen Headed Cap Screw. The overall appearance is quite neat and not unlike the fittings seen on some locomotives.

Valves and Valve Spindles

As valves have been dealt with in the chapter on cylinders there is little that need be added. The fitting of valve spindles is generally dependent on the type of valve and is often a thread on the end of the spindle, particularly where slide valves are concerned. If possible some form of cross head should be devised to offer support to the spindle and prevent undue wear caused by the tendency of it to move up and down. If Walschaerts gear is in use there will be a knuckle joint connecting to the radius rod. With Stephensons and most other gears the joint connects directly to the valve rod and it is near this point that support is needed, although the actual joint is a comparatively simple affair.

Return Cranks

Where a return crank is used, such as with Walschaerts Gear, we again need to look at full-sized practice when it comes to securing it in position on the crank pin. Probably the most popular way is to split it and put bolts through the split to draw it tight round the pin. This is quite effective and has the advantage of allowing us to adjust its position and thus set the valve gear, but there is always the possibility that in use it might slip out of position and so defeat its own purpose. Once a suitable setting has been reached, which should be either in advance or behind dead centre depending on whether slide or piston valve cylinders are in use, insert a pin to stop it from moving. This need only be a piece of round bar pushed in a hole that dissects both crank pin and return crank.

A system frequently used in full-size practice is to have a square on the end of the crank pin - the return crank is located on this and it is automatically set at the required angle. The return crank is still split and a bolt passed through as a means of tightening up. It looks right and is nice and neat, as well as being a permanent fitting. The square has to be milled on the crank pin before it is fitted into the wheels and care must be taken to ensure that when it is fitted to the wheels it does not rotate, which would make nonsense of the setting angle.

Another form of common fitting in full-size practice is the use of four bolts or studs, which pass through the return crank into the crank pin. As with the square end the difficulty is in lining the return crank accurately. Both the latter methods can be simulated and a round fitting used. The square section is made

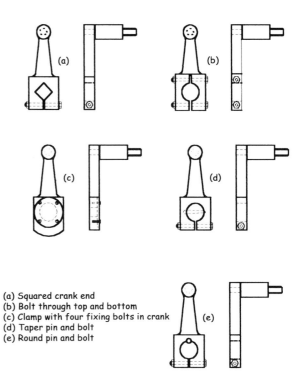

(a) Squared crank end
(b) Bolt through top and bottom
(c) Clamp with four fixing bolts in crank
(d) Taper pin and bolt
(e) Round pin and bolt

and pushed into a hole in the crank pin after assembly and likewise a round plate with four bolt heads can be fitted in the same way.

Anyone modelling the smaller scales, such as garden gauges, may find that any attempt at clamping the return crank gives an out of scale appearance, and it is best to fit one with a simple round hole and pin it in position. Once again a dummy fitting of some sort can be made to make it look more realistic.

Reach Rod

Attached to the reversing lever or screw, the reach rod is usually made from flat steel and is not difficult to construct. As usual there are many variations in design and some call for a comparatively thin rod with round bosses for the bearings on the ends. These are probably best made from mild steel rod and silver soldered to the end of the rod; wherever possible bronze bushes should be used. Care must be taken to get the length of the rod accurate in order to achieve full travel of the reversing arm.

Many reach rods call for a curve to be made at the reverse arm end. This means curving against the widest part of the metal and invariably it will tend to want to twist round to the narrow section. One way to prevent this is to put the rod on a hardwood block, screw a length of flat steel over the rod to the block and then generate the curve, the steel section on top will stop it twisting. The idea can be taken a step further and with judicious use of a few pins a

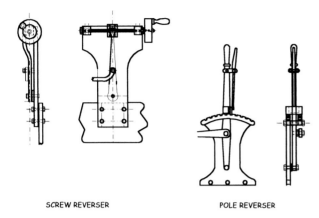

SCREW REVERSER   POLE REVERSER

length of bar can be used to generate the curve and keep the rod flat as well. Some reach rods pass inside the boiler lagging and, if this is the case, stainless steel should be used to prevent problems with rust.

Reversing Levers and Screws

A shunting type locomotive will usually have a reversing lever, and an express or heavy goods a reversing screw. It is far quicker to operate a locomotive with a lever and if the model is to be used on a track which involves a great deal of reversing then, if possible, fit one. If continuous running on a circuit is to be the order of the day a screw may give greater control.

Reversing Stands

The lever is very easy to make as it is just a case of cutting metal to shape and drilling a few holes. The catch should be fitted so that it releases easily and a small round headed screw, without a slot, is ideal for the purpose. Sometimes a small coil spring is used to hold the release mechanism which holds the lever in position, although a flat spring on the arm pressing in the block can be manufactured and used instead; this looks better, even if it is a so-and-so to make in the smaller gauges. The locating slots should be

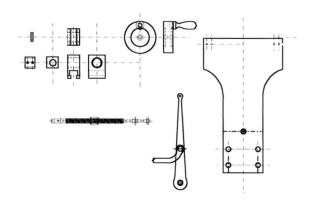

The parts required to construct a Pole or Screw Reverser.

cut after the valve gear has been assembled to ensure that the best advantage of the cut off positions is taken.

The screw reversing stand is not too much of a problem either, but it is necessary to use as coarse a thread as possible, otherwise the advantages of the screw will be lost, as it will take too long to operate. It should also have a left hand thread; if a commercial thread is to be used, *British Standard Whitworth* is about the coarsest. It is better to make one's own by screw cutting and, if possible, make a two start thread that will give even faster travel. If making one's own thread there is no reason whatever why it should not be made to a square section as in full-size practice. Doing this makes a great deal of difference to the appearance of the reversing stand.

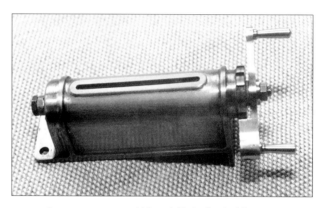

A screw reverser would invariably be fitted with a cover. This is an example built by Tony Meek. The slot will house a pointer to show at what position the screw is in, and a catch is fitted so that the handle can be maintained in that position.

Many people do not mind attempting the screw cutting of the outside thread but will fight shy of the internal one; certainly it will require the construction of a very tiny internal screw cutting tool and care will have to be taken not to break it. If the nut is made of brass or very free cutting bronze it should not be all that difficult.

For those who are not used to the procedure here are a few tips. Cut the outer one first and without changing the setting cut a second one in silver steel, to be used as a tap for cleaning out the other thread. File or mill three slots lengthways along it to form the tap and if you don't fancy making three slots settle for one. Harden and temper to a mid blue colour.

Machine the inner thread on a suitable piece of brass or bronze and clean it out with the home-made tap. In theory both parts should screw together without any slop or binding. In fact it is much more likely that the thread will bind up and that is good, as we

The weighshaft and balance weights for "Princess of Wales" by Tony Meek. Once again an excellent example of workmanship. Note the use of correct type spit bearings for the shaft, rather than the usual method of using bushes.

A lot has been written about attention to detail and this is a fine example from Eric Brown. A carefully shaped anchor link and combination lever, held as per North American practice, with split pins. In Britain the use of castellated nuts and split pins would be more likely.

do not want any slop on it. Coat the outer thread with a grinding paste of the type used to grind in car valves and gently work it backwards and forwards until a nice free running fit is obtained. Clean it off well with paraffin or white spirit. Make sure it is absolutely clean - if need be, soak it overnight. There we have it, it is that easy.

The reversing stand, whether a lever or screw, is mounted either by using a piece of angle or by bolting it direct to the frames. As it is a difficult component to keep clean when using the model, it must either be thoroughly treated with a rust proofer or painted and, in all probability, this will have to be done before the model is finally assembled. Most screw reversers were covered in a shroud and had a catch to stop them moving during running. The shroud or casing would vary from designer to designer and once again for good appearance some reference should be made to full-size practice.

The Weighshaft

A high sounding name that relates to a simple rod that connects both sides of the valve gear to the reversing lever. It is a made from a piece of mild steel rod of suitable size and passes through bearings either in or attached to the frames. Sometimes the reversing arms and or lifting links will be fitted to a step, machined on the ends. Where inside valve gear is in use then obviously the lifting links will be inside and arrangements must be made for them to be secured to the shaft. A taper pin is as good a way of doing this as any, but care must be taken to ensure that the pin is not large enough to weaken the link. Some designers call for an increased diameter of the shaft at the point where the links are to be fitted, which is sound practice as it offers extra support where it is most needed.

Generally parts to be fitted to the weighshaft should be keyed in position with a square key to prevent movement. In smaller models this might not be practical and small taper pins are recommended. Getting correct adjustment can be difficult and some people prefer to use small grub screws to hold parts in position. There is always the danger of these failing and causing problems when the model is in use. It is, therefore, advisable to use grub screws only for the purposes of adjustment and to pin the parts afterwards.

Making valve gear can be time-consuming work; careful and accurate construction will pay dividends later, as can be seen from some of the very fine examples in the photographs. Readers are therefore urged to ensure that they take every care to get the required accuracy, in order to ensure a free running locomotive, as well as a good looking one.

This is how it is done in full-size practice as per Sir Nigel Gresley. Details worth copying would be the motion bracket and valve crosshead. The slide bars are typical Gresley three-bar type. Even the anchor link is fluted to save weight.

A large scale 'Scenic' Line

'Scenic' lines are generally found in Gauge 1 and smaller gauges, but these photographs show what can be achieved in a larger gauge, in this case 5".

Starting with suitable terrain, the owner has laid his track at ground level incorporating one engineering feature, has added some infrastructure including a station (or 'depot' for this line) and a water tower. With some appropriate rolling stock, suitable for sitting or lying on, he

has created a miniature railway, in the Belgian Ardennes, which absolutely reeks of the American West in the 1880s. Introducing the driver ruins this illusion of course, other than for the driver, but as he built and owns the line, he doesn't care.

The plot on which this railway was built was smaller than might be thought and

was sloping, the house, the corner of which can just be seen on at the top left of the photo on the left, being at the highest point. The line emerged from the basement of the house and then ran in a 'dogbone' loop around two sides of the house, the

circuit being around 250 metres long. As well as a workshop, another delight in the basement was a huge American 'S' gauge electric layout, with full scenery and tracks from floor to ceiling. Trains, with full and very realistic electronic sound, were all around and it was difficult to know where to look at any one time.

Chapter 11: Slide Bars, Motion Brackets & Crossheads

On tin plate toy locomotives we used to see the piston rod moving in and out of the cylinder unsupported, there was no power to the piston and so the movement caused no great damage. With a steam locomotive things are very different - the power is being applied to the piston and therefore causing the movement and, if the piston rod is left unsupported, wear would take place in no time at all. From the very beginning of steam power this was realised by designers and crossheads working in slide bars were fitted.

Slide Bars

These are exactly as the name describes them, bars of metal in or on which the crosshead will slide. Most are plain metal bars secured to the cylinder at one end and to a device called a motion bracket at the other. They vary somewhat in design, the most common idea being to use two evenly spaced either side of the piston rod with the crosshead running in between. In some instances the bars are shaped to improve strength, those used by *Great Western Railway* locomotives being the most obvious example. Some companies favoured the use of a single slide bar, the crosshead having a box-like structure all round it above the piston rod. Another system that was used was the three-bar type. Outwardly this appeared to use two bars very close together with the top of the crosshead sandwiched in between. In fact there were two lower bars, one supporting each side of the crosshead.

In model form the slide bars will mostly be easy to make, consisting of just flat bars drilled at each end to accept bolts which allow them to be retained in position. The Great Western type may have to be

A typical motion bracket casting. Small sections of angle will be fitted to it to marry with the slide bars and form an anchorage.

fabricated or may be obtainable as castings but other than that construction will be similar.

Motion Brackets

The motion bracket supports the end of the slide bars furthest away from the cylinder. They can be either fabricated or made from castings. Brackets are used for securing them to the slide bars. The faces of these must be machined to exactly the same measurement as the fixing points on the cylinders, any variation will result in either a very tight or very loose spot, both of which will create problems over a period. In order to get the required accuracy, either the actual crosshead or a specially prepared spacer should be used. Bolt the slide bars to the cylinders and use a feeler gauge to ensure that the gap between those and the spacer is identical through the whole length of movement. If by any chance the distance between the bars is too great at the bracket end it should be possible to fit shims to get it right.

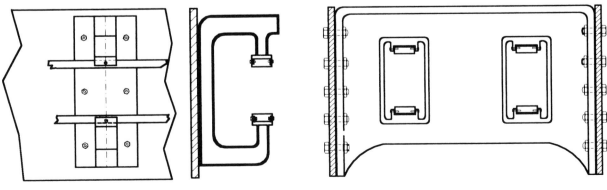

MOTION BRACKET CONSTRUCTION

Outside Cylinder Locomotive   Inside Cylinder Locomotive

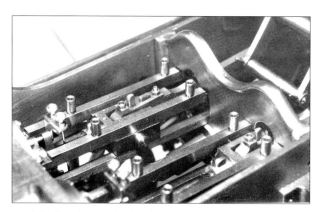

A fabricated motion bracket for an inside cylindered locomotive. Four slide bars are used for each crosshead in order to give plenty of support.

The crosshead from an American Locomotive supported by four slide bars.

Generally it is possible to drill through both fixing brackets and slide bars at one go. The motion brackets will have to be aligned on the frames, in all probability holes having already been made in those. This calls for careful lining up using spacers and measuring not only that the angle is correct but also that the distance at the cylinder end from the frames is the same as that at the motion bracket. Once the correct position is established it will be possible to clamp the brackets to the frames ready for drilling.

Crossheads

Like motion brackets, crossheads may either be fabricated or machined from castings. A personal preference is for fabrication as it is felt that this makes it easier to get measurements right. The end of the crosshead has to be drilled for the piston rod and this should be done in the lathe to ensure accuracy and that it is at ninety degrees to the slide surfaces, some people screw the piston rods in place in the crosshead, others like to secure them by cross drilling and fitting taper pins, if screwed in it is advisable to fit a locknut so the rod cannot unscrew itself when running.

The grooves for the slide bars can be milled and finished with a smooth file to give a nice easy running fit. When they are fabricated it is quite usual

for lips to be bolted on rather than machining grooves. Which ever way it is done the fit must be free running with no high spots to cause binding. Although the fitting of slide bars and motion brackets plus the crosshead construction may be one

A crosshead for two slide bars, with a difference as the bars fit in grooves at the side of the crosshead. This allows the cylinder to be moved slightly further away from the frames and accommodate Stephensons Link Motion outside the frames.

of the easier tasks undertaken when building a model, it should not be skimped in any way as doing so may lead to excessive piston wear at an early stage.

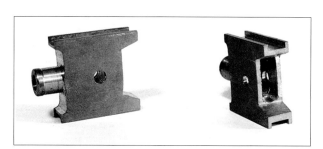

Two views of a crosshead casting that has been machined. Note how in this instance the connecting rod fits in a recess in the casting.

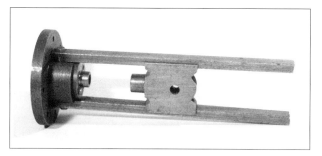

Complete assembly of cylinder head, with gland, slide bars and crosshead.

Chapter 12: The Front End

The Smokebox

One of the most important things in locomotive construction is the design of a good front end; by this we generally mean the smokebox and all it contains, plus the chimney. In most instances the smokebox will consist of a tube that fits on to the boiler shell, and contains the main steam pipe, superheaters, blast pipe and the blower, and is sealed with a door. This is usually hinged to a metal ring, which forms the front part of the tube and is

A cast smokebox, which is an unusual type as it bolts directly to the frames and does not require a saddle. There are no front or rear rings as they are cast integral with the smokebox.

sealed when closed by a catch or catches of one form or another. The chimney fits in a hole at the top and we will come to that shortly. The smokebox is best made from mild steel, it can either be a length of tube or rolled from sheet, if brass or other non ferrous metals are used, because of the extreme heat involved, it is difficult to prevent paint from peeling off. There are, however, bronze and aluminium castings available for smokeboxes that are of a shape which is different to the plain tube. These are excellent as a means of saving work but extra care will be required when it comes to painting them and at least two coats of primer should be applied, one of which must be self etching, the finishing coat should be of the special heat resisting paints available for motor cycle engines.

The end of the smokebox connected to the boiler should always be screwed into position using brass or bronze screws. If it is rivetted it will not be easy to remove should that become necessary; sometimes the smokebox tube fits on to a metal ring in a similar method to the front. The front part can be rivetted to the ring and the rivets either filed flush or left proud as required. Getting a riveting dolly inside a smokebox can be a problem and a simple device can be made with a bar of steel fitted with a rotating ring. A hole is drilled in the ring and a riveting dolly pushed into that, allowing it to be used at any required angle. The bar can be held in a vice and the fact that the ring can rotate will give sufficient flexibility for the dolly to line up with the rivet head.

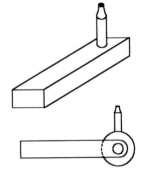

Rivet Dollies for working inside the smokebox. Intended to be held in a vise, the lower swivels for greater versatility

The device should be made as heavy as possible, whilst allowing as much room as possible inside the smokebox to operate.

The most important thing about the smokebox is that it be completely airtight on all joints. If it is, all exhaust gases will be forced out up the chimney, and so create a powerful draught that will draw the fire to a nice red heat - any leaks will prevent this from happening. To achieve this means that the part which is attached to the boiler must also be well sealed, and the door a first-class fit. The hole made to accept the steam and exhaust pipes must be sealed once these are in place. There are various ways of doing this, in full-size practice it was quite common to use concrete but this is a little drastic for model making. A good material is fire clay, which can be rammed hard in any gaps, alternatives are epoxy resin or a silicone that will accept high temperatures, another is a mix of Hessian strands and Plumbers' Boss White. This is very pliable while soft, so it can easily be moulded to shape yet sets very hard, whilst still retaining enough flexibility to prevent it cracking and although an old fashioned idea it is still very effective.

The importance of getting this and any other gap sealed cannot be over stressed. If a locomotive starts to become shy of steam when it is running, the first place to look for a problem is the smokebox. If the door is not quite done up or there are any gaps in the seals, it is almost certain this will be the cause of the trouble. The result of thorough sealing is to create a partial vacuum in the smokebox, in full-size a vacuum gauge was fitted so the crew could see how things were going, on a model this would only be practical in the larger gauges.

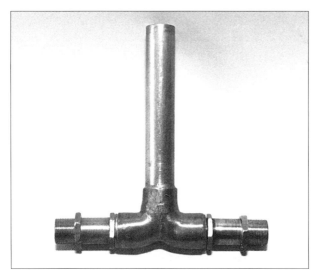

To get a smooth flow of gases this exhaust pipe for a 5″ gauge model has been given a nice curved profile. It is made using two plumbers' joints cut away and then rejoined, which is easier than attempting to make two matching bends.

The Blast Pipe

The blast pipe consists mainly of a tube which connects to the cylinder exhausts and tapers towards the top, this taper gives greater velocity to the exhaust steam and so aids the creation of a good draught. It does not mean that we can reduce the size of the orifice just for the sake of doing so, as if it is made too small it has the effect of strangling the steam, which cannot escape quickly enough. It is not possible to give exact figures for the reduction, as there are too many variables to be dealt with, depending on the particular locomotive. It is best to make the final exit in the form of a screw fitting which will allow a number of nozzles to be made and experiments to be made with different sizes. Then use whichever gives the best performance.

The optimum size will depend on a number of things. For example, if the locomotive is to pull only a driver a smaller nozzle will be more efficient, but if hauling a heavy load, a small nozzle might well create too much draught and actually pull the fire to a point where small cinders and burning coal are thrown out of the chimney. It is hardly practical to change blast nozzles according to the number of passengers being hauled and so a compromise has to be reached.

It was quite common for the shed foreman and the foreman fitter at a depot to carry out experiments of this nature in order to get the best performance from a full-size locomotive. This was quite a difficult task as the blast quality also depends to some degree on how the locomotive is driven; at one time a locomotive would be handled only by a single crew, or at the most two, but in the search for higher utilisation it became common practice for any crew to use whatever locomotive was available, and the blast arrangements that suited one did not always suit another. On the Continent a device called the *Giesel Ejector* became quite popular with designers. This replaced a single exhaust nozzle with a row of considerably smaller nozzles, with a greater total area than the single nozzle, thus reducing back pressure and increasing smokebox vacuum. Although used in many other countries, in Britain it did not find a great deal of favour, but the *Kylchap Exhaust*, usually consisting of a double blast nozzle and a double chimney did. The odd thing about the system was that both nozzles were of diameters that were almost identical with that used on the old-fashioned single exhaust system. The end result was a much softer exhaust that was inclined to drift downwards, instead of being thrown high above the engine. This resulted in obstruction of the driver's view and so smoke deflectors had to be fitted. Efficiency was definitely improved but it is a matter of debate as to whether locomotives looked as good when fitted with the *Kylchap*.

Not all British locomotives by any means received the *Kylchap* system, it being mainly applied to express engines. The crews on more mundane work were left with engines with the original system, which would not steam well at all. Although strictly forbidden, the crews used to fit something which became known as a "jimmy". Quite simply it was a metal bar placed across the top of the blast nozzle and secured in some way; this had the effect of splitting the blast and creating more force. The results could be quite spectacular with red-hot cinders flying from the chimney. This led to complaints from passengers and caused lineside fires, so woe betide any crew found using one. At the end of a shift it would be secreted away, to be brought out again when the crew were allocated a locomotive that would not steam. Use of the device became particularly prevalent as the days of steam drew to an end and locomotives suffered from lack of maintenance, with leaky boilers and badly fitting smoke box doors making it difficult at time to maintain pressure.

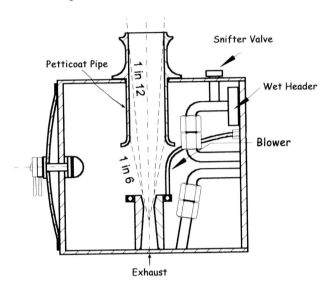

Layout of Smokebox
showing angles of exhaust

Petticoat Pipe

The chimney is located over a petticoat pipe, which on models is fitted via a block and screws to the top of the smokebox. The design must be such that it will allow the exhaust to evacuate as quickly as possible and it is a good idea to make the height adjustable as the position in which it is fitted has a considerable bearing on the steaming capabilities of the locomotive. There are various ways of making the petticoat, probably the easiest being to make a former for it and to hammer a length of tube round that, it can also be machined from bar stock, using the top slide of the lathe to get the required angle and working with that and the cross slide to generate a curve. Whichever method is used it is desirable to get a nice smooth finish as this allows both free movement of the gases and prevents a build up of oil and soot which can soon reduce the size of the opening. The block which is screwed to the inside of the smokebox has to be shaped to match the curve of the smokebox. The petticoat pipe extends through the top of the smokebox providing seating for the chimney that fits over it.

Proportions

Of great importance is the relationship between the blast nozzle and petticoat pipe. As well as the diameter of the blast nozzle, the angle at which the blast will escape up the chimney will be the factor that decides on how well the blast will keep the fire going and, therefore, how efficient the locomotive will be. A rough guide is to make both the blast nozzle and petticoat pipe one third of the smokebox diameter in length, leaving a third as a gap through which gases are drawn. With the suggested adjustable petticoat pipe it is then possible to fiddle around to get the best results, although in general little addition or decrease to the third is likely to be needed. The usual angle quoted for the escape of the gases is 1 in 6 to the bottom of the petticoat pipe and 1 in 12 to the top of the chimney. This leads us to yet another measurement as it now becomes evident that to achieve these figures the internal diameter of the chimney must be sufficient to give the required clearance. A method suggested for getting these angles is to cut a piece of card or thin metal and to push this down the chimney, adjusting the petticoat pipe and blast nozzle until the required angle is obtained.

The Blower

The blower is used to draw the fire when the locomotive is stationary and there is no cylinder exhaust. Most British models have a blower in the form of a hollow boiler stay, steam being taken from the top of the boiler, via a valve, through the stay to a small pipe in the smokebox that directs the jet of steam centrally up the chimney. The section in the smokebox consists of a pipe with a union which fits the hollow stay, on the exit end of the pipe a small nozzle is fitted, the actual orifice is very tiny indeed allowing the minimum use of steam while ensuring sufficient draught. The blower will be needed whenever the locomotive is stationary as well as when raising steam. Going once again to full-size practice, the crew were under strict instructions to open the blower valve before closing the regulator, failure to do so could result in a blow back of the fire and, if the fire hole door was open, serious injury could be caused to the crew.

Multiple Jets

While there is no objection to the use of a single pipe and nozzle as a blower and many models use the system, it is far better to use multiple jets, which are even smaller than the single one and are placed in a sealed ring that fits around the blast pipe. The ring can be made to screw on to the blast pipe and used as the nozzle. The main advantage is that the jets for the blower are accurately directed up the chimney. Some builders go a little further and even have individual blower screw in jets.

In full-size the blower tube from cab to smokebox

A blast nozzle, which incorporates a blower ring with four ¹⁄₆₄"
diameter holes. A Primus pricker is used to clean them
should they become blocked.

would more likely be put along the side of the boiler, either in front of or behind the cladding, instead of having a hollow stay as we do on models. Running it along the outside is easy enough if one wants to emulate full-size operations, but it is not so practical to put it inside the cladding. Some model makers have found ingenious methods such as using a hollow

Another example of a combined blast nozzle and blower ring,
which was made by Tony Meek and, in this case, includes small
nozzles to ensure the correct direction of the fine jets of steam. It is for
use on an inside cylindered locomotive and requires only a simple
block to secure it to the cylinders. The pipe in front of the nozzle
is the main steam pipe.

handrail as the blower tube. For true scale appearance, whilst still being practical, it may be necessary to make a dummy blower pipe and the fixture that takes it into the smokebox, whilst still using a hollow stay to do the job.

Superheaters

The superheaters do not directly form part of the exhaust system with which we associate the front end of a locomotive, but one end of them is to be found in the smokebox and so it is as well to think

about them while on that subject. Basically superheaters consist of a tube or tubes that travel from the regulator outlet, known as the wet header and is in the form of a block. In full size, a locomotive if fitted with superheaters, and in the early days not very many were, would have lots of small pipes, possibly running into hundreds, doing the job. In model form it is usual to have one, or at the most two, to each cylinder and sometimes there is only one feeding both cylinders.

Construction of a Superheater

As the steam in the superheater is travelling down the pipe towards the firebox and returning again to the smokebox it follows that there must be a return bend of some sort. An easy way is to take a pipe from the wet header, through which the steam emerges from the front of the boiler, down the superheater flue to a hollow block, and from there another pipe back to the smokebox. The block can be of copper or bronze but because it is adjacent to the firebox, the joint with the pipes has to be made either by screwing the pipes in or brazing them with a very high temperature spelter. This is because when the locomotive is not working, while steam is being maintained in the boiler the superheater pipes are empty. This can raise the temperature to a point where copper tubes can become red hot and is sufficient to melt most silver solders, as well as over a period actually burning through the tubes.

Radiant Superheaters

To prevent exposing the tubes to this excessive heat it is customary for the block joining the pipes to be kept near, but not in, the firebox. With a radiant

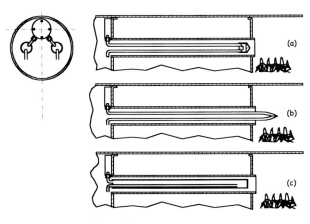

Three Superheater Types

(a) Regular system using a block for the return
(b) Radiant stainless steel type with welded ends
(c) Steam enters the large tube and returns via the small one. Requires a good seal at the smokebox end

superheater the pipes actually travel into the box and this makes the use of copper impossible as the heat of the fire would burn through it in a very short period of time. The alternative is to use stainless steel, which will withstand the temperatures involved. It is usual to weld the two pipes together in the form of a spearhead, but a competent welder should carry this out; it is always necessary to weld stainless steel through a film of gas, Argon being the usual one, the process being known as *Argon Arc Welding*.

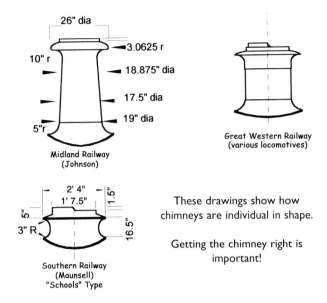

Midland Railway
(Johnson)

Great Western Railway
(various locomotives)

Southern Railway
(Maunsell)
"Schools" Type

These drawings show how chimneys are individual in shape.

Getting the chimney right is important!

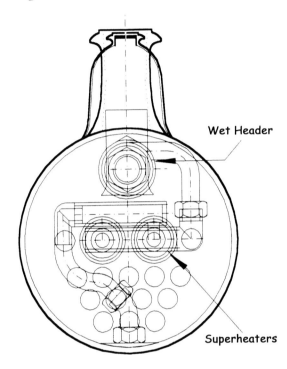

Layout of the Front End,
showing superheater connections.

If possible stainless steel superheaters should be screwed directly into the wet header, silver soldering copper to stainless steel is not recommended as after a period of time the joint will break down. This may take several years but break down it most certainly will. There are modern welding techniques, which make a suitable joint, but these are not generally available to a model engineer.

Chimneys

Although mainly functional, the chimney of a locomotive must look right as well. In the case of a freelance design, as long as it is proportion with the rest of the locomotive, the shape is not too important. Where a scale model is concerned only if the chimney is correct will the model look right. One way to ensure the shape is finally as required is to make a template out of cardboard or plastic sheet

and use that as a guide when machining to get the correct shape, it is easier to get it right on a piece of flat material than on a circular one.

The chimney may be made from either bar stock or a casting. If bar stock is used it can be bored, the outer shape formed and it can then be parted off for machining the flare. Where a casting is used it will almost certainly come with the bore already in, although that will need to be machined both to size and shape. Chimney castings and those of dome covers as well can be tricky to machine, particularly the short type found on express locomotives and most people have their own ideas on how to carry out the various machining processes.

The casting will probably have a ridge along its length where it has been drawn from the mould and will not run properly in a steady, so it will be necessary to machine the outside first and to do this a piece of hard wood is required on which the casting can be rammed, the wood is put in the four jaw chuck and supported at the other end by a centre in the tailstock. Some people may prefer to push a piece of wood in each end rather than have one piece right through. Providing the wood fits nice and tightly the outside can be machined and mostly the work is quite straightforward. The difficult part is the flare that fits on the smokebox and here again individuals will have their own ideas on how to go about it. One way is to machine a series of minute steps using a combination of top and cross slide and then smooth it out with a hand tool, using a hand tool rest, and using the previously made template to get the right contours.

With the outside shaped, put the chimney in the four-jaw chuck holding the top lip. If the casting is

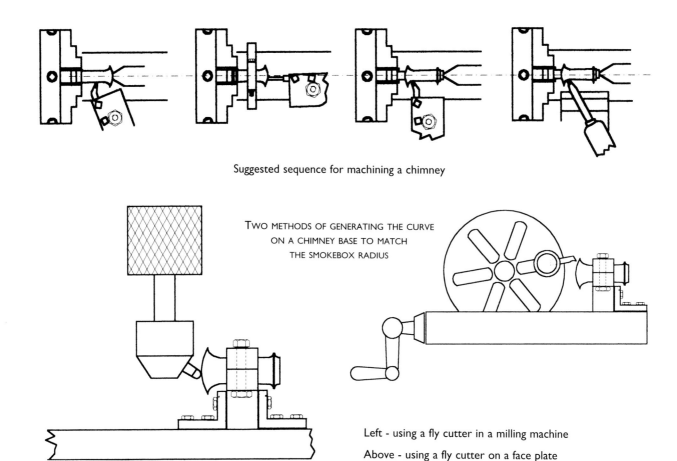

Suggested sequence for machining a chimney

TWO METHODS OF GENERATING THE CURVE
ON A CHIMNEY BASE TO MATCH
THE SMOKEBOX RADIUS

Left - using a fly cutter in a milling machine

Above - using a fly cutter on a face plate

brass or bronze protect it by sticking small pieces of brass shim to the jaws with double-sided transparent tape. Support it with a three point steady somewhere towards the end of its length and again protect it from damage, this time stick pieces of plastic to the pads of the steady. It is now possible to machine the bore to the correct shape and there are two things to remember. Firstly the end near the flare has to be machined to a good fit on the tube used as a petticoat pipe and secondly almost certainly there will be a taper on the bore. It is essential to get the bore really smooth as otherwise it will collect a mixture of oil and soot and rapidly become blocked up.

At this stage the casting should be looking exactly right and all that remains is to machine the inside of the flare, which can be done on a either a milling machine or a lathe, using a fly-cutter. This is set to cut at the correct radius of the smokebox. The casting is mounted either on the cross slide of the lathe or on an angle plate in the milling machine and the base fly-cut to shape and size. The actual mounting may be difficult. By far the most secure way of doing so is to make a mandrel of the correct diameter and taper to fit in the chimney, soft solder it in and then clamp the mandrel in place. Not everyone will have a chunk of metal available to use for such a mandrel

and the alternative is to hollow out a pair of hardwood blocks to accept the casting and use them as a clamp to mount it in position. As each circumstance will vary, in the end it has to be a case for individual judgement.

To finish the bottom of the flare and remove all the marks, which almost inevitably will be there as a result of the machining, stick a piece of emery cloth

A chimney casting incorporating an extension as a Ventura or petticoat pipe fitting.

Two typical dome cover castings, which are totally different. The taller of the two is comparatively easy to machine, the shorter one will need to be soldered to a spigot in order to work on it.

to the smokebox, using our old friend double sided tape. Rub the casting backwards and forwards on that until there is a nice smooth surface which should be a perfect fit on the smokebox.

Dome Covers

Dome covers are machined in the same way as chimneys, but sometimes the castings have chucking pieces that make life considerably easier. Both chimneys and dome covers can be fitted to the model with small screws, into the smokebox in the case of a chimney and into the top of the inner dome for the cover. The alternative which is both neat and useful, should the need to dismantle arise, is to make them a tight push fit. This is easy enough with the chimney but in the case of the dome, the inner

Something very unusual is this attractive dome cover made by the late Eric Brown.

section should be lagged and so the lagging will need to be capable of offering support. One way of doing this is to mould the lagging in fibreglass and machine it to a push fit when it has set.

Snifting Valves

When a locomotive coasts with the regulator turned off, the movement of the valves and pistons causes the cylinders to act like large pumps and to draw in air continuously from the steam chest, this creates a partial vacuum inside the cylinder and steam chest. As the valves alternately uncover the ports to exhaust, air rushes back down the blast pipe carrying with it hot gasses and all too often fine particles of ash and grit. An anti-vacuum valve or snifting valve is fitted to prevent this from happening, being designed to lift and admit air immediately the pressure within falls below that of the atmosphere outside. The effect is more noticeable on a piston valve engine than with slide valves where the valves tend to fall away from their seats when steam is shut off, creating a by-passing effect. Even so it is advisable to fit a snifting valve.

The placing of a snifting valve will depend largely on the prototype being modelled, on some engines on the old *Southern Railway* and quite few on the *London North Eastern Railway* the snifting valves were often a feature of the outline. In the case of *Southern Railway* Locomotives there were two situated just behind the chimney and on the *London North Eastern Railway* a single one. Other companies tended to put them low down on the smokebox where they were hardly visible.

Snifting Valve Construction

There is nothing special about the construction of the snifting valve. It is a simple non-return valve as described in the chapter on cab fittings. It only has one connection and this is straight into the steam pipe to the cylinder. The pressure in that pipe, when the regulator opens, closes the valve. When there is no pressure the valve opens to air, so the valve must be situated in such a way that cool air can enter when it opens.

The shape of the valve can easily be made to conform to full-size practice, which usually included a small cowl covering the air intake and preventing as much dirt as possible from entering. It is essential to examine the snifting valve at regular intervals as, by their very nature, they attract a great deal of dirt, which can get under the ball and on the ball seat and stop the valve from closing. This also will result in bad steaming of the locomotive and there are many model engineers who have had a great deal of trouble trying to trace the cause of this, when the answer was really quite simple.

Spark Arrestors

Many societies now insist that locomotives are fitted with spark arrestors, resulting from complaints by members of the public who have had clothing scorched by hot cinders ejected from the chimney. A filter of some sort is all that is needed and it can be a simple piece of wire mesh in a frame, which is either hinged, or slots in place. The wire mesh that is used should be of stainless steel and an ideal source for this is an old tea strainer Many overseas locomotives particularly wood burners and those running in hot, dry countries had spark arrestors fitted to the chimneys which are easily distinguished by their bulbous shape. They do not generally work on the principle of a mesh to prevent hot ash being thrown out, but on a double skinned device which cools the ash and allows it to return to the smokebox.

It will be seen that the smokebox can get very crowded if everything possible is put in it. We must have in mind the fact that it needs to be kept clean to ensure good steaming, and so every effort should be made to keep all pipes and fittings in a position that ensures it is possible to work inside. Some people have made life easier for themselves by making a split along the smokebox, enabling them to lift the top half off. It certainly is an aid to maintenance but the joint line is very hard to disguise and can spoil the appearance of the model.

Smokebox Doors

The general shape of the smokebox door will be known to most people. The back of it must be machined as smooth as possible in order that it fits snugly against the outer ring. Machining the curvature of the door may cause a little head scratching, even if a casting is used, but it is not difficult to do and the simple equipment required takes very little time to make. It requires a pivot from a fixed point in line with the door, connected via a bar that can swivel to the cross slide. The saddle lead screw is disconnected and as it is traversed the arm and pivot make it create an arc, the length of the bar sets the radius. The door needs to be mounted on the lathe in such a way that it can be machined overall and for this it can be fixed to the faceplate with double sided adhesive tape. It is essential to ensure that the flat side is machined accurately first with a smooth finish and that all oil and grease has been removed from both that and the faceplate, otherwise the tape will not grip. Take very light cuts and test

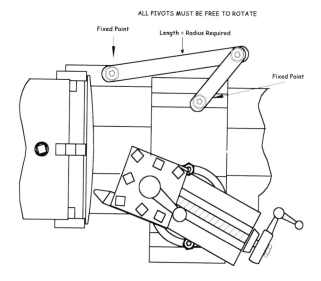

A simple device for turning large diameter radii such as smokebox doors. The length between pivot points of the pivot bar must equal the required radius.

the security of the casting first by giving it a tap with a plastic hammer before commencing machining.

Hinges

Some castings come with hinges cast on, these are not intended to be machined, simply cleaned up with a file and emery cloth and drilled for the pin. Where hinges are not cast on, or stock material is used, they can be fabricated from thin mild steel strip and rivetted to the smokebox door. The section of the hinge which fits on the front ring, can be screwed in position, or alternatively secured with nuts inside the smokebox.

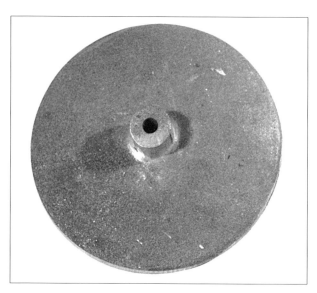

A cast smokebox door.

Darts

Most smokebox doors are secured with a device known as a dart, which fits in a slot in a bar inside; the bar can be fabricated from two pieces of flat section mild or stainless steel or milled from a single piece. It needs to be quite substantial as it takes quite a bit of pressure when the dart is screwed home. The dart is also fabricated from mild steel or stainless, and is quite easy to make; it is fitted with two handles, one of which has a square hole that fits a square on the dart and the other is screwed home. Stainless steel is preferable here to mild steel which is more easily destroyed by the high temperatures involved.

Some locomotives had a different means of securing the smokebox door, consisting of a series of clamps that were tightened with bolts. It is a useful system on models as it helps create a seal right round the edge of the door, rather than just being pulled in from the middle. The shape of the clamps varied according to the company or country using them and some research might be needed to get them the right shape. The securing bolts also varied considerably, some being ordinary hexagon headed type while others required a special key.

Securing the Smokebox

The smokebox is secured to the frames via a piece known as a saddle. Saddles vary greatly in their shape and size and as far as the model maker is concerned they can either be machined from a casting, if a suitable one is available, or fabricated from mild steel. The saddle is either bolted or rivetted to the frames depending on the whim of the designer, and should always be bolted to the smokebox, ensuring a rigid construction. As the boiler will expand when heated, the firebox end is fitted via a clip which allows longitudinal movement, whilst preventing any vertical lift.

The main steam pipes on a locomotive may vary considerably. On most models they will be taken out of the bottom of the smokebox but on some of the later larger locomotives with outside cylinders, particularly if there were more than two, the pipes come from low down on the side of the smokebox. They are brought out through holes, which are sealed off and almost certainly they will be fitted with some form of cover, which can be fabricated from thin mild steel. The covers are bolted in position with small hexagon headed bolts; before doing so the steam pipes should be covered with some form of lagging.

The front end may be only a small part of a locomotive and, at first sight, may appear to be rather insignificant. It is actually quite complex and a great deal of care must be taken with it to ensure the best is obtained from the locomotive.

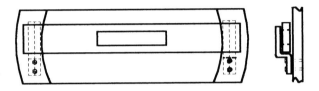

Construction of Smokebox Dart and Securing Bracket

Fix Bracket to Smokebox front with bolts

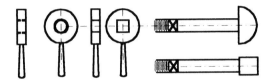

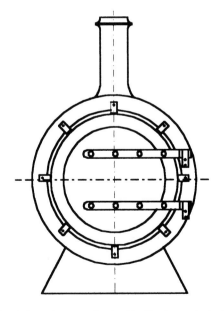

Smokebox door retained with clips instead of a Dart

Four Ways to Secure your Smokebox Door

1 *(right)*:
Two levers are used on the very neat smokebox of 15″ gauge freelance 2-4-2 "Siân".

2 *(above)*:
One wheel and one lever are used to close the smokebox door of this 5″ gauge Caledonian Railway 'Jumbo' 0-6-0, built by Alec Wilson.

3 *(below right)*:
Clips only are used on this Gauge 1 model of an LMS 4F class 0-6-0, to the popular "Project" design.

4 *(below)*:
A combination of both a central dart and clips around the circumference can be seen on Heinz Lehman's 5″ gauge model of a Prussian 2-8-0.

Chapter 13: Boilers
(the heart of a steam locomotive)

The Problems - Real or Imagined ?

Boilers cause more heartaches than any part of model locomotive construction and in this day and age some model makers purchase the boiler, because it is a major component which they are unwilling to build. If one just wants a model to run and wants it as quickly as possible then this is fine but somehow there does not seem to be the same satisfaction in having a model with a boiler built by someone else, as there is when it is built by oneself. It should be made clear at this point that it is copper boilers under discussion, not steel, which will be dealt with later in this chapter.

There are various reasons given for buying a boiler. "I haven't got the equipment" is a fairly usual one, and yet the equipment can be hired quite cheaply, so that is hardly valid, particularly as buying the equipment and the material to build ones own boiler will work out at a quarter of the price of purchasing one. "I do not know how to go about it" is a better one but when this chapter has been read all should be clear and that excuse no longer valid. "It is as cheap to buy one as to make it." That is nonsense. It is possible to make three or four boilers for what it would cost to buy one. Well, that is just three such excuses, none of which are valid, so let us get on with the actual job.

There is another point which should be considered. Anyone can advertise that they will make boilers for payment, even if they have never built one, or had any sort of experience in doing so. There have been cases of people ordering a boiler and paying a lot of money for it, only to find out when, or indeed if, it ever arrives, that it is of no use. This is not to say that everyone that builds model boilers is a charlatan, there are some people who are first class workmen and will do a first class job. But beware of the other sort, remember that there is no official boiler making qualification, no examinations for people to pass, and who can say whether or not such a person is competent. Making ones own boiler is the only way to be absolutely certain but, if purchase it you must, then make sure that, before doing so, a sample of the work of the trader can be seen to be satisfactory.

Principles and Aims

We are looking to make a vessel that will hold a high pressure with adequate spare strength, and that will leak as little as possible or, better still, not at all.

Originally full sized boilers were made mainly of iron and were riveted together. The seams around the rivets were hammered as tight as possible to prevent leakage. There were quite a few early examples in full-size practice of boiler explosions, these were rarely if ever caused by a weakness in the construction but, almost without exception, by the crew tightening the safety valves in an effort to raise more pressure than the boiler was designed to hold. As long as the stated working pressure was adhered to little was likely to go wrong, even with a boiler using comparatively primitive materials and methods.

With the coming of steel, the same principle was still applied to boiler construction. Properly spaced rivets and plenty of hammering to caulk the seams. Of course it was not possible to get a boiler perfectly steam tight by these methods, and locomotive crews were inclined to assist things by putting various substances in the water, such as oatmeal. This congealed round leaking seams and stopped any leakage; most crews had their own pet formula for the purpose. Later boilers were welded together instead of riveted, and matters improved no end, they are still made in this way for preserved railways around the world.

Quite how the first model boilers were made we know not, but certainly the author has had the pleasure of renovating models made in the late eighteen hundreds, and the boilers were inevitably riveted. They were copper, and the difference between them and full-sized practice, was that the caulking was carried out with soft solder. This method of boiler construction was still used right up until the early 1950s, when silver soldering took over, more or less in the form that it is used today. Many of these riveted and caulked boilers are still in use and as sound as the day they were made.

It would be nice to be able to describe how to make a riveted and caulked boiler but space will not allow it. In case anyone is considering the idea at any time, then it should be understood that it is an art that is not quite as easy as it sounds. Firstly the rivets required must conform to standard engineering practice, regarding rivet diameter and spacing, not just put in where the builder thinks is suitable. All holes must be thoroughly deburred to prevent leakage around the rivets themselves. Tubes are

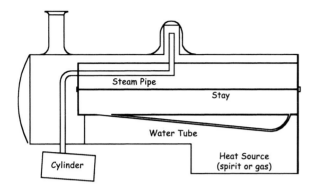

A simple water tube boiler for small scale steam locomotives. It can be gas or spirit fired.

slightly thicker than used on a silver soldered boiler and they are screwed into the firebox and expanded at the smokebox end. If superheaters are used then the superheater tubes are expanded at both ends. All stays are threaded into the copper and secured with nuts. Finally all seams are soft soldered, the soft solder is not used for strength but merely as a caulking medium, a job it does far better than the traditional method of hammering seams and tubes over to make them tight. Thicker material is used for the backhead, allowing bushes for fittings to be screwed in (some builders used to put a nut on the inside for greater security) these too were sealed with soft solder. It is probably harder to make a good riveted and soft soldered boiler than it is to make one with silver soldered tubes, although the end result is a boiler that is just as strong, or perhaps even stronger, than one that is silver soldered.

In general boilers for locomotives of 2½" gauge and over all follow the same overall pattern of construction. An outer shell, a firebox inside and tubes running from that to the front end. The design may differ according to the locomotive, some having wide fireboxes and tapered boilers and others having the squared off *Belpaire* firebox. These types call for different methods of staying and, in some cases, outer shell construction as well. An exception is the use in some narrow gauge models of a marine type of boiler which, while still following similar principles, has a large tube as the firebox. On smaller models there are a whole host of designs in use, from simple pot types to more complicated centre flue versions.

Equipment Required

We must start by giving thought to the tools that will be needed and to quite a large extent these are going to depend on the size of the boiler. Whatever the size there are two things that are necessary, a suitable heat source and a hearth on which to do the work. The latter is a posh name given to a tray of sheet

metal that may or may not be folded up at the edges, although it is desirable that it should be. On this we need some means of retaining the heat. At one time coke was recommended but that is now not easy to obtain and so the next best thing is good quality firebricks.

Firebricks

These come in several types. There is the type that is used to line the domestic hearth. They are not ideal for boiler making as there is no reflected heat from them, but can be useful if a permanent hearth is to be made, as they can be cemented together with fireclay and used as a base. Then there are silicone bricks, which are white in colour and are used frequently in furnaces for firing pottery. They have wonderful heat reflecting properties and can be highly recommended. There is a problem as they do break rather easily, but the broken bits can still be used and, while inconvenient, a broken brick is not the end of the world. In fact as the pieces get smaller and smaller they become useful for packing in nooks and crannies. The bricks can be obtained from art suppliers as well as specialists in the manufacture of hearths or foundry gear. The third type is also a refractory type of brick but it is not white, it is a sort of yellow

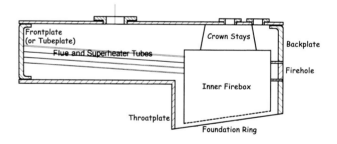

Standard large scale locomotive type boiler.
It can be fired on numerous fuels.

colour, its heat reflecting properties are not as good as the silicone brick but is good enough for what we want and has the advantage of being less inclined to break up than the silicone brick. These can often be obtained at a really good builders merchant, if not it is worth exploring to see where your nearest brick yard is, as they will usually be able to help. *Thermalite* bricks used by builders also reflect heat and while the reflective properties are not as good as silicone they will do the job.

Finally it is possible to use a bed of silicone chips instead of bricks. These are becoming more and more popular with people making jewellry. They are very good indeed as the boiler can be literally buried in them to retain heat. However they are very expensive.

Do not use the bricks taken from electric night storage heaters, it is a mistake to think that these will reflect heat back to the work; their function is to absorb it and release it slowly, whereas what is needed is something that will discharge the heat as quickly as possible.

Tools for the Job: Gases

With the hearth sorted out we now need to consider the actual heat source. We can use a gas mixed with air or mix it with oxygen. The latter gives us a greater and more concentrated heat, it does mean the hire of an oxygen cylinder and this in turn needs special equipment in order to use it. If we think in terms of gas and air, then a simple blowlamp will do, but it will have to be large enough to supply the heat required, which on a large boiler is considerable. There is a choice of three gases, ordinary town gas as it is sometimes known, which is piped to our homes and used for domestic cookers and boilers, and Butane or Propane which are both known as l.p.g's (liquid petroleum gas). Most readers will already be familiar with them in some form or another. As the name implies, they are actually liquids. They are bottled at pressure and the vapour created by that pressure at the top of the bottle supplies the gas to burn. Both give more heat than town gas. Butane has the distinct disadvantage of the liquid cooling rapidly as the gas is drawn off, which could even result in it freezing in cold weather and, overall, the best type to use is Propane.

Regulators

Whether Propane or Butane, the gas cylinder must be fitted with a regulator. This need be nothing more than a tap to turn the gas on and off, but the inclusion of an anti blow back device is essential for ones own safety. It is possible, even if very rare, for the gas to burn back in the pipe between the torch and cylinder, but should it do so, this immediately exposes the whole cylinder to the flame which could result in an explosion. With the operator standing close to the cylinder it is he or she who will get, at the very least, badly injured if not killed.

Sophisticated regulators can be obtained which include safety devices built in, others have various settings for gas pressures and some even include gauges. It is largely a matter of cost, and must depend on the frequency of use as to how much one wishes to spend.

Burners

A torch, maybe two, will be needed and it must be able to supply enough heat, so the size will depend on the size of the boiler. For a small locomotive, say gauge '0' or '1' it is possible to use a domestic blowlamp. When it comes to larger size models a torch attached to a cylinder with a flexible hose is required, again the size depending on the size of the boiler. The position at which air is collected by the torch can also be important and if possible one that collects it from as far from the actual heat as possible is desirable. Torches with auxiliary air valves can be obtained which are very useful. When the valve is closed a pilot light burns and when it is opened by a squeeze of the trigger full power comes on.

There are two main reasons why people find they have not made a success of boiler making, the first and most usual is lack of a good mechanical fit of the parts prior to silver soldering, and the second is insufficient heat. This is usually, but not always, caused through the use of blowlamps of insufficient size, but it may well be the fault of the operator who has been unwilling to heat the copper sufficiently. To some extent lack of size of the blowlamp can be compensated for by good packing to prevent heat loss, but this should not be relied on.

The heat generated by the torch will depend on the type of gas used, the quantity of air or oxygen with which it is mixed and the volume of gas the torch will burn. This volume is in relation to the size of the torch; frequently small propane torches are advertised, the advertisement saying something like 'Burns at 2300 degrees centigrade'. Certainly it will burn at that temperature at the tip of the flame but the quantity of that heat is minute and as soon as the flame touches the copper of the boiler the heat will flash away. There will never be sufficient to raise it to the temperature required which is why it is stressed that the burner must be of a suitable size and the boiler should be packed to conserve as much heat as possible. It is impossible to emphasise too much that if the torch will not supply the volume of heat it will not be possible to raise the temperature of the boiler sufficiently for the silver solder to flow properly.

Clothing

The final thing to consider before getting on with the job is the clothing to be worn. In industry, people working as we are proposing to do would require all sorts of sophisticated safety clothing; boots, gloves, aprons and helmets, all of which makes one look like an out-of-work spaceman. The safety people are quite right of course, and their standards should be respected. Few readers, one suspects, will be inclined to invest in all the equipment and if they do, take the trouble to wear it. Fortunately what one does in ones own back yard, as long as it interferes with nobody else, is still for us to decide, but the would-be boiler maker would be a complete fool to set about the work without adequate protection.

The first and most obvious thing is shoes and, unless special industrial boots are bought, then we must make do with ordinary footwear. Above all be sensible, sandals and other open toe shoes are definitely out, as are house slippers, plimsolls and trainers. If a piece of heavy or hot metal were to drop on the foot the very least needed for protection is a reasonable pair of shoes. Preferably they should be made of leather, as plastic will melt if the metal is hot and, rather than shoes, boots would be preferable.

Equally, because there is going to be a lot of heat about, do not think that working in a thin shirt is a good idea, clothing gets hot and the thinner it is the quicker the heat gets through to the flesh. A jacket can provide reasonable protection without being too hot to wear, a good quality cotton overall is ideal if worn over other clothing. Man-made fibres such as nylon should be treated with care as they can melt and stick to the flesh and, anyway, they get hotter than natural materials. People working in foundries are forbidden to wear man-made fibre for this reason.

A little story that illustrates very clearly the absorption of heat is worth repeating. The model engineer who was boiler making enlisted the aid of his wife to hold the blowlamp while he applied the silver solder. Just as the boiler was reaching the required temperature his good lady started squirming around and then departed quickly from the area. "What on earth is the matter?" he asked "It's all right for you," she said, "I've got metal straps in my bra and they have got so hot I can't bear it". A true story which illustrates just how much heat there will be.

Wear safety glasses (but then that is a good idea for all work in the workshop) and a pair of gloves is also needed. Although we shall come to special tools that keep hands as far from the work as possible, it is still a good idea to prevent the hands from getting too hot and possibly dropping things as a result, so gloves are an essential. The gloves used must again not be plastic and heavy chrome leather gardening gloves are a good and cheap way of getting the required protection.

Wearing a hat is also a good idea - it is doubtful if many people will have a full head and face cover as used by professionals, but an ordinary cap or something similar will again make life a little more comfortable while working.

Some silver solders contain cadmium and breathing the fumes can be dangerous to health but many silver solders are now cadmium free, and the use of these is highly recommended. Failing that, or if the composition of the silver solder is not known, use a face mask.

Other tools

As well as blowlamps, certain other tools are desirable, these are very simple items but they can make life easier. Firstly a pair of large pliers with which to pick up smaller items, the pliers will be ruined in no time, at least as far as appearance is concerned, so don't dash out and buy a brand new pair, get the largest pair you can find at a jumble sale or something similar. It is possible to obtain a type known as gas pliers and these generally seem to have been treated in such a way that the heat has less effect on them but if you cannot get these then the bull nosed type will do. Better than pliers would be a pair of blacksmiths short tongs; not easy to come by, but who knows what one will find at a sale?

A specially shaped pair of tongs is needed to pick up the boiler barrel when hot and can easily be made from strip steel to suit ones own individual requirements. It is nice, if not essential, just to rivet a piece of tubing on the handles as that makes the tongs more comfortable to use, as well as preventing too much heat from transferring up them.

A pricker to stir flux and silver solder which fails to run as required is useful and this should be made of stainless steel - mild steel cannot be used, as the silver solder will build up on it, but it is less inclined to stick to stainless. Clamps can be useful but easily get ruined, in particular the threads twist and become useless after a few heatings, once again stainless steel can come to the rescue, and is the best material to make clamps from.

A shield for holding the silver solder makes life much easier and again is simple to make as will be seen from the drawing. The only other item is a special tool for raising ridges on small tubing, which will be described at the appropriate place.

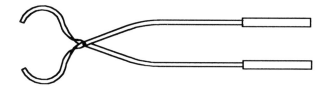

Homemade tongs for holding boilers

Materials

Copper when annealed is very ductile and easy to work with, it also readily accepts silver solder. Bushes for fittings should be made of bronze, it is explained in the chapter of fittings how the zinc content of brass will tend to leach out during use and this applies to bushes as well as fittings. Stays should be of copper with *Monel Metal* as an alternative. The flux used for silver soldering must be one designed for prolonged heating at high temperatures rather than the ordinary standard silver solder flux, it is a good idea to mix it to a

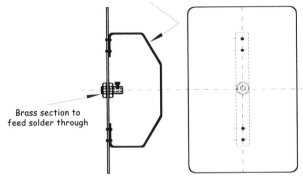

Shield for feeding silver solder to work

creamy consistency with water, adding just a drop or so of washing up liquid to assist it to flow into the joints. One of the problems is the tendency of the flux to run all over the place and to take the solder with it. This does not necessarily mean a bad joint but it does mean a messy looking job. The flux and therefore the solder can be contained in areas by drawing a heavy lead pencil line around the area where it is necessary to retain it - an alternative to the lead pencil is typing fluid.

Construction

Describing every aspect of the construction of a copper boiler would be a lengthy process. From hereon a series of photographs are produced which will give readers the opportunity to see most of the necessary stages.

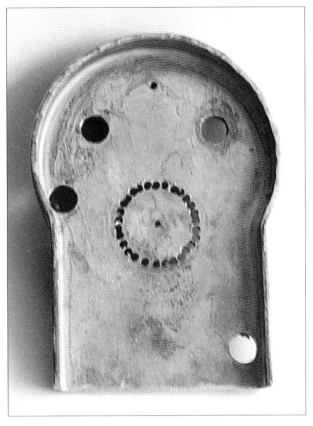

Flanged plates are formed by knocking the edges over a former made from steel, aluminium or hard wood. Holes for safety valves, dome, non-return valves, etc. should be cut very carefully, to avoid unsightly gaps round the edges.

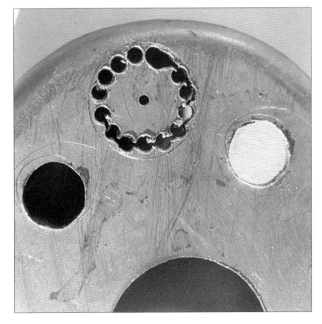

Still with the backhead, the hole for the regulator bush will be too large for drilling and chain drilling may be the answer. The two holes underneath are for the longitudinal stays. These can be fitted directly into the backhead and then such large diameter holes will not be necessary. In this photograph the stays are to be screwed into bushes, a system that allows some slight adjustment if measurements are not quite right. Note the firehole has now been finished with a file and is perfectly shaped.

Mechanical means of making large holes include using a boring head as shown in the photograph, in which case it is necessary to ensure the work is very securely clamped down while boring takes place. An alternative is to mount the work on the lathe faceplate and use a boring tool.

A finished set of flange plates with all holes made and awaiting cleaning in acid ready for assembly.

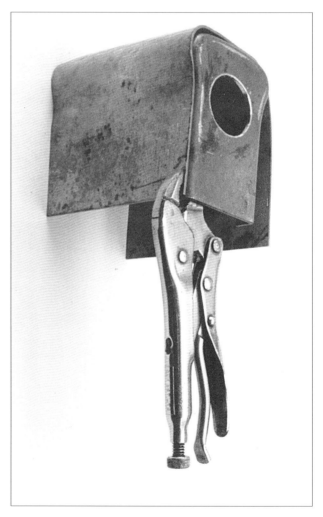

The inner firebox may be shaped in a variety of ways. Whichever shape it takes, it is best to use a former for bending the copper, although in very small boilers for small gauge models it might be practical to use the actual firebox flange plates. This former is a simple plywood box with pieces of beading glued along the edge.

With the wrapper bent to shape it is necessary to drill it for riveting to the plates. After drilling the holes through both parts, separate them and ensure that all burrs are removed. Any burrs that are left are a potential source of trouble as they create pockets where the gap is too wide for the silver solder to fill it.

The wrapper has been riveted in place and the inner firebox is ready for silver soldering, using a high melting point solder. Heating it for this will anneal the copper and allow the crown of the firebox to be flattened, it having risen into a dome during the bending. Copper rapidly work hardens under these conditions and two or more annealings may be required to get it to shape. It was this work hardening effect which allowed the doming effect to occur.

The crown stays are fitted to the firebox with rivets and silver soldered using a high melting point solder. In this instance the firehole is only chain drilled at this stage, the holes of the drilling are to be transferred to the backhead later as a means of lining up the two large diameter holes. One of the many optional constructional variations which are a matter for personal preference, is to only rivet the firebox together, combining the silver soldering with other operations later on.

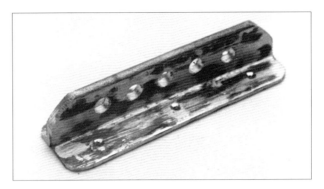

Crown stays fit on top of the firebox to prevent distortion under pressure. The one shown is a simple type folded from copper sheet; modern safety rules now demand that they are secured to the outer shell as well as the firebox top. In full sized practice rod stays were used connecting both inner and outer fireboxes. Some model makers prefer to use that type of stay that has much to commend it for both simplicity and strength.

With the firebox complete the next task is to fit the flue tubes. These are pushed into the firebox and supported by the front plate while silver soldering takes place. There is one big snag - as the copper on the firebox is heated, the holes for the tubes expand faster than the tubes do. If care is not taken the tubes slowly slide down into the firebox and, if any silver solder has been applied, the result is a disgusting mess. To avoid this a simple tool can be used to raise a ridge on the tubes and prevent them sliding in.

The tool is easy to use, the fixed part with the raised ridge is put in the lathe chuck and the tube which is hand held slipped over it. The lathe is rotated very slowly while the wheel part is gently wound in and the ridge on the tube formed.

Two tubes which have been suitably dealt with.
Another tip is to make the tubes slightly different lengths. At a later
stage of assembly it will be necessary to put the front plate over them,
at the same time sliding it in the main barrel. The tubes never line up
exactly with the holes and if they are all the same length we end up
fishing for them with bits of rod. If they are fractionally different the
longest can be drawn in first to hold the plate in position
while it is slid over the remaining ones.

It is time to prepare the main boiler barrel and the first task is to trim
it to length. This means supporting each end, which can be done using
wooden blocks. There is no need to make these completely round.
Simply taking off the corners to make a nice fit in the barrel is
sufficient and to ensure a tight fit the machining should have a taper
of about one degree. The block that is to be used at the tailstock end is
drilled through so that a centre can be used as support.
It may be possible to use the chuck jaws to support the other end;
care must be taken not to over tighten and distort the tube -
alternatively a similar block to that at the tailstock can be used.
If one is used at the headstock end it is left in the chuck,
or on the faceplate, until machining the barrel is completed.

Silver soldering the tubes in position. Note the firebrick has
been packed right up to the edge of the firebox to conserve heat. Flux
has been applied round the tubes and, although it cannot be seen, a
ring of silver solder has been made and slipped round each one, this
will melt and run as heat builds up, saving the necessity of applying
any. The tubes are lined up by temporarily slipping the front plate in
position. Note that there is another variation in construction in this
case as the front of the firebox is being silver soldered at the same time.
This saves one heating operation. Pencil lines to prevent silver solder
from running all over the place can be clearly seen.

With the barrel suitably supported use a nice sharp tool to
trim the edge. Take it slowly as copper is inclined to snatch and we do
not want the precious barrel coming off the lathe. Do not, on any
machining operations, use cutting oils as these can prevent silver
solder from flowing. If lubrication is thought to be necessary use
diluted washing-up liquid.

The barrel having been trimmed, two longitudinal lines must be scribed. One for the line of the dome, safety valve, etc. the other exactly opposite for the outer firebox. It is best to mount the barrel on vee blocks and use either a height gauge or scribing block.

Drill any holes required in the barrel then use a scribing block to mark a line to be cut for the copper to be folded back to make the outer firebox.

There are two ways of making the outer firebox. One is to fit a separate section of copper suitably shaped to the barrel, using either an overlap or a butt strip. The other is the method used here of cutting and opening out the end section of the barrel and fitting an extension on either end.

An extension is required for the outer firebox and this should be supported with butt strips, which can be fitted either inside or outside the firebox. In the photograph the butt strip is clamped in place ready for drilling for the rivets which will hold it. To support the outer firebox the throat plate has been riveted in place and the backhead screwed into position. The backhead is best screwed rather than riveted even at assembly, as it is difficult to close rivets in the confined space.

The finished outer firebox with the extensions supported by the butt strips held in place with rivets, The backhead is removed while silver soldering operations take place.

The throat plate set up for silver soldering. Once again note pencil marks to prevent the solder from running. Before heating, the bricks will be packed up tight against the copper, leaving the minimum area exposed.

Additional support should be given to the join between throat plate and barrel and here we see a piece of home made copper angle riveted in place. In theory this can be done before the throat plate is silver soldered but in fact it is quite difficult to get it accurate if only held with rivets. It was still possible to save a heating by silver soldering the front section of the foundation ring at the same time.

A piece of thick tubing is used as the firehole ring and is machined to fit in both the firebox and backhead. The operation calls for some careful lining up of the parts to ensure that the end result will be a good fit in both.

The ring is silver soldered into the firebox using high melting point solder. Once again we see a variation in construction with the final part of the firebox being soldered at the same time, even though tubes and front end are complete.

The backhead complete with all bushes is screwed into position and fluxed ready for soldering, note the brick which is built right to the top. The next job can be to fit and solder the foundation ring, although some people prefer to leave it until after the boiler has been stayed.

Nearly finished. The tubes and front plate fluxed ready for soldering. Rings of solder are passed round the joints and allowed to melt with the heat rather than applying the solder from a stick. The wet header bush is in position but not drilled and tapped at this point. It can be done after soldering using the header as a guide for the holes.

Soldering the front plate and tubes. Steel pegs have been made to fit the tubes and prevent heat running down them and possibly causing damage. The superheater flues are covered with small stainless steel plates.

The top bushes, dome, safety valves, etc. are a straightforward operation, and here in particular it is necessary to use some means of preventing the solder from running. Once again the brick is packed as high as possible to conserve heat.

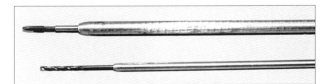

The boiler needs now to be stayed. The stays can either be screwed into position or silver soldered both sides. Silver soldering inside the firebox can be difficult without equipment including oxygen and it may be as well to screw the stays as well. A belt and braces effort of fitting nuts is even better. Drilling for stays is generally easy enough except for those on the throat plate which need extensions for the drill and tap as shown. To make these simply drill suitable sized holes in lengths of mild steel and secure the drill or tap with a retaining compound - this should be quite sufficient to hold them in position while the work is carried out.

The drilling operation for fitting the throat plate stays, using the extended drill.

Testing

When the boiler is completed it will be necessary to test it to twice the working pressure. Plug all holes not in use for the test, ensuring they will not leak by fitting gaskets. Connect a hand pump to one in the lower part of the backhead. Fill the boiler with water and try to ensure that there is no air left by gently shaking it. Partly screw in the pressure gauge leaving it sufficiently loose for water to escape around the threads. Give a single stroke of the pump to force water out, and with it any air that might

A photograph showing test equipment, the use of which is easier than connecting both pump and pressure gauge to a boiler.

have been lurking around. Tighten the pressure gauge and pump water in until the required pressure is reached. Maintain the pressure for half an hour; if it is necessary to pump a little, that does not matter. Note any leaks in the boiler and then slowly reduce the pressure. Examine the boiler for distortion or bad seams. The test is not specifically

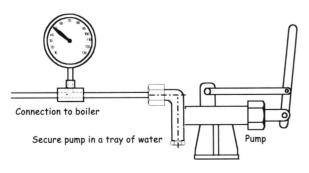

Set up of a boiler testing rig, with one connection to the boiler

for leaks, as these do not make the boiler unsafe - it is to ensure the workmanship and material is sound. Leaks are something we do not want for ourselves, as every leak makes it harder to maintain boiler pressure; in fact if there are too many it will not be possible to reach the boiler test pressure anyway.

If there are any leaks they have to be sealed. Generally they will appear round the foundation ring and stays. Heating the boiler to re-solder the foundation ring is no joke and so it is best to plug any holes there are by drilling a small hole where the leak occurs and tapping it 8 or 10BA, thread a piece of bronze and screw it in, leave 1/16" or so proud and then hammer it over to seal it completely. Oxygen assisted equipment may be needed to repair leaks inside the firebox with silver solder. Providing any leaks are very small there is no technical reason why a good quality soft solder cannot be used; this was common practice in years gone by, but today's boiler maker should ascertain the attitude of those who will ultimately issue any boiler certificate to this procedure before actually using soft solder to seal minor leaks.

A full sized boiler demonstrating the technique of riveting the plates, a system once used by model engineers. Note the rivet spacing and remember it is important that, if making a boiler in this way, this is the type of spacing involved.

With the leaks sealed, start the test again and see how successful you have been. Tiny leaks will disappear on the first steaming of the boiler, and as the water test should be followed by one with steam pressure, things will probably sort themselves out. It might, anyway, be a good idea to steam the boiler before repairing any small leaks; providing of course it is otherwise sound, as a rule they will seal themselves off as soon as a steam is raised.

At the the time of publication, new Pressure Vessel Regulations are being introduced at the behest of Brussels. However the present understanding is that these do not affect boilers made for personal use.

Chapter 14: Regulators

The Mystery Explained

For some reason, to many people regulators seem to be shrouded in mystery but, like most parts they should be considered in simple terms, and the regulator related to a common everyday object, as its function is simply that of a tap, just like those indoors. It is merely a means of getting steam from the boiler to the cylinders when it is needed and turning it off at other times. The most basic of regulators are literally taps and nothing else, and like a tap can be regulated to allow a trickle or a quantity; in this case it is steam - with the domestic tap it is water. Some regulator designs are a little more sophisticated than that and these will be dealt with later in the chapter but, keeping things in their simplest form, all that is needed is a screw-down tap and we have a regulator. There is one big difference, if the tap at home leaks a little it is annoying but not a desperate matter, but care must be taken to get a regulator as steam tight as possible. Failure to do so results in a continuous leak of steam into the cylinders, which means that even when the steam should be turned off it is not and the engine will still want to move. Putting the locomotive in mid gear can rectify this, but the end result of such a practice is the cylinders fill with condensed steam far more rapidly than usual, and this is something which is definitely not wanted. However, it is always a good idea when the locomotive is stationary to open the cylinder drain cocks, just in case for some reason the regulator does have a leak.

Screw-Down Regulators

It should not be all that difficult to get things steam tight - if we go back to the screw-down tap, this generally works via a flat washer, which when worn causes the tap to leak, whereas regulators based on the tap principle and used on model locomotives rely as a rule on a pointed piece of metal screwing hard into a hole. The more it is used the more compatible those two surfaces become and the less likely there will be a leak. It is best if the screw that operates the plug is made with a left hand thread, allowing the clockwise movement to close things down. This is in keeping with full-size practice where invariably the regulator opens when turned clockwise. If the builder is unhappy with the idea of cutting left hand threads, or going to the expense of buying a left hand tap and die, by all means use a right hand one. It does not take very long to become used to operating the steam supply in this way, although it can, and sometimes does, have a pretty disastrous effect when a friend has a drive and forgets that turning the handle anti-clockwise actually makes the model go faster.

The thread should always be as coarse as possible, otherwise it can take quite a while to keep turning the handle sufficiently to make a smart getaway. The Whitworth range works reasonably well but cutting ones own threads to an even coarser pitch is a better idea. There are two schools of thought about where the thread should be: should it be near the orifice or

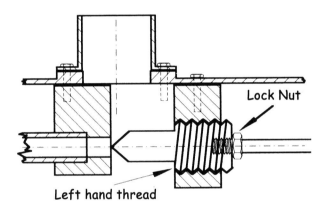

Screw Down Regulator

somewhere within the gland at the handle end? A personal preference is to make it as near the orifice as possible, in an attempt to avoid excessive flexing caused by the rod, this can be troublesome when the thread starts to get a little furred up, and any eccentric movement caused by the furring is multiplied by the length of the rod. So although it is easier to make the thread at that end, and assembly does not require any fiddling in fitting the screwed block near the boiler, as shown in the drawing, in the long run the extra trouble is probably worthwhile.

Steam Collection

Where possible the steam to the regulator should be taken from the hottest area, which is the highest point on the boiler, usually inside a dome, if the locomotive has one. Some designers did not like domed boilers, Patrick Stirling, for example, believed they created a weakness. In that case the regulator is usually placed close to the backhead, picking up steam from above the firebox, working

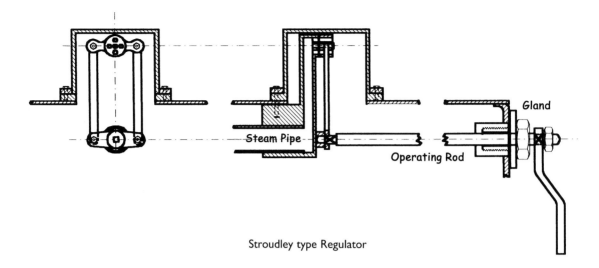

Stroudley type Regulator

on the principle that the heat of the fire will increase the heat of the steam, at that point.

Although very rarely used in full-size practice, there is nothing whatever wrong with the use of a screw-down type on a model. If they have a fault it is that sometimes they will stick a little for one reason or another, otherwise they work well. Probably in full size the larger areas involved would cause problems with sticking, and so various other types were used. All used the same basic principle of a hole to let the steam into the cylinders, and something to bung over the hole somehow or another, when steam was not needed.

Stroudley Type Regulator

Quite popular and very useful in models is the regulator design of *William Stroudley*, one of the early locomotive designers. The drawing shows how the arrangement works. A pillar is erected in the dome and attached to this is a disc with two arms. In the disc are two or more holes to act as ports. When steam goes through these, if the regulator is open it can pass through matching ports in the pillar and then into the main steam pipe. The arms are operated via levers from the rod attached to the regulator arm, which is fitted to the backhead with a steam-tight gland. It is essential when making this type of regulator to ensure that good tight threads are used to hold the pivot pins in place as otherwise they can work loose, drop out and be lost forever in the bottom of the boiler. (It is strange they rarely ever come to light again.) The other thing is to ensure that the faces of the ports are well ground in to prevent leakage, but this applies to the port faces on all regulators. Given that these two precautions are taken, the Stroudley Regulator is very reliable and smooth to operate, as well as being easy to maintain.

Disc Type Regulator

The Stroudley regulator is a disc type, and the main difference between it, and the type that is actually referred to as the disc, is that with the Stroudley operation takes place high in the dome, while with the disk it takes place in line with the main steam pipe. The control is via a rod set in a square hole as against the two arms of the Stroudley and generally the ports are elongated, as they can be on the Stroudley type, if sufficient room can be found. The steam collection pipe is taken from the dome top as it is with a screw down regulator.

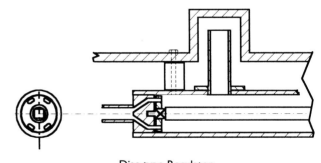

Disc type Regulator

Slide Valve Type

The slide valve type is used as a rule where space is limited and was very popular on the *London North Eastern Railway*. It is literally a tiny slide valve in a block, the movement of which opens a port to steam which passes to the cylinders, once again it is essential to ensure the valve is ground well in. To make certain the valve does not leak it is also necessary to apply pressure from above, which can be done by either putting a spring in between the top of the inner dome and the valve or fitting an '0' ring, the same principle is sometimes applied to slide valves

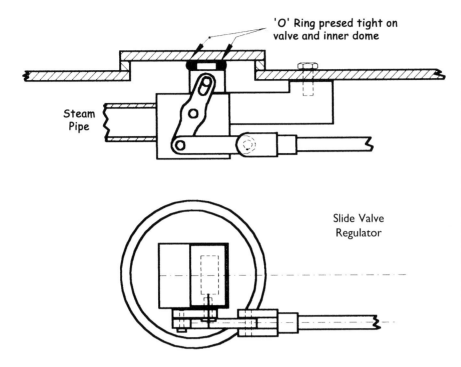

'O' Ring presed tight on valve and inner dome

Steam Pipe

Slide Valve Regulator

in cylinders. As the valve is usually used when there is limited room above it, there is unlikely to be a steam collecting pipe.

Poppet Valve Regulators

Poppet valve regulators are smooth in operation and are used quite a lot in the United States, where generally there is more room for them in the boiler. They are fitted close to the backhead and the steam collection pipe runs parallel with the main steam pipe. If a reasonable sized dome is fitted, an extension can be taken into it to get steam from a higher point but as a rule the type is used for boilers with small domes. Builders of models of any of the British Railways bigger "Standard" classes will also come across this type of regulator, in a slightly different configuration, as they were fitted in the smokebox, close to the wet header

Tubular Design

This type of regulator is particularly useful on a domeless boiler and is fitted close to the backhead, above the firebox. It consists of a steam pipe with a series of tiny holes drilled in it and fitted inside is another pipe that can rotate, also with holes matching those in the outer tube and which line up when the regulator is open. When the regulator is only partly open a limited number of the holes match, thus restricting the flow of steam. The main difficulty with making this type is ensuring that all the holes inside the steam pipe are completely deburred and likewise with the outside of the rotating pipe. It is best to use some form of lap to ensure the two pieces fit together in such a way that they will be steam tight. It is also a good idea to use two different metals for the two perforated sections, possibly bronze on the outer one and stainless steel for the inner rotating one. If these objects can be achieved it is a particularly sensitive and easy to operate regulator, but extra care must be taken at the end of a running season to make sure that the two sections do not fur up. Once they become bound together it is almost impossible to separate them and the regulator is no longer of use. Good maintenance will ensure a lengthy service and it is well worth considering making this type of regulator.

Handles

The regulator handle was invariably a distinctive feature of the cab and varied greatly, not just from company to company, but also from design to design, and even from one individual locomotive to another. Often it was nothing more than a shaped metal bar, sometimes bent to allow clearance of various fittings. It could be positioned almost anywhere, some went up above the regulator bush while others dropped below and yet others would be at one side or another. When slide valve regulators were fitted, instead of rotating the handle would pull outwards. At times this could cause a rather greater movement than was really wanted as it would at first stick under the pressure and then suddenly release without warning. This was no problem for regular crews on that type of locomotive but frequently caught out those not used to that type

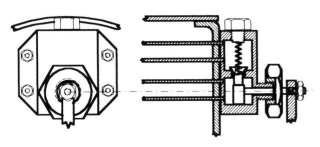

Poppet Valve Regulator

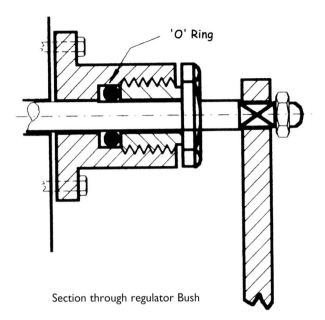

'O' Ring

Section through regulator Bush

of regulator. The pull-out regulator on some locomotives was connected via cross bars to two handles so that it could be operated from either side of the cab, which was quite a useful feature.

In the case of rotary operated levers they should be made a push fit over a square section of the operating rod and secured with a nut. The bush itself contains a gland and would be tightened as a rule with a ring of bolts, but occasionally a series of studs might be used. The packing for the gland can be in the form of soft material, or an '0' ring can be used. A point to watch for is the size of the bush and fitting. On most models these are greatly oversized and if we look at a full-sized locomotive it will be seen that they are actually fairly small. A quite usual specification for a 5" gauge model is for a ⅛" square and a 6BA nut, which is probably about twice the size required to get a good scale appearance. It is always difficult without special equipment to make square holes a good tight fit and the smaller they are the more difficult life becomes, and is no doubt one reason why an oversize specification is given. The usual way to make a square is to drill a hole to the size across flats and file out the corners. It is possible to

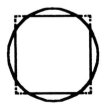

A simple way to fit a Square is to make an oversized hole, and just nick out flats, as shown by the dotted lines, with a file.

cheat by making the initial hole a slightly larger diameter and with a small square needle file just nick out the corners. With the nut in place the difference does not notice and it is much easier to get a good fit in this way.

Materials

Handles should be made of stainless steel, which prevents quite a lot of the transfer of heat and remains relatively cool, the bush and glands should always be of gunmetal or phosphor bronze. Some people with sensitive fingers like to put a small sleeve over the handle to make it easier to operate and although it spoils the appearance it can make life easier when driving. Neoprene fuel tubing as sold for model racing motor cars is the ideal material for this purpose, as it does not stretch except under extreme heat.

Smokebox Regulators.

Finally it is worth mentioning the smoke box regulator, which is sometimes used in full-sized practice, particularly on the continent. The obvious advantage to having the regulator in the smoke box is the fact that the extra heat keeps the steam at a higher temperature than when it is brought from the boiler. The regulator is usually a poppet valve type and is operated by a rod running alongside the boiler and cranked where it enters the smoke box, sometimes the operating rod will be inside the boiler cladding. The actual construction of such a regulator is not in itself a great deal more difficult than making one that fits in the boiler. The reason that smoke box regulators are not more popular on models is probably because the extra heat tends to distort the components and give operating problems as well as causing a stickiness in operation. The regulator also quickly becomes covered with a mixture of soot and oil, making maintenance difficult, plus the fact that the smoke box becomes very crowded.

The gland and handle of a regulator are very much a feature of the cab and so it is worth spending time and thought on their manufacture in order to give the cab a really nice appearance. In particular we all too often see regulator handles covered in file marks and scratches. It can be time consuming to get a good polish on stainless steel but doing so is time well spent. Most of us have seen the footplate of a locomotive and it is quite noticeable how the regulator handle always has a nice polished appearance, so it is worth trying to achieve this in model form.

Chapter 15: Safety Valves

The importance of good quality, well maintained safety valves cannot be over emphasised. The very least damage a faulty safety valve will do, if the trouble is not spotted in time, is to ruin the boiler, at its worst it could result in injury or worse to those who happen to be around at the time. They are without doubt the most important fitting on a boiler and should be treated as such.

The first question we need to know the answer to is how large should the safety valve be for a particular boiler? It is a difficult question to answer, most published drawings have satisfactory figures worked out, so if you work to the design there should not be any disasters. For anyone designing their own boiler the figures given in the appendix will serve as a guide, but it must be emphasised that a guide is all they are and, if in any doubt, it is far better to have a larger area of escape. It does no harm if the escape area is larger than quoted, as the valve or valves will automatically shut off at the desired pressure.

In small gauge models it is quite usual to have a single safety valve but generally models from 2½" gauge upwards should have two, unless the design of the original is such that only one is called for. This is very rare and although the *Ramsbottom* and *Midland* type of valves at first glance would seem to have only one escape orifice, in fact there are two. Each orifice should be capable of relieving the pressure on the boiler of its own accord, and generally they should be adjusted so that one opens at about ten pounds per square inch lower than the other. This takes care of any tendency for the boiler to raise pressure at a faster rate than usual, which may temporarily overwhelm the first valve.

The construction of safety valves is quite straight-forward and, in the case of an ordinary standard type of valve, no silver soldering need be involved. If it is to be threaded into a bush in the boiler it is essential to ensure that the thread is a good full-sized and well made one. A loose and badly made thread can, when under pressure, come undone, causing the valve, plus a quantity of steam and hot water to fly out and possibly cause injury. All safety valves should be made of bronze and if a ball is used for release purposes it must be a good quality non-rusting type. Springs if possible should be stainless steel or bronze, although if made of ordinary spring steel will be quite efficient, but **must be checked regularly for signs of deterioration** and must be replaced immediately if this is found. A drop of thin oil into a safety valve just before running can improve performance, but it can also cause a sticking effect if the oil is allowed to congeal and this again is a reason to regularly clean and check the valve.

In many areas of Britain, and other parts of the world as well, calcium in the water soon creates deposits on boiler fittings, which has two effects on the safety valve. Firstly, if small deposits form underneath the ball or whatever other surface is used as the sealing device, the valve will start to leak. If a considerable amount is allowed to form it can cause the valve to stick down so hard that it is impossible to release it. Before running and while steam is being raised, release the valve and let a little steam escape, this should at least ensure that during running the valve is unlikely to leak. Frequently soak the whole valve in vinegar or some form of water descaler and this will ensure that harmful deposits are removed. If for any reason it is difficult to take the whole valve out to do this, just pour a few drops of the solution into the relief holes and allow it to soak, which will have the desired effect.

The drawings show a number of types of safety valve that one may come across when building models. The first is a modification of the type that is used on toy steam engines. Putting the spring inside the boiler allows a good-sized safety valve to be fitted without it looking ugly. A dummy cover can be made and pushed on if required to give the effect of something like the *Great Western Railway* type of valve. Of course the top must be left clear to allow the escape of steam and the spring must definitely be of the non rusting variety. It is neat and effective but suffers

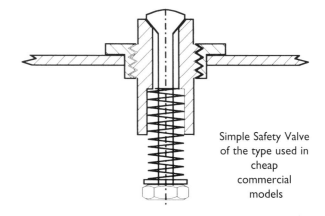

Simple Safety Valve of the type used in cheap commercial models

from the problem that for adjustment it has to be taken out of the boiler.

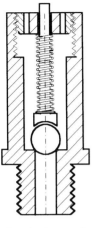 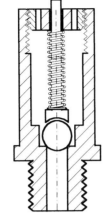

Standard type of safety valve

"Pop" or quick release safety valve

The second drawing shows two valves; the one on the left is the more or less standard type of construction, which is shown using a ball. Different sealing devices can be used to replace the ball if one wishes. The valve on the right is very similar but it will be seen that the ball is set in a recess, this gives an action which makes it release with a loud popping sound and it is therefore hardly surprising to find that it is called a pop valve, it also releases and seals off more quickly than the plain type. This type of safety valve was common in full-size practice and, as well as ensuring a quick release of pressure, it also often caused quite an alarm to people standing on the platform. As more power was required locomotive boilers got bigger and bigger until they had just about reached the limit of the loading gauge. Designers found the usual types of valve could not be fitted, so a flatter version was devised and is shown in the third drawing

The next two drawings take us back to a more leisurely age when things were designed for appearance as well as how they would function. The *Salter* type

of valve was set in a dome and was adjusted from the outside by the tension on the spring. Many early valves had a similar arrangement of an external spring and were a constant source of worry, as the crews had a habit of tightening them down to increase boiler pressure in an attempt to gain more power, resulting in a number of boiler explosions. Sometimes the dome might contain two valves side by side.

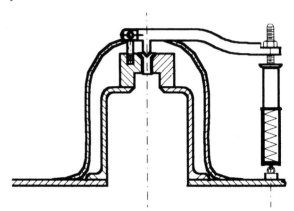

The Salter type Safety Valve is usually situated on top of the Dome

Drawing number five shows the *Ramsbottom* valve, which will be familiar particularly to anyone with an interest in the old *Great Northern Railway*. Crews often kept them highly polished and at some sheds there was often something of a competition to see who had the brightest safety valve. As well as looking smart the valve was functional and it was not very easy for the crew to tighten it. At the same time a little downward push on the lever would release boiler pressure, if it was thought to be necessary to do so. It proved to be a highly popular valve and was used until very late in the life of steam traction.

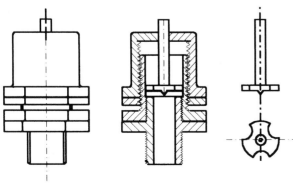

Safety Valve designed for use where room is limited above the boiler

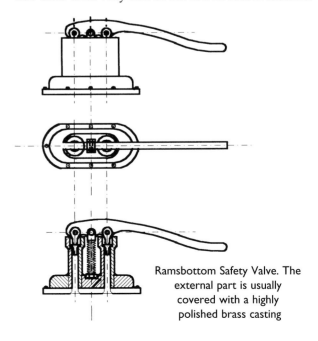

Ramsbottom Safety Valve. The external part is usually covered with a highly polished brass casting

Chapter 16: Firedoors and Grates

The idea of lighting a fire and keeping it burning brightly sounds the easiest thing in the world but it certainly is not in model locomotives, and in order to make it burn efficiently, as well as having a good boiler and front end, the design of the fire hole door and grate are also very important. The fire hole on a working model steam locomotive will almost certainly be oversize as it is necessary to feed the fire with the locomotive running, and that in itself requires something of a balancing act. As scales get progressively larger it is possible to get the hole nearer to scale proportions but unless a really large engine is built, this side of things is never going to be quite right. Size, therefore, will always be something of a compromise but this does not mean that it needs to be obtrusive or unsightly.

Drop Down Doors

The fact that the hole is possibly oversize does not in itself affect the design of the door which should be similar to full-size practice and, as well as trying to copy the full-size article, thought will have to be given regarding what will be practical. One of the easiest types of door to make is a drop down, which does literally what is suggested, a catch at the top is undone and the door, which is hinged at the bottom, drops down and lays flat on the footplate. It is in many ways very convenient as there is no obstruction of any sort to prevent coal being fed to the fire the door is simple to make and so why, we must ask ourselves, do we not see this type of door more often on models? There are two reasons, the first is plainly that a drop down door on a full sized locomotive did not drop down and lay on the floor. There was a catch and chain that prevented it from going below ninety degrees. On a model this can make life very awkward as the chain tends to get between the door and back head when it is being closed, also it has to be so fine that it is easily broken. One answer is to make these removable so that when the locomotive is being used, the door will drop right down, at other times the correct fittings are in place. So far so good, but there is another more difficult problem to overcome; it is almost impossible to prevent little bits of coal falling in to the hinge when firing, these will wedge themselves between it and the back head and make the door impossible to close. If a model is being used in a situation where it will be stationary when fired, something which is common on club tracks, where a model does a circuit and then stops for the fire to be made up and to take on water, this

does not matter very much as the pieces can be swept out with a small brush and the door closed before starting off. This is something that is not possible when running and it is essential to give some thought to the matter before deciding whether this type of door is suitable.

Sideways Opening Doors

The sideways opening door is also easy to make and on many models would conform to full-size practice. Spilled fuel usually falls straight to the floor, in the event of coal or ash falling in the hinges it is a simple thing to clean it out and in addition a well made catch can easily be opened with a flick of the shovel if need be. After driving model steam locomotives

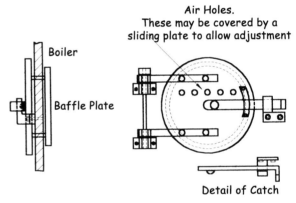

Side Opening Firedoor,
suitable for round or oval fireholes

for some time most people actually find their hands harden against heat and they can open this type of door with their fingers. The door is suitable for round or oval fire holes and is very versatile; on smaller models it can be made as a single piece and consist only of a hinged metal plate that will cover the hole. For larger and more sophisticated models it should be fitted with a baffle plate that is a reasonable fit in the hole, and an outer plate that extends right over. It is also a good idea to fit some form of adjustable vent that allows adjustment of the amount of air that can be drawn over the top of the fire.

Sliding Doors

In many ways sliding doors are the ideal type to use, although they do take a little longer to construct and there is still some chance of unburnt fuel preventing closure. The drawing shows the principle and

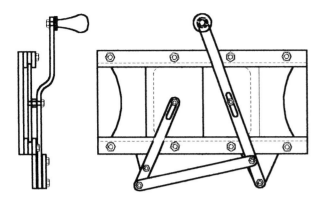

Sliding Doors; a little harder to make but effective

although shapes sometimes vary, basically all sliding doors follow the same system. A door working on a similar principle is referred to as the butterfly type and a look at the drawing will soon explain why. From the modellers point of view it is not quite so easy to make as it requires gears, but if that is the type of door that is wanted, don't be put off. The usual practice is to cut a gear wheel in pieces and silver solder it in position; it is also possible to file the teeth to shape and make ones own gear. They follow about a quarter of a circle and need no more than half a dozen coarse teeth for a full opening, which isn't such a terribly daunting task.

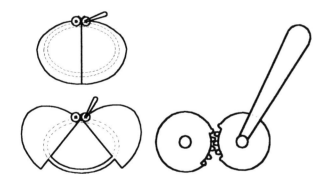

Butterfly Door, showing operating mechanism

So far only the shape and operation of the door has been dealt with, but for efficiency something more sophisticated than an ordinary piece of metal to cover the hole is required in order to have good control over a fire. This control requires a suitable draught and while the action of the exhaust provides this to some extent, we have little or no control over the amount of draught that is produced. There are other factors involved in maintaining a steady steam output and the firebox, including grate and ash pan should be constructed in such a way that the draught is drawn from behind and through the fire

bars, subsequently going out along the boiler tubes. If the fire hole door is left open, air is drawn over the top of the fire instead of through it, and this has the effect of reducing the heat into the boiler, partly because the fire will not burn so brightly and partly because cold air is being drawn through into the boiler tubes. One way we use to extinguish the fire when running is finished is to open the door, which assists in allowing the fire to die off. At the same time when a locomotive is working hard it is possible for the draught to be too strong and this too is a bad thing. It is to prevent this that a series of small holes are drilled in the door, and a cover fitted which can be adjusted, so that the number of holes that are uncovered are just enough for the fire to generate the exact amount of heat needed.

The door would sometimes also include a plate that fitted closely in the fire hole, this prevented air from around the door from being drawn in unintentionally. Usually there would also be a plate just above the door which could be dropped down when the door was opened for firing, it prevented too much cold air from being drawn in while the fireman was doing his work. So important was it to prevent cold air being drawn in when not wanted that the usual practice would be to close the door between each shovel full, the fireman was sometimes assisted in this by the driver who would swing it shut between each one, but on some locomotives the door would be operated by a foot pedal, and the fireman would place his foot on that so the door opened as he swung the shovel full of coal in. Neither of these practices is available for the modeller who, of necessity, will have to leave his door open for as long as it takes to make up the fire. The answer therefore is to do so very frequently, so that the door need remain open only long enough for one or two shovels full to be put on, preventing large quantities of cold air from having an adverse effect.

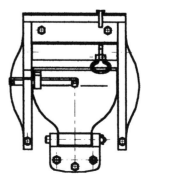 

A Drop down Firedoor of scale appearance.
There are two flaps, the lower to feed the fuel through, and the upper for inspection purposes
Drawing courtesy of Tony Meek

The Grate

The grate consists of a series of bars spaced out to allow air to pass through. The best material to use for grate construction is stainless steel, but cast iron and mild steel are used and, although not so long lasting as stainless, will work quite well for a period. If home made then the usual way is to use strip material and fit spacers in between the bars. It is possible to purchase cast iron and stainless steel grates. Usually the grate would be made as a series of separate bars which could be removed individually, the advantage being that when one or two bars

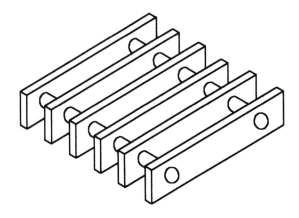

Construction of a Grate using steel flats and spacers

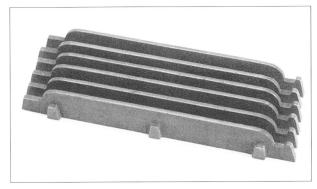

A particularly fine example of a grate made by the late Fred Beard, copying full sized practice. The shape of the fire bars can clearly be seen and how they slot into cross bars so that each can be removed individually.

became worn they could be replaced without the need to replace them all. Although some advanced modellers have used the idea, this is not always practical in model form, so generally the grate will be in one or possibly two complete pieces. When making a grate we once again come across the problem of the quantity of air to be drawn through the bars, too much is almost as bad as too little, and a good general figure to work on is the space between the bars to be equal to one, or one and half times, the thickness of the bars themselves. The bars should if possible taper towards the bottom to allow ash and small clinker particles to slide away, this is not always practical when using stock sized steel, but well worth aiming for. One mistake that is fairly common is not to make the bars deep enough. The depth should be a minimum of three times the width, with four being possibly the maximum required, making them deep means that they remain cooler, and do not burn out so quickly. Additionally the depth can act as something of a funnel to induce air to flow quickly through the gaps. It is usually possible to

Ideal shape of firebars

purchase grates made from cast iron, the best material to use when making one is stainless steel, mild steel tends to burn out rather quickly,

Having carefully explained the basic principles to look for in grate making, these theories have been somewhat challenged in recent years by a few modellers who have used a completely different concept. They have been successful using just a thick sheet of stainless steel with a series of holes drilled in it. Being flat metal it follows that the holes cannot be too close together, or the strength of the material would be weakened to the point where it would collapse when heated, nevertheless the system appears to work well and such a grate is much easier to make than the more conventional type.

When building a model the design should include the facility to drop the grate right out, not only for cleaning purposes but also as a safety measure; should some unforeseen circumstance mean the boiler is running out of water, the grate can be removed complete with the fire, preventing any further build up of steam. Frequently a grate will be designed to slope towards the front of a firebox allowing the fire to work its way forward when running, and bringing it to the point where it is most needed. Some locomotive designs call for a grate to be bent in shape and others to be hinged in the middle. A grate is usually fitted by allowing it to rest against the foundation ring and supporting it with pins through the frames, which some people screw in to the frames, while others rely on a good tight fit.

The Ash Pan

The ash pan should be large enough to allow for a decent period of running before it needs emptying and, like the grate, it must be capable of being dropped quickly if need be. Most modern designs have a hinged flap that allows ash to be removed

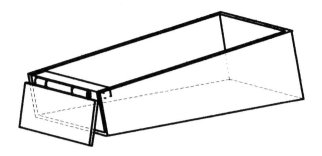

Typical ashpan made from sheet metal

A complete Rocking Grate assembly,
ready for mounting in place.

while the engine is still in steam. Air openings should be at the front so that air is drawn across the bottom of the fire bars and it is a good idea to fit flaps, or dampers, at each end which will allow some adjustment of the quantity of air that is admitted; these can be operated via a lever from the cab. Other than these hinged openings the ash pan is simply folded up from thin sheet metal - mild steel works quite well but, as always, stainless will be longer lasting.

Rocking Grates

Usually the grate will sit on the ashpan, and lie flush with the boiler foundation ring, being released for fire removal by removing pins pushed through, or screwed into, the frames. On some locomotives this will not be practical, as the grate is directly above an axle or possibly a bogie frame. It has already been explained how, in full-size practice, the individual

bars of a grate could be removed, and a flap allowed the ashpan to be raked out. Many locomotives also had rocking grates which allowed some movement to shake the fire and release ash. In a model it is possible to use the idea of a rocking grate to empty the firebars completely, by tipping them further than would have been normal in full sized practice, and the drawing illustrates how this is done. The grate is operated by the central pivot shown as a square section at point 'B'. It can be attached to a lever in the cab, but it is perhaps better to operate it from out- side, making a special box spanner to fit the square. If possible, all parts should be machined from stainless steel for longer life. The assembly is still held in position by pins through the frame, but saves the necessity of taking it out, and putting it

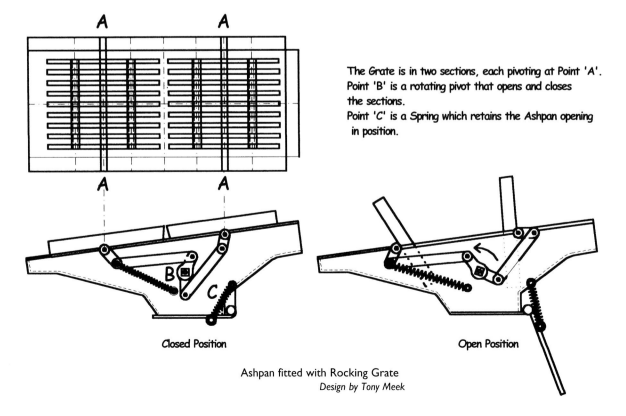

A   A

The Grate is in two sections, each pivoting at Point 'A'.
Point 'B' is a rotating pivot that opens and closes
the sections.
Point 'C' is a Spring which retains the Ashpan opening
in position.

A   A

B   C

Closed Position   Open Position

Ashpan fitted with Rocking Grate
Design by Tony Meek

back, after each run. In the unlikely event of this even being possible, it is, at the least, going to be a very awkward, and probably frustrating, job.

Brick Arches

In full size a brick arch was fitted under the lower boiler tube plates, this deflected the hot air coming through the grate is such a way that the top of the firebox received a considerable amount. There have been examples of arches fitted to model boilers but generally they are a nuisance as it is difficult to clean the top, which quickly becomes clogged with a mixture of soot, and ash that congeals on the arch as it mixes with water vapour from the fuel, but there is no doubt that an arch will improve efficiency if it can be used.

Even without the refinements of a brick arch there is no reason why the driver should not be able to keep a bright fire burning, but always remember too much air is almost as bad as too little, Close the fire hole door as soon as practical to prevent cold air being drawn across the fire and through the flue tubes, and ensure that it fits properly.

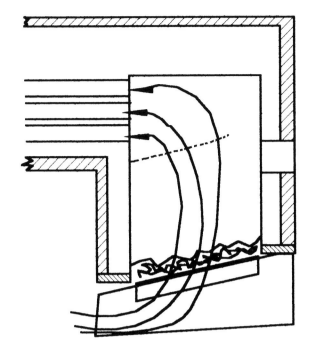

Diagram showing the passage of air through the grate and fire, and into the tubes. A Brick Arch, if fitted, would be in the position of the dotted line, forcing the heated air round the back, and roof, of the firebox, before it entered the tubes

Driving Positions - up or down?

Historically, for ease of driving, and for safety, tracks of 5″ gauge and under have been raised, the driver and passengers sitting astride trollies, with tracks of 7¼″ gauge and over being laid at ground level. On a raised track, points are not possible and the trains just go round and round the track. At ground level a more realistic railway can be laid, complete with points, turntables etc., and operations can also be more realistic.

Of recent years 5″ ground level tracks have become common, especially in Europe, Australia and Japan and a number can also be found in Great Britain where there is a national society dedicated to the realistic running of 5″ gauge locomotives and trains at ground level. Such tracks have proved to be as safe as raised ones, and more interesting for drivers.

With a very few exceptions, 3½″ gauge tracks remain raised to make driving easier. Gordon Dando had a ground level 3½″ track at his home in Bath, but this was essentially a scenic line, with scale stations, infrastructure, coaches and wagons, but which it was possible to drive a locomotive

round with care. A few European club tracks also have their 3½″ tracks at ground level, which can give rise to interesting driving positions as shown on the following page; the prone position has the benefit that the driver is at cab level so obtains a very realistic view of the track ahead.

Conversely, the running of a 5″ gauge locomotive, intended for ground level use, on a raised track can call for strong nerves, as may also be seen.

To complicate matters further, some raised 3½″ and 5″ gauge tracks also have a 7¼″ track intended to take the passenger trollies, on the Brunelian principle that the broader gauge increases stability. Inevitably some 7¼″ gauge locomotives are run on these tracks.

None of which should affect your choice of locomotive to build, but if you are building a 5″ gauge locomotive, it is as well to consider the type of track you will run on before starting to build the tender or driving trolley, so that any modifications required to suit the driving position may be built into them from the start.

The SUPPLICANT: face precisely positioned in the exhaust, even with a cushion the knees ache. This position also requires considerable balancing skills and is not really recommended!

The TOBOGGAN: relaxed driving stance, face can be brought lower to give realistic forward view and escape exhaust. Requires two flat trollies-and attention paid to body position over middle coupling!

Ground level locomotives on raised track: First - MOUNT YOUR TENDER!

THEN: Sit still, Hold On, Open your eyes, Keep your fingers crossed and don't forget you have a train to drive.

Unusual Driving Positions

Nick Stothard, suitably attired for the first run of his 7¼" gauge "Raritan", on the usually passenger trolley only rails of the Sunderland Society's track. This loco is a doubled up American 3½" gauge design.

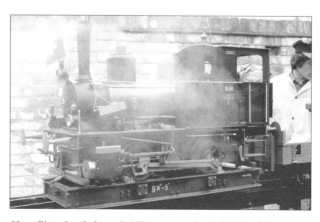

Hans-Pieter Landerberger's 150 mm gauge Swiss 0-4-0 tank locomotive has its own adaptor wagon to run on 5" - 9¼" gauge tracks. It works well, although the locomotive's wheels revolve the opposite way to the direction of travel. The simplicity of the wagon may be seen below.

Chapter 17: Drain Cocks

The function of drain cocks is fairly obvious - they release water from the cylinders, but it is worth asking ourselves why we need to do this and how the water gets there in the first place. Whenever a locomotive in steam has the regulator turned off, there is a certain amount of steam clinging to the walls of cylinders and pipes leading to them. This rapidly condenses and finds its way into the bottom of the cylinders. With no steam coming through, to either maintain it at steam temperature or force it out with the exhaust, it will lie in the bottom of the cylinder. If steam is only turned off for a short period the amount of condensation is of little consequence and will automatically exhaust when the regulator is next opened. If there has been a time lapse, too much water will have accumulated and we need to get rid of it, as otherwise it can create problems. With water in the cylinders, there is less room for steam to expand and so, when the regulator is opened, there is an increase in pressure in the cylinders. This is the opposite to the normal situation where the pressure in the cylinders is generally lower than that in the boiler. In theory we could use this to our advantage and half fill the cylinder with water, using the extra pressure to give power. It does not actually work quite like that, the pressure increase is very temporary and opening the regulator can have several effects. It can cause the wheels to spin furiously, in which case the locomotive will slip and waste valuable steam. With a slide valve engine the valve will be forced from its seat and the water ejected through the chimney, showering everyone, including the driver and upsetting bystanders. Experience shows that mum is not often pleased when little Johnny, dressed in his best white shirt suddenly is covered in thick, hot, oily water. Wives of drivers have also been known to be less than pleased, when he arrives home in a shirt that is completely ruined. Could there then be a better reason for fitting drain cocks? In the long run it could be a prudent thing to do. In full-size, water in cylinders has been known to have serious results and there are recorded instances of cylinder end covers being blown off, and even of locomotive running temporarily out of control. The increase in pressure is a very short and is immediately followed by a drop in the steam pressure.

In the garden gauges it is not very often practical to fit drain cocks because of the size. Most models are slide valve and the amount of exhaust is tiny, so probably is of no consequence. A little water and oil coming from the chimney will hardly matter and as a rule pressure is low enough to prevent the residue travelling very far. This also applies to small 2½″ gauge models, but if these small engines have piston valves, then some method of draining the cylinders should be fitted. It can be a simple screw device operated by hand at the cylinder which would save fitting a fiddly little linkage, as long as it is sufficient to allow the release of any water. If they are not fitted the least that will happen is that the locomotive will be difficult to start and, at the worst, it may lock up completely until the cylinders can be drained off. Larger engines of 2½″ gauge and all 3½″ gauge models upwards should have them fitted.

Construction

Drain cocks are made in the same way as any taper cock, but generally the angle will be steeper because of their small size. To make them, simply chuck a piece of brass or bronze rod of suitable diameter, turn down one end and thread it to the size required for the cylinders. Drill the water release hole and then shape the cock. This can be done with a form tool made from a piece of silver steel. Part off and you have the beginnings of the drain cock. It helps in this sort of operation to have a rear mounted tool post to hold the parting tool. The shape can then be formed and the metal parted at a single setting.

Form Tools

To make the form tool to shape the body, simply file the reverse of the contour in the end of a piece of silver steel of the required diameter. Make sure that all file marks are smoothed out with emery cloth. File the steel flat to half its diameter for a distance that just clears the shape. Then file a cutting edge to an angle of about ten degrees, it is not that critical. Once again finish with emery paper and remove all marks. Any marks left on the tool will show up on the finished drain cocks and so the smoother the better, in order to end up with good looking and well operating drains. Cut the silver steel to a length of about one inch and remove any burrs. Dip the shaped end in some washing-up liquid and then heat it with a blowlamp until it is the colour of a boiled carrot. Immediately quench it in a solution of salt water. Many people recommend quenching in oil to prevent the metal cracking. This should not be necessary in such a small size, but if oil is preferred use something like Sunflower Oil, rather than a mineral oil as used on a car. The oil traditionally used in industry for this purpose was Whale Oil, something to which the average model engineer is unlikely to have access.

The steel needs to be polished bright with a piece of fine emery cloth. This is where the original dipping in washing-up liquid proves its worth. If it is not done it is very difficult to clean the metal, dipped as suggested it is easy. Get an old flat tin. Sardine tins do nicely, or an old tobacco tin if you have one. Half fill it with sand, garden silver sand is good for this, failing that it is always possible to rob the family budgie. Put the tool on the sand and heat the tin until the tool turns a dark straw colour, immediately quench it either in brine or oil. It is now suitably tempered. It is quite possible to heat the tool away from the cutting edge and allow the colour to run along it, before quenching, but there is a chance that the colour will run more rapidly than expected, with sand, control over the job is easier.

We now need a simple holder for the tool. This can be a piece of square mild steel, drilled centrally along its length, using the four-jaw chuck in the lathe. Cross drill it to accept a suitable screw to hold the tool tight and just grind a tiny flat on the actual tool where the screw will go, this prevents it turning round in use. Use a piece of bar of suitable size so that the cutting edge of the tool will be exactly at centre height when set. The setting of tools to the exact height is most important in all turning operations and more work is spoiled through getting that wrong than for any other reason.

Taper Reamer

The next job is to make the taper reamer and we start by turning the required taper (about ten degrees) on a piece of silver steel, turn the top slide over to do so. When finished leave the top slide at the angle used, do not under any circumstances alter it. From then on the steps are virtually the same as for the form tool. File the steel flat to exactly half its diameter and harden and temper as before. As the reamer is to be used in a chuck, a tool holder will not be required. Unfortunately it will only be of use for the one job as the chances of later on setting the top slide to exactly the same angle are about as good as winning the National Lottery. The obvious thing, therefore, is to make a few drain cocks while we are at it. There is every chance that spares will be needed as in the case of a derailment drain cocks have a nasty habit of getting badly damaged - and then there is always the next locomotive.

Taper Plugs

The taper plugs are a simple turning job using the same set over on the top slide. A thread is put on the smaller end and this can cause some complications. It is rather nice if we can keep the readings of our slide. In that way we can wind the tool to the required length and diameter and then wind it back to the original settings. It makes life very easy and taper plugs can be made by the hundred if we like. The thread diameter is machined by moving the saddle so we keep the angled settings used for the tapers. Parting the plugs off may cause more of a problem; even if we use a rear tool post, which is ideal for the job, care is required to return to the original setting figure and backlash will have to be taken into account.

Hole Drilling

To cross drill and ream the bodies to accept the taper plugs, it is necessary to ensure that the drill, (which should be the same diameter as the thin end on the taper plug) goes centrally through the body and a simple jig will take care of this. A piece of mild steel, brass or even hard wood is bolted or stuck to the drilling table. A centre drill of suitable size is run into it to make a dimple deep enough to accept the bulge on the body. Providing the table is not moved it is possible to centre drill, drill and ream knowing that the tools are going to go through exactly the same spot each time. Before starting file a small flat on the body, this will make a platform to start the drill and provide a nice flat surface for the spring. Holding the drain cock body, particularly in the smaller sizes can be difficult but if a piece of square bar is tapped with a thread to fit the drain cock body this will hold it quite nicely.

The taper plug also needs cross drilling, the correct position can be picked up by pushing the plug into the cock which it will be used in and rotating a drill by hand until there is a decent enough mark on the plug to act as a starting point for the drill. A groove filed at an angle in a piece of hardwood will make a suitable seat for the actual drilling operation, it can again be held by the thread as was the body. Make sure all burrs are removed. A square is needed for the control arm and here again a simple jig will help. Put a piece of square brass in the four jaw chuck, drill and ream a hole using the taper reamer to accept the tapers. Push the cock in this to file squares on the ends, count the number of file strokes and then rotate until all four sides are done. Check for size and repeat until it is right. It is quite surprising how accurate it is possible to be using this method.

Springs

Small springs can be wound from phosphor bronze wire, using a piece of steel rod in the lathe chuck. With a very small central core to the spring, it may be necessary to put a piece of brass with a hole of the same diameter as the winding mandrel, in the tailstock chuck and use that as a support. In the case of large diameter springs it is usual to drill a hole through the steel being used as a core winder. The idea is not practical in many cases as drilling the hole would weaken the steel former sufficiently for it to break under strain, so the wire will have to be nipped between a chuck jaw and the winding mandrel.

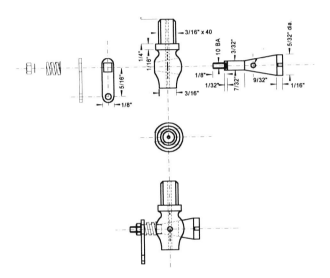

Standard type of Drain Cock.
Body shapes may vary according to locomotive

Linkage

Two drain cocks are required for each cylinder, one front and one at the rear. In order to operate them, a linkage to the cab has to be provided, as shown on the drawing. Small bearings will have to be made for the rod to run in and screwed to the frames, a thin rod, usually supported somewhere along its length can go to the lever in the locomotive cab. Somewhere along the rod, which is parallel to the frame bottom, it is useful to make a screw joint that can be adjusted; nothing fancy just a screw, a collar and a locknut to ensure that the drain cocks open evenly at a set position of the lever.

Automatic Drain Cocks.

It is possible to make relatively simple automatic drain cocks and the device shown in the drawing

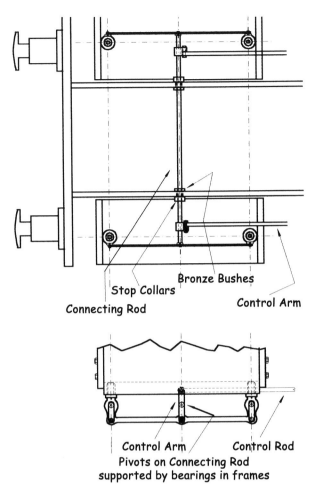

Drain Cock control linkage

works quite well, being particularly suitable for the smaller gauges. When there is no steam pressure the ball rolls clear of the exhaust opening but as soon as pressure is applied it is forced over. Any water remaining in position between steam and exhaust port is pushed out of the way. There is a slight tendency for this type to leak, but it is not a disaster when they do, and in fact the effect can be quite attractive.

For larger models a spring is included in the construction although the principal is similar, in that they rely on the initial increase in pressure when there is water in the cylinders to push against the spring, and so release

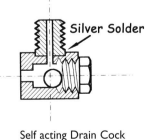

Self acting Drain Cock
for small models

water that has condensed. The drawings show how they are made and good operation relies on the ability to set the spring to a suitable tension, and that will almost certainly have to be by trial and error.

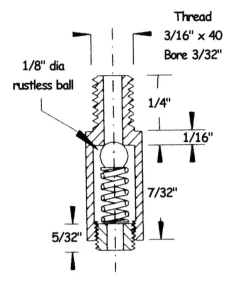

Automatic Drain Cock

Steam Operation

Although some full-size locomotives had lever and rod operated drain cocks, most in later years were steam operated. There is nothing magic about them, a jet of steam direct from the boiler pushes a plug away from a hole, allowing the water to escape. The plug can be made in various forms. Some people prefer a taper and others a straight arrangement, either seem to work well, although steam operation sometimes means a slightly leaky form of operation. Once again readers can make the drain cocks from the drawings and, whilst no measurements are given, they should not be difficult to calculate for oneself.

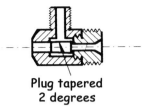

Steam Operated Drain Cock with tapered plug

Operating The Cocks

Drain cocks should always be opened when the model is in steam and has stood for a while and they should be closed as soon as it is on the move. It really is not good practice to have clouds of steam coming from them as they are purely to release water. Steam operated drain cocks may be controlled by a small rotary valve placed on the backhead, or by a lever type, both of which were used in full size. Rod operated cocks must operate from a lever and the size of this is a matter of choice. Often when they were fitted to full-size locomotives, particularly industrial types, the lever was very short and would be set in the cab floor. It was kicked open by the driver or fireman when need be, generally got in the way and caused some unusual words to be used. Larger levers were fitted as time went on and these were operated by hand in the normal way. For operational purposes the longer lever is preferred on a model, as the short type can be difficult to use as it is difficult to get a hand in to them. Because of this problem, some model makers operate them via a lever underneath the cab and, whilst not strictly correct, it does make opening them a lot easier.

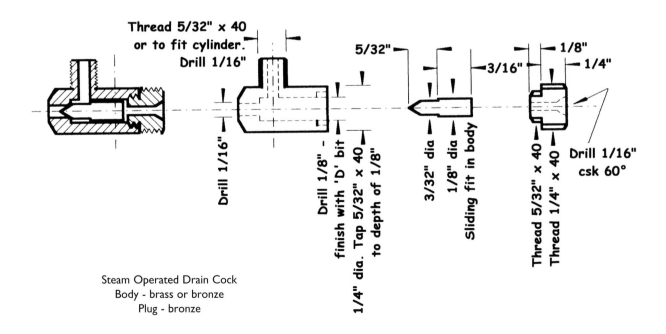

Steam Operated Drain Cock
Body - brass or bronze
Plug - bronze

Chapter 18: Brakes

Hand Brakes

For the sake of appearance if nothing else, brakes should be fitted to locomotives. Unless the model is very big, such as a narrow gauge prototype running on 7¼″ track, they are not going to be effective as the weight of the passenger or passengers will be sufficient to push the locomotive along and, if the brakes have been applied, it will just skid. Ultimately one supposes that this could wear the treads of the wheels down until instead of being circular they became a series of flats, although it would take a considerable time to happen. Therefore any brakes designed to actually stop a train should be fitted to the passenger cars rather than the locomotive. Brakes do considerably enhance the appearance of a model and can be useful when it is in a position of rest to prevent it rolling away. In full-size practice the hand brake would only ever be used when the locomotive was likely to remain stationary for a period rather than for the purpose of stopping and, in the interests of safety, all passenger trains were continuously braked. Various forms of power were used to work them, each company using their own favourite system. At times this created difficulties as it meant that locomotives and rolling stock from one company were not compatible with those of another.

For many years the practice was to couple goods trains with three link couplings and the only brakes used were those on the engine, plus a hand brake in

the guards van. Older readers will no doubt recall the noise created by a goods train, particularly a long one coming to a stop, as each wagon pushed into the one in the front and then rebounded as the springs in the buffers expanded after the initial shock. The action was like a rubber ball with a bouncing effect and when we think of some of the trains of nearly a hundred wagons all bouncing backwards and forwards, it now seems almost beyond belief. Spare a thought too for the poor old guard who was at the end of all this and was hanging on for dear life trying desperately to screw down his hand brake, usually to little avail. Goods trains were limited as a result to very slow speeds and sauntered around the countryside in a stately fashion. On certain trains it became necessary to travel at faster speeds, for example those carrying perishable produce, and special wagons were constructed fitted with continuous fail-safe brakes, leading eventually to modern day practice where a guards van is no longer required.

Most models are fitted only with a hand brake that is operated by a simple screw down column in the cab, a similar one being fitted to the brakes on the tender. Brake shoes are usually made from a casting, which generally comes in the form of a ring allowing

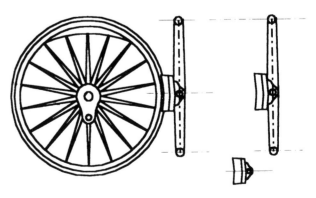

Brake Hangers

the correct radius to be machined, after which it is separated into sections and fitted to mild steel hangers which are no more than strips of steel with three holes in them. The hangers are pivoted and rods push them in and out as the screw of the brake handle is revolved. In some cases a central rod is used to operate the brakes but this can mean that it becomes difficult to remove the ash pan and so a rod along either side is more desirable. This also has the advantage that adjustment of the positions of the

A brake ring casting machined to the correct radius and about to be cut in to individual brake blocks.

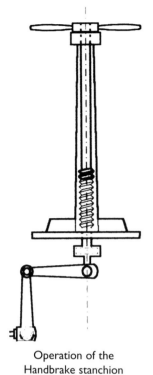

Operation of the
Handbrake stanchion

shoes is easier than when they are centrally operated.

Tender hand brakes are made in a similar fashion with the stanchion placed on the tender footplate, again the brakes are of little use in stopping a loaded train but do enhance the final appearance of the model.

Steam Brakes

For various reasons many modellers like to fit other braking systems to their engines, in addition to the hand brakes. The most popular of these seems to be simple steam operated ones. In addition to the handbrake stanchion

A steam brake cylinder, machined from solid material, attached to the bar frame of a locomotive under construction by Roger Nicholls. In this case a cylinder is needed for each side.

a steam cylinder is fitted and the piston, when steam is admitted, pushes the operating rods and applies the brakes. To release them the steam is turned off and released through a valve, and a spring ensures

The hangers to which the brake blocks are attached, On this model they are curved but on many they are straight. Note the assembly of rods using split pins rather than nuts which are likely to come loose during operation.

The cross for a centrally operated braking system, here again split pins have been used rather than nuts.

The two steam brake cylinders, in this case fitted to the inside of the frames. A larger single cylinder mounted centrally may also be used.

the return of the brakes to the off position. It is used in conjunction with a hand brake and uses the same operating gear working independently. Obviously the steam brake cannot be used unless the engine is actually in steam.

Vacuum Brakes

The vacuum brake was commonly used in full-size practice and now has become quite popular with modellers, particularly in societies where public passenger hauling is carried out. Once again we are looking at a basically simple idea, a vacuum is created in a cylinder and this draws in the operating mechanism. It can be worked in two ways, either creating the vacuum putting the brakes on, or maintaining it while the locomotive is running and releasing it causing the brakes to go on. The latter system is used in full-sized practice and is much quicker in operation as it works immediately the vacuum is released, whereas to create a vacuum to apply the brakes takes a little time, as all air from the cylinder has to be excluded. The big advantage of the vacuum brake is that the system can be extended to all passenger carrying stock, enabling brakes to be applied along the whole train at once from the cab of the locomotive. The disadvantage of the system on a model is the necessity to maintain the vacuum all the time it is running, which requires steam to be continually passed through a simple device called an ejector and, if boiler pressure drops, the brakes start to be applied and cannot be released until pressure is raised again. It rules out the system for models below the gauge of 5″ and even in that gauge some of the smaller prototypes may not be able to cope. There is no doubt that, as long as the locomotive boiler can supply the necessary steam to keep the brakes in the 'off' position, it is the ideal system for miniature railways. Applying the brakes to the

whole train requires nothing more than to open a valve and destroy the vacuum in the cylinder.

The drawings and photographs show details of how the various braking systems are made; brakes work via a bell crank, which either pushes or pulls the brake blocks on to the wheels when the brake is applied. Some locomotives have the blocks in front of the wheels, others have them behind and this will

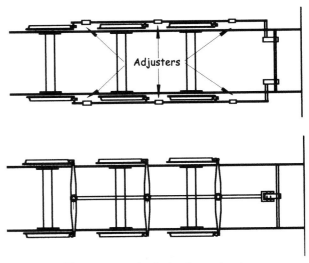

Two positions for Brake Control rods

be the deciding factor on the angle of the crank. The cranks and levers are made from mild steel strip, and it is worthwhile fitting small bronze bearings to prevent undue wear. The pins that act as pivots should be made of silver steel and hardened, again with the intention of reducing wear. The control rods that connect to the brake hangers are usually made of mild steel rod and threaded adjusters are included which consist of internally screwed rod and lock nuts. They are screwed to the control rods and the screw action provides the adjustment.

Cylinders for steam brakes ideally should be of bronze, although on large models, cast iron is frequently used. In this case care must be taken to avoid the brake cylinder becoming corroded when the model is not used for a period of time, and the same advice that has been given for locomotive cylinders applies. Some castings are available for steam brake cylinders and while they may be intended for a particular prototype they are, in general, quite universal and will serve for a number of different types.

Vacuum brakes require both an ejector and a cylinder, neither of which are very complicated to make, and there are castings available for both. If no suitable casting is available, ejectors can be made from brass, there are no parts that are likely to suffer

The operating cylinder of a vacuum brake. Note the return spring, which helps to ensure the vacuum is maintained and keeps the brakes off until it is released.

from rapid wear; cylinders should be made from a non-ferrous material, but although in theory internal rusting should not be a problem, as steam is not applied to the cylinder, condensation is present and can be a cause for concern.

There are a number of other braking systems that were used in full-size practice, and no doubt many readers who visited Liverpool Street Station in London during steam days will be only too aware of the sound of the Westinghouse Pumps that were extensively used by trains using that station. This and other systems that were used in other countries are not really applicable to model work and, should a prototype of the model being made require a Westinghouse Pump, it will be as well to make it as a dummy, or use it as a water pump, rather than try and use it for braking purposes.

Full size German locomotives had complex braking systems working on both sides of the driving and coupled wheels and, in some cases, on the pony and trailing trucks as well, as can be seen on this very nice 3½" gauge 2-6-2.

Luc Tennstedt from Belgium is one of the founding fathers of the hobby in Europe and builds fine 7¼" gauge locomotives, all of which are fitted with a very effective air brake system, on both engines and the passenger coaches shown here, driven by a steam compressor, which can be seen on Luc's Royal Scot, also fitted with a steam driven generator for lighting.

Chapter 19: How to get Water into the Boiler
(pumps and injectors)

For many years axle pumps were the mainstay for supplying water to boilers on models when running, and a hand pump acted as an emergency back up. More recently injectors have been used, usually in addition to the mechanical pumps. It is absolutely essential that the correct water level is maintained, so pumps should always be made large enough to supply more than sufficient and any excess returned to the tank or tender via a by-pass valve. Some model makers rely entirely on injectors and providing they are reliable there is no reason why this should not be so; if it was good enough for full-size it is good enough for us.

Most axle pumps are operated by one of the driving or coupled axles, using an eccentric to supply the necessary reciprocating motion. A few modellers fit the pump so that it is driven from an axle on the tender but this is far from common. Pumps can also be driven from the locomotive crosshead and these will be discussed later. Whether one relies on a pump or injectors or both, in addition it is always advisable to fit a hand pump for emergency use, or perhaps to fill the boiler when preparing to raise steam. This too should be as large as possible so as to fill the boiler against pressure as quickly as possible, as it is used basically as an emergency pump - if the water level is low then the quicker it is replenished the better.

A word of warning here. In the event of a mishap where the boiler runs completely dry:

Never try and pump in water. It will flash into steam so quickly that pressure will rise to several times the safe working pressure of the boiler.

It is both a remarkable and frightening experience to see one movement of the hand pump send the pressure so high the gauge cannot record it. It is very easy to think that one will never let a boiler run dry, but the author once loaned a locomotive to someone who did just that. Fortunately all ended quite safely, but it was a potentially dangerous situation.

Using Castings

Axle driven pumps can either be made from a casting or from basic material. There is nothing to choose between the end results and little as far as time is concerned. The casting will usually come as a tee shaped piece and it can be held in a four-jaw chuck

and bored for the ram. A drill and reamer can be used but a boring tool will always do a better job, if possible lap the bore as well. The outside of the casting will also need to be machined and threaded to take a gland.

The two non-return valves can be drilled straight through by holding the casting by the outside of the valve as accurately as possible in a four-jaw chuck. Initially drill right through, open out for the ball that will act as the valve and finish with a 'D' bit to give a seating to the ball. Later the seat will need to be

A part-machined casting for a mechanical pump incorporating a frame stay, the alternative is a separate stay with the pump body bolted to it.

either ground in or flattened by tapping a ball of similar size with a hammer, as to be described in the chapter on cab fittings. The ends of the valves are threaded and countersunk to accept the olives on the pipes. This operation involves turning the casting round and re-setting it as accurately as possible and should be set up using a wobbler and clock gauge. The drawing of a pump makes the basic method of construction fairly obvious and it remains to make the insert at one end, which acts as a seat, plus the union nuts, and the main body is completed. How it is fitted to the locomotive will depend on both the design of the pump and the design of the locomotive. On smaller gauge models it is quite usual for the body of the pump to be threaded into a spacer. On larger models it may be bolted to a spacer via a couple of lugs.

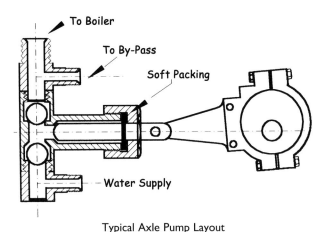

Typical Axle Pump Layout

The Ram

The ram should be stainless steel and a slot is required at the end to accept the pump operating rod, this is cross-drilled for a pin to hold this in position. Some people like to make a groove or grooves and fit either soft packing or an '0' ring in order to get a better delivery. Pumps for small models will usually work quite well without such refinement, relying on the fit of the ram to give the required pressure. It is difficult to be definite about the size of ram required for a locomotive. Generally speaking about seven sixteenths of an inch will be sufficient for even a large 5″ gauge model. Five sixteenths for 3½″ gauge, with a quarter or even seven-thirty seconds for 2½″ gauge; garden gauge models require nothing more than an eighth of an inch, if an axle pump is fitted at all. These figures can only be used as a guide and if in doubt start with a smaller size but allow enough material to ream out to a larger size if it is necessary.

Twin Pumps

Some models use twin axle pumps which is a good idea, because a single large pump can cause a model to run very unevenly as the water is pushed against boiler pressure; two pumps set at a hundred and eighty degrees to each other offset this effect. The pumps are made half the capacity of the single one they are to replace. In many cases there is not

A cross head pump of the vertical type, made by Roger Nicholls. There were no castings used in the construction, it being completely fabricated from brass and bronze

sufficient room for two axle pumps and we have to settle for a single one.

Crosshead Pumps

As the name implies these are pumps worked by the crosshead of the cylinders, and are usually bolted to the frames via a bracket. They are of necessity smaller than the axle driven pump but otherwise follow the same pattern of construction, and are remarkably efficient, particularly when their small size is considered. American Locomotives are the most common types that have crosshead pumps but there are also many examples of British and Continental Locomotives which used them, notably on the *Great Western Railway.*

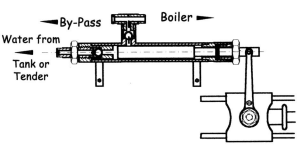

Crosshead Pump Layout

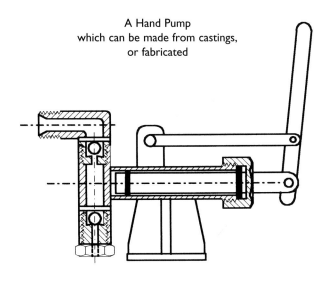

A Hand Pump
which can be made from castings,
or fabricated

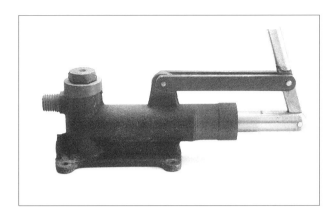

A hand pump built from a casting. Although it is easier to make a flat handle this one has deliberately been made round so that it is easier to fit the necessary extension, required to enable the pump to be worked from outside the tank or tender.

Hand Pumps

Hand pumps are generally placed either in the tender or a tank of the locomotive, although on small models they are sometimes located in the cab. Construction is similar to that of an axle driven one, except that a bracket is required for a linkage that allows the handle to operate the ram. Some form of base is also needed to enable the pump to be bolted down. A gasket must always be fitted between the base and the tender or tank floor to prevent water from leaking. Once again sizes will depend on individual models but the ram diameter should always be larger than that of the axle driven pump.

Where a hand pump is fitted in a tender, a flexible pipe will be needed to carry the water from the pump to the check valve on the locomotive boiler. That connection must be made strong enough to withstand a pressure higher than that in the boiler. It is no use just slipping a piece of rubber or plastic tube on each end of a pipe as it will simply fall off as soon as water is pumped when the locomotive is in steam. The connection must be capable of being dismantled so the tender can be moved away from the locomotive. No doubt readers will have their own ideas on how to make such a connection, there is no reason why one of the special plastic tubes used for carrying fuel in model aircraft should not be used as these are quite strong enough, but suitable compression type connections must be fitted. People making large sized models can obtain compression fittings from plumbers merchants, these are rather large and only take a small-bore tube but they are very efficient at high pressures.

Starting From Scratch

The idea of fabrication of pumps has already been suggested. In some ways this is easier than using

castings, as stock material is not so difficult to hold in the lathe. The valves can be silver soldered in position after having been made in the normal fashion and the use of hexagon bar enables valves to be located on the flat surfaces rather than round ones where drills are likely to wander off line. Although bronze is the best material to use, brass can make a quite long lasting pump and is easier to obtain, as well as being cheaper.

Injectors

Henri Giffard, a Frenchman, invented the injector in 1859. Prior to that locomotives had used mechanical pumps. There had been instances where these had caused the build up of exceptionally high pressures in the pipes leading from them, causing burst pipes and fittings, and so the injector was immediately seized upon by locomotive builders. The patent rights were taken up by *Sharp Stewart and Co* in 1860 and a number of people in the following years made various improvements to the design. From then on the use of mechanical pumps for feeding boilers in full size locomotives became rare; few, if any, did not use injectors. There were cases of the use of steam pumps but even then they were generally used in conjunction with injectors.

Nowadays the use of injectors on model steam locomotives is common practice. It was not always so and to many people they are still something of a mystery. Small injectors are readily available from model engineering suppliers but there is no reason why they should not be home-made as long as care is taken in their construction.

The Mystery Explained

Before making anything, it is a good idea to understand how it will work, so we know what we are trying to achieve, and it is to be hoped that the following notes will give readers some idea of what makes the injector work. Use the simplified diagram on the following page as a rough guide with which to familiarise yourself, read the explanation and from there it is possible to go to the more detailed drawing.

Injectors use the pressure of steam in the boiler to push water into that same boiler by increasing the pressure to above that inside, all of which seems to be something of a paradox but is not quite so impossible as it sounds.

Let us pretend that steam is cold, we can stand in a jet of it if we so wish and will not get scalded. We will stand a couple of yards from the nozzle which is

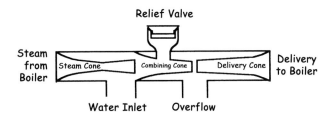

Basic layout of an Injector

ejecting the steam; because it is a gas there is no great force even with the steam leaving the nozzle at around sixty pounds per square inch. There was a force of 60 psi at the nozzle but once it entered the atmosphere all that force has gone. Instead of striking us with a force of 60 psi it will simply find its way around. Of course we cannot actually do this as the steam would be too hot and even though it did not strike us with force, we would be scalded, but that is how it would happen if it were cold. If we were to try the same thing with a jet of cold water, standing at the same distance from the nozzle at that pressure we would probably be knocked over. Because it is a gas the steam has no power and is unstable, while the water has power by virtue of it being a more stable substance. If we could miniaturise ourselves and stand inside the nozzle the steam would then have force because it is confined around the periphery. Looked at simply, a small jet of steam which is confined to a given area can give a quantity of water a shove and in doing so will increase its power.

A home-made injector. Of comparatively simple construction and made from a casting it has none of the refinements of the full-size artefact.

Generally it is essential that the water is cold, if it is warm the steam has less effect, as it will tend to mix with the warm water rather than shoving it along.

The injector is mounted below the level of the water supply, which can run into it without the need for any additional power. With no steam it will simply run through the combining cone and out of the overflow. When steam (which, as we have already established, is at considerable velocity because of the cone) is allowed in, as soon as it meets the water in the combining cone, it condenses which creates a vacuum and brings the release valve down tightly on its seat. When it condenses the steam gives up its own velocity to the water, which shoots forward and enters the delivery cone, through the non-return valve and into the boiler. This action will not happen immediately as there will be a very short period when the jet will fluctuate in its intensity and some of the water will go out through the overflow pipe. In no time at all it will "pick up" and flow directly into the boiler. If any water is still coming from the overflow it will be because there is more than the steam flow can cope with through the cones or nozzles, and adjustment of the water flow will be necessary.

What is required to make an injector, therefore, is a device that will direct water and steam in the right direction and at the right velocity. Like many things in model form it will be of a simplified design when compared with full-size practice.

Full-Size Injectors

Injectors are classed as either lifting or non-lifting, the former again being divided into horizontal, vertical and combination. They are constructed to lift water and are in many ways similar to the water lifters used on traction engines. The combination type is usually bolted directly to the back head of the locomotive and has both water and steam valves more or less built in to make operation and maintenance easy. The whole assembly can be taken off by undoing a few bolts.

We rarely see the lifting injector in model form. Most model injectors are of the non-lifting type and they are placed somewhere below the cab of the locomotive. This also makes them convenient to get at and allows them to remain comparatively cool, which is important if they are to function properly. It also means that water can flow into them by gravity, simply by running a pipe via a valve from the tank or tender. The non-lifting injector was used in full-size practice and sometimes both types might be fitted.

Exhaust Steam Injectors

Exhaust steam injectors are a development of the original Giffard design and in principle follow the original idea. The cones are differently designed and duplicated. Exhaust steam enters the chamber first, via a very large cone and picks up the water. Then the admission of a little live steam gives the impetus required to overcome boiler pressure. The feed water, having had two lots of steam condensed in it, is at a very high temperature, and to prevent it forming into steam as it passes the overflow outlet, a valve is introduced which closes. A small piston connected to the delivery pipe usually operates this. There are obvious advantages in the use of exhaust steam injectors but it is doubtful whether working models could be made except for the very large gauges.

Making Model Injectors

Although many people are worried about making model injectors, if care is taken in making the original tooling that is required, there is no reason why the results should not be good.

The first thing required is the body, and the hole in this, which accepts the cones, must be reamed accurately. The release valve must also seat well and not allow any escape of steam once it has seated. It usually consists of a separate section, silver soldered on top of the main body; however, some people prefer to make the injector from a single piece of metal, cutting out any surplus. Most model injectors have the release valve arranged so that any steam that is released will exit via the overflow together with excess water. The cones must be a good fit in the body, ensuring that air cannot pass along the edges. (Remember we are trying to create a vacuum.)

Whilst some latitude can be allowed on the angle of the cones and indeed there are a number of learned opinions on what these should be, everyone agrees it is essential that there are no sharp edges and the bore is smooth and nicely tapered.

Making cones obviously involves making taper reamers, details of which are given in the chapter on cab fittings. It is essential that the tapers in the cones are smooth and without burrs. While the top slide is at an angle to make a reamer some people use the setting to make an identical shape from a piece of hardwood. When making the cones this piece of wood is soaked in a mild abrasive, such as a brass polish and used as a lap, to ensure the cone bore really is smooth. It is always a good idea to make spare cones, they might be required if the injector does not work immediately as the fault may well lie in a badly fitting cone. Spares can also be useful when cones wear as a result of the abrasive action of the water.

Piping an Injector

Good fittings that will allow plenty of steam and water through are essential for piping up an injector. There are differing schools of thought on whether the taps to turn on steam and water should be direct acting or screw down. It all seems a matter of personal preference, as both appear to work quite well. The water supply must be higher than the injector and it is essential that all pipes to and from the injector are air tight; if air is taken in, the injector will not work properly. A good fine mesh filter should be fitted in the water supply to prevent dirt blocking the cones. The pipe from the tender water supply obviously has to be flexible and plastic tubing will work quite well. The only problem likely

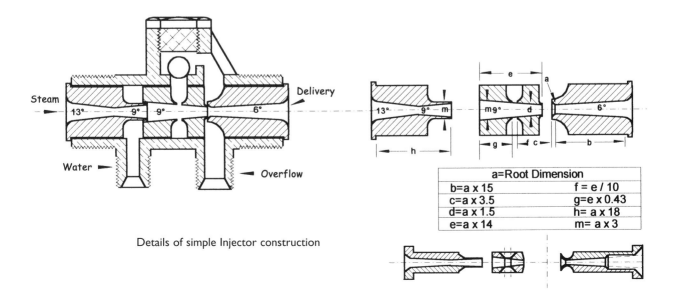

Details of simple Injector construction

a=Root Dimension	
b=a x 15	f = e / 10
c=a x 3.5	g=e x 0.43
d=a x 1.5	h= a x 18
e=a x 14	m= a x 3

to arise from using this is if the non-return valve on the boiler becomes faulty, and allows hot water to return down the pipe. Not only will the injector not work properly, but the heat is likely to warm the plastic tube to a point where it will fall off.

Both steam and water pipes should be as straight as possible to prevent restriction of the flow - avoid sharp bends. This also applies to the delivery pipe taking the water to the boiler; steam and delivery pipes should be kept as short as possible. A check valve should be fitted as close as is practical to the injector on the delivery side.

Injectors, properly made and fitted, are a reliable means of ensuring the correct level of water in the boiler. They have the advantage of working whilst the locomotive is stationary and not exerting any physical pressure against movement when running and, as the water is warmer than that supplied with a pump, there is less pressure drop in the boiler.

Maintenance

Generally speaking injectors require little attention, other than regular cleaning. It is as well to check connections regularly to ensure air cannot enter and periodically the injector should be removed and left soaking for a short while in a mild acid such as vinegar to remove any alkaline deposits. In some hard water areas these deposits can actually close nozzles right up if care is not taken; do not poke bits of wire down the cones, that is a recipe for disaster with scored surfaces or oversized holes.

It has been stressed at great length that the water supply needs to be cold and, in the case of tank

engines, the water tanks often heat up during running which makes them unsuitable as a supply for the injector. It is often a good idea to put a small tank underneath the cab of the locomotive and take water from that. There is usually no reason why it should not have connecting pipes to the main tanks, the water generally will cool down sufficiently for our purposes once it is in the auxiliary tank. If a quantity of coal is not to be carried in the bunker this too can be a useful place to put a tank for cooling water. It is easy enough to put a false top on it and cover it with a small quantity of coal for the sake of appearances.

It is not only on model locomotives that warm water can cause injector problems, it also frequently happened in full-size practice. It was usually cured by playing a hose on the injector, the equivalent in model form is a quick dowsing from a jug or something similar. Leaking steam valves and badly sealing non return valves on the delivery side are often the cause of an injector getting hot and these should be checked regularly.

It is to be hoped that the modeller does not have to go to the lengths of British soldiers in World War Two. Winston Churchill promised the Russians that they would receive supplies of essential materials in considerable quantities, and part of the plan for so doing was the construction of a railway from Iran to Russia by British troops. Working under great difficulty, steady progress was made and a large number of locomotives were sent out from Britain to run the railway. None of the injectors would work and the heat was diagnosed as the problem. The solution was to paint the tenders white. Ingenious but hardly attractive.

Injectors are usually mounted under the cab, as on this 7¼" gauge 0-4-0 tank locomotive, which also shows the correct way round the injector should be fitted, with the overflow on the delivery side. In this picture the overflow is emitting steam indicating that the steam or water valves need adjusting, that the boiler is full, or the check valve is sticking.

Chapter 20: Lubrication

All things mechanical need lubrication and model locomotives are no exception. It is essential when making a model, whether steam driven or otherwise, that thought should be given to supplying sufficient lubrication points. Most of the places where these will be are fairly obvious; axle boxes, valve gear, etc. are those that immediately spring to mind and so let us deal with them first.

Axle Boxes

Again we should think back to full-size practice where it was customary to fit oil boxes with pipes running to the bearings. There is no reason why this

Carefully lubricating axles and motion before starting a run is good practice.

method should not be followed on a model and it certainly makes life easier than scratching around trying to put drops of oil in holes in the top of axle boxes. Particularly if the locomotive is of the outside framed type it can be a devil of a job. Many locomotives have axles that are close to or even underneath the ash pan. If oil holes are left in the top of these they can quickly fill with ash, which is very abrasive. The result is a lot of wear on the axles as well as the boxes and the use of a piped system obviates these problems.

If for any reason it is not possible to fit oil boxes, try and put some form of cover over the oil holes, to prevent dirt and grit from entering. A simple push-on cap will do, but make a few spares as they are easily lost - small oil caps can be purchased and are excellent as they keep out all the dirt and the cover springs up to allow oil to be poured in. Although they do the job well, somehow they do not look right on a standard gauge engine, but possibly would be in place on a narrow gauge prototype.

Valve Gear

It is usual to provide a small hole in each bearing surface on the valve gear and to put oil in these at

regular intervals. There is nothing wrong with this method and it is simply a case of going round the locomotive every so often oiling the various points. Care should be taken not to over lubricate as oil from motion work tends to splash around. A useful idea to prevent over oiling is to fit a short length of very thin tubing, say about $1/16''$, to the spout of an oil can, the reduced diameter preventing too much oil being applied. As well as being unsightly, if surplus oil is splashed around, almost inevitably some will get on the track, causing trains to slip badly. The actual hole which provides a passage for the oil in the bearing can be very tiny, say about $0.03''$ or 0.8mm, this will allow sufficient lubricant through, but it is very difficult to get oil into such a small hole, so the top should be counter bored, or to use a technical term, opened out a bit. The counter bore also acts as a reservoir so that oiling is needed at less frequent intervals

Cylinders

It is essential that the cylinders are kept lubricated, this particularly applies if the steam is superheated, as it is then very dry. Early locomotives had oil cups on top of the cylinders and these had oil poured into them at frequent intervals. Sometimes the fireman would climb out along the running plate and drop oil in while the train was going along, which sounds a horrendous thing to do. Not only did he have to make his way along a narrow ledge on a swaying locomotive, he had to undo the oil cap, often in driving rain or snow. We can imagine that, at this stage, steam would almost certainly escape, even if the driver closed the regulator. But enginemen were tough in those days and did far worse things than that. An alternative to holes, with or without caps was to use a wick. There was still a hole of course but this would be filled with a wick of some sort, usually asbestos. It was kept well soaked in oil or grease and the moving piston against which it was rubbing would drag the lubricant down into the cylinder, the heat inside thinning the lubricant so that it spread throughout the bore. These primitive arrangements were superseded, no doubt to the relief of firemen all over the world, by mechanical lubricators, one of which, usually driven by the valve gear, would be fitted for the cylinders. This would frequently be on the running board and is a practice difficult to follow in model form, as generally the lubricator is oversized so it is often hidden somewhere between the frames.

Displacement Lubricators

On small gauge models the displacement lubricator is very popular. A simple device, it consists of a closed tank with two small diameter pipes fitted to it. The tank has a drain plug at the bottom and is partly filled with oil. Steam from the boiler travels along one of the pipes and passes into the other, which in turn is connected to the cylinders. It passes through the tank and condenses on top of the oil, which is drawn up and joins with the steam, eventually going into the cylinder and supplying the lubrication. Any steam that condenses falls to the bottom of the tank, displacing the oil upwards, and can be drained off at a later stage. It is a simple system and the lubricator is very easy to make.

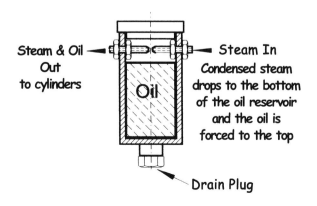

Simple Displacement Type Lubricator

Although very efficient, displacement lubricators are not often seen on larger scale models because it is difficult to control the flow of oil and frequently too much is drawn in. In particular this is likely to happen when the model has been stationary, with steam raised, the initial surge as the regulator opens draws oil into the cylinder and, as the piston is not at that point moving and so cannot use it, it is released through the chimney. This hardly matters with a tiny locomotive, but where we have one with large cylinders and a driver sitting immediately behind, the oil tends to blow all over the place, and particularly all over the driver.

Mechanical Lubricators

Most models of passenger hauling size, therefore, use mechanical lubricators, which are tiny pumps set into a tank and operated by a rod from one of the reciprocating parts, frequently the eccentric of either the axle pump, or from part of the valve gear. The most common type is based on an oscillating cylinder, rather like the simple steam engines that are bought as children's toys. The cylinder has a hole in it and a port face has two holes that line up alternately with it as it oscillates on a pivot. When it passes one of these, the piston is travelling down the cylinder and the suction it creates pulls oil in. When the piston returns, the hole in the cylinder lines up with the other hole in the port face and the oil is forced out, into the locomotive main steam pipe, a small non-return valve preventing it being sucked back into the tank. The oscillating effect is governed by a pawl which locates with a ratchet wheel and allows rotation in one direction only. Some locomotives will have two such lubricators, one for each cylinder, or there may be two outlets from the pump, otherwise oil is pumped into the main steam pipe below the smoke box. The oil reservoir is usually made from a piece of square brass tubing and the completed lubricator bolted to a convenient surface. It is often hidden behind the front buffer beam as, in general, model lubricators are very much over scale and, if mounted on the running plate as they are in full sized practice, would look rather odd.

The Ratchet

It is possible to purchase completed pawls and ratchet wheels, in which case one just makes the tank and inside parts of the lubricator, but it is not difficult to make the ratchet and pawl. The ratchet wheel can be made by putting a straight coarse knurl on a piece of silver steel rod. The teeth are then made a little deeper with a small file. The pawl is filed to shape from strip metal. Both the ratchet wheel and the pawl should be hardened. In the case of the

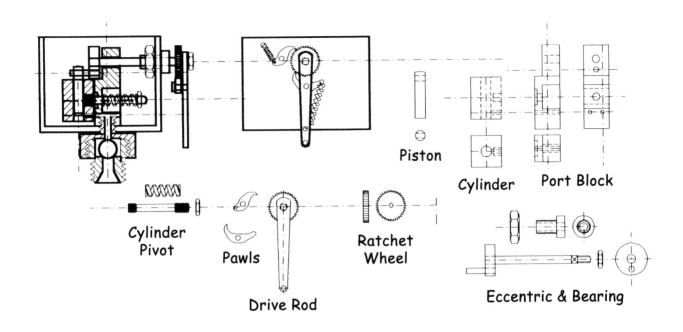

The most commonly used lubricator is the oscillating type,
shown here with its component parts

latter, if gauge plate is used, hardening is no problem. If mild steel has been used then it must be case hardened before use.

It is also possible to purchase tiny one-way ball races, i.e. ball races that only move in one direction. If they can be obtained they may be used in place of a ratchet and pawl and will make a neater job, as well as almost certainly wearing better than the ratchet wheel. In addition it is easier to construct the lubricator using one of these.

An alternative to the oscillating type of pump is one with a plunger or ram. Rather like the water pump this just goes up and down the bore alternately sucking oil in and pushing it out again. Because it is not usually practical to have a ram connected to an eccentric the pump is operated by pressure from a cam and is returned by a spring; the drawing shows

how such a device is made. The cam and plunger are likely to wear with constant use and it is a good idea to make one from bronze and the other from hardened steel, it matters not which way round this is done - it is simply a case of using two metals that will give long lasting service.

Hydrostatic Lubricators

These are non-mechanical lubricators working in some ways in a similar fashion to the displacement type and are sometimes called sight glass lubricators. The oil is housed in a tank to which steam is admitted. This forces oil along a pipe and through a sight feed arrangement, which is a small glass tank full of salt water. From there it goes to the cylinders. It is a very simple, but at the same time very efficient, arrangement and has the advantage that the driver can see the oil passing through the sight glass so that he, or she, knows the quantity going to the cylinders. A needle valve at the bottom of the sight glass allows control over the quantity passed to the cylinders. The oil tank must be situated below the sight glass, and it is essential that both the oil tank and the sight glass are made to withstand at least the same pressure the boiler will be working at, so they should be hydraulically tested in the same way as a boiler. The sight glass should be about a half inch diameter and can be sealed with '0' rings, piping is very small and the lubricator can be made very neat to enhance the appearance of a cab. It is also quite fascinating to watch blobs of oil passing through the water whilst running.

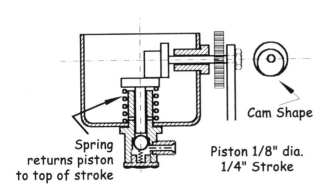

Lubricator with cam operated Pump

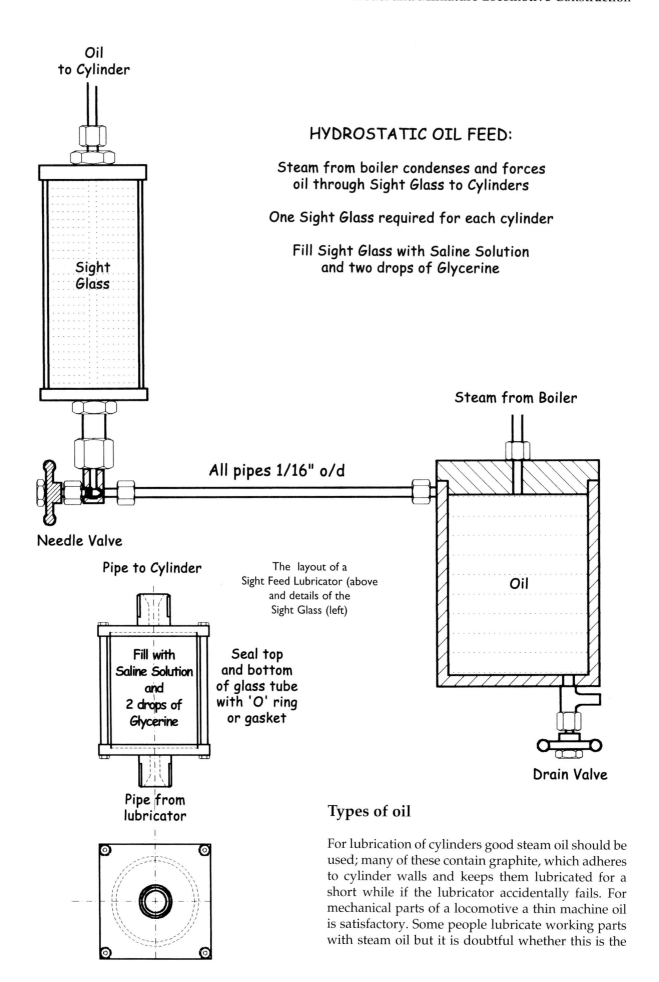

Oil
to Cylinder

HYDROSTATIC OIL FEED:

Steam from boiler condenses and forces
oil through Sight Glass to Cylinders

One Sight Glass required for each cylinder

Fill Sight Glass with Saline Solution
and two drops of Glycerine

Sight
Glass

Steam from Boiler

All pipes 1/16" o/d

Needle Valve

Oil

Pipe to Cylinder

The layout of a
Sight Feed Lubricator (above
and details of the
Sight Glass (left)

Fill with
Saline Solution
and
2 drops of
Glycerine

Seal top
and bottom
of glass tube
with 'O' ring
or gasket

Drain Valve

Pipe from
lubricator

Types of oil

For lubrication of cylinders good steam oil should be
used; many of these contain graphite, which adheres
to cylinder walls and keeps them lubricated for a
short while if the lubricator accidentally fails. For
mechanical parts of a locomotive a thin machine oil
is satisfactory. Some people lubricate working parts
with steam oil but it is doubtful whether this is the

best thing to use, although it does have the ability to cling to the working parts. Some of the modern synthetic oils are particularly good for lubricating working parts, although they must not be used in cylinders. Things such as reversing quadrants, couplings, etc. should be lubricated with a thin grease, here again modern materials have much to commend them, and copper based grease is particularly good for this type of application. In the case of a non-steam locomotive the bearings need lubricating with a thin oil and, if chain drives are used, an application of light grease to the chain is desirable. Many people leave steam fittings dry and this is not good practice. A silicone grease applied to threads and to valve stems will keep the fittings free,

and save the need to keep stripping them down for maintenance. However, under no circumstances should oil or grease be allowed to get on to the balls used for valves as it goes hard after a period of time and causes bad seating - in addition, when first applied, it can act like an adhesive and prevent the ball from lifting as required.

Finally, although hardly under the heading of locomotive construction or maintenance, do not forget to lubricate the bearings of driving and passenger vehicles. If they are allowed to dry out and become stiff the locomotive will have to work much harder than need be and obviously will not perform so well.

On this freelance, but Americanised, 5" gauge 0-6-0 a mechanical lubricator has been fitted on the running board just above the cylinder. Drive is from the top of the expansion link, which gives a degree of automatic adjustment to the delivery if the locomotive is 'notched up' on the reverser when running. Judging by the top of the boiler, the feed from the lubricator needs reducing by moving the drive rod up the lubricator arm. Another common position for mechanical lubricators is between the frames in front of the smokebox but, on this locomotive, there is not sufficient space between the smokebox and buffer beam to do this. Note also the boiler mounted oil box with individual pipes to the axleboxes. Not a prototypical location for the oil box, but very practical, especially when running at ground level which this Zimmermann built engine was intended for.

Something entirely different!

Pierre Bender from France likes a challenge, and modelling the unusual. Definitely in both categories are the two 3½″ gauge steam turbine locomotives, and the 7¼″ gauge steam turbine locomotive he has built, the first being shown on the left, and below, during a visit to Britain.

This locomotive is a scale model of a French steam turbine locomotive built just before World War II; the model runs well, although its power is limited. Removing the streamlined casing reveals the more or less conventional boiler, the turbine and the drive mechanism, as seen below.

The 7¼″ gauge steam turbine locomotive is a freelance design. On the left it is seen on the *Antony Vapeur Club de France* track near Paris, with Pierre's son Lionel at the controls, whilst Pierre himself is driving his second steam turbine locomotive, fitted with a flash steam boiler on the raised 3½″ gauge track in the background.

Pierre is currently working on developing a 7¼″ gauge **gas turbine** locomotive, using mainly automotive turbo-charger parts; the prototype test locomotive was demonstrated at the 2003 Guildford Meeting where it made a number of impressive runs. Unlike the steam turbine locomotives, the gas turbine locomotive is remarkably quiet when running.

Chapter 21: Cab Fittings

Cab, or boiler fittings as they are more correctly known, are used to control the flow of water and steam and basically fall into two types, taps and non-return valves. Although they look different, the tap type works in a similar fashion to the domestic tap and are normally referred to as stop valves. Non-return valves are frequently called clack valves because, in the construction of some of them a ball is used, and this can bounce up and down making a clacking sound. They are one-way valves to ensure the flow of either water or steam passes only in one direction. For example if water is pumped into a boiler the non-return valve will open to allow it in, but close against the pressure of the steam or water in the boiler and prevent it from flowing out. Many models are spoilt by ghastly oversized fittings; this is not necessary as they can be produced to near scale size while still being fully working.

Materials

All fittings that are likely to come into contact with boiler water should be made of bronze. At one time brass was used and was quite satisfactory, but modern water treatments include chemicals which cause the zinc content of brass to leach away. Eventually parts of the fitting will disintegrate. The effect is particularly noticeable on the fine threads usually used to screw fittings into boiler bushes, they are attacked and gradually turn into powder, the fitting then coming away from the boiler. In full size, fittings are usually bolted to flanges using studs, this makes assembly and dismantling much easier also, in full-size, boilers are made of steel which does not have the same chemical reaction with brass, only on small narrow gauge engines are we likely to see fittings screwed in. Some model makers also secure fittings as per full-size practice and, if possible, it is desirable to do so. This is not always practical though, as the studs and nuts need to be very small and any corrosion that occurs makes them difficult to remove. It will be seen that an alternative is often used of fitting dummy bolts to fittings that screw in, giving the best of both worlds, ease of fitting and enhancement of the appearance of the model.

Stop Valves

Two main types of stop valves are used, the screw down and the straight on and off version. We will deal first with the screw down type, which usually involves a bronze body with stainless steel screw and plug. Sometimes the body will be angled and the angle section is silver soldered in place; that apart the work is quite straightforward, consisting of little more than drilling and threading. The plug is usually machined complete with its stem from stainless steel, and screws into a seat in the body, which is finished with a "D" Bit. If there is any pressure involved the valve will need a gland, which should be packed to make it steam or watertight. A variety of materials is available for this purpose and a personal preference is for PTFE tape but many people use graphited string, others use "0" rings and a more modern idea is to machine a washer from Teflon.

By-Pass Valves

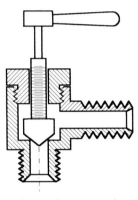

Screw-down type of
Bye-Pass Valve

Possibly the simplest type of valve, it diverts water from the pump back into the tender or tank of the locomotive to prevent the boiler from becoming too full. When carefully adjusted the locomotive should be able to run and maintain the correct quantity of water in the boiler with little need for further adjustment. The valve can take a variety of forms, it can be screw down, or be a simple rotating type that allows water to flow through a hole. The length of the spindle will vary depending on how one wishes to operate it. Because no great pressure is involved, frequently there is no gland on the valve.

Handles

All stop valves, except those used for blowing down the boiler, will be fitted with a handle of some sort

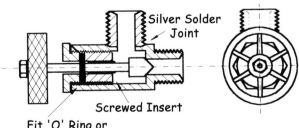

Type of Screw-down Valve used for Blower
and other purposes

*A square being milled on a shaft using
a piece of square stock for indexing.*

and the best way to attach this is to make a square on the shaft with a corresponding square hole in the handle. A nut on the end of the spindle ensures the handle does not fall off. A simple set up can be used to file or mill a square on the shaft. It is made from square bar, the flats are used in the vice as a means of indexing. When milling, work to the graduations; if filing, count the number of strokes before each rotation and there is no reason why a good square section should not be formed.

Handles can be in the form of a wheel or a lever and should be made from stainless steel, which does not conduct too much heat and is easy to handle. When making a wheel the spokes can be filed out after drilling and knurling the edge, then parting off a suitable slice of material. A square hole is needed to match the shaft and this can be made in two ways. The first is to file it with a needle file, which can be a

little bit tricky. Life can be made a bit easier by drilling a hole a little over the distance across flats and just squaring off the corners, it will work perfectly well and unless you tell someone what you have done nobody will be any the wiser. The alternative is to make a square broach from silver steel, the drawing shows how this should be shaped. It is made from silver steel and hardened and tempered to a light blue colour. To use it, use plenty of lubricate, ensure it is at ninety degrees to the handle and tap it through with a small hammer, doing a little at a time, brute force doesn't usually work in this case, frequent light taps giving the best results. Another little dodge is to put a square

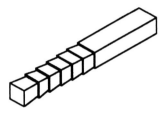

Design of a broach for
making square holes

needle file in the chuck of the drilling machine, then raise and lower it through the hole in the handle until a square is formed. The machine must not be rotating during this operation.

Blowdown Valves

The blowdown valve is situated at the bottom of the boiler near the foundation ring and differs from other stop valves, as it does not usually have a handle. A large square end is fitted on the spindle, either by machining, or by silver soldering an additional piece in position. The valve is used to empty the boiler and opened with a spanner when need be, don't be tempted to use a hexagon as the corners quickly get knocked off and it becomes difficult to use.

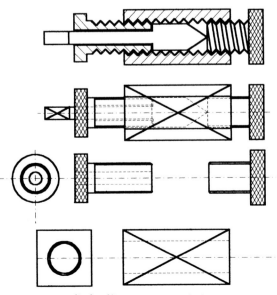

Jig for filing squares on shafts

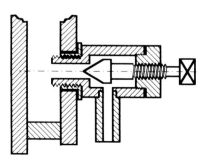

Blowdown Valve

The Blower

The blower takes steam from the boiler to the front end and from there up the chimney to draw the fire when the engine is not working. The valve is a simple one similar to the blowdown, but fitted with a handle either in the form of wheel or a lever. It usually differs from other stop valves as, on most models, it fits into a small bore, thick walled hollow tube that goes through the length of the boiler, this is secured in a tapped bush which the blower valve then screws into.

Unsafe Type of Construction

Readers will no doubt notice from the drawings that invariably on stop valves the plug is larger than the stem. This is for safety reasons because if it is the same size, or smaller, it will be possible to unscrew it right out, with the release of steam and the danger of scalding, not only the driver but interested bystanders too. Some drawings specify valves with small plugs and these should be changed for reasons of safety. While it is obviously much easier to make the valve with the small plug **the temptation to do so must be avoided at all costs**.

A globe valve, the body of which has been machined from a casting.

as the name suggests. The manufacture of this calls for a form tool of suitable size and shape, and a slightly different form of construction as can be seen from the drawings. They come in two types, the angle form in which construction, other than the body shape, is similar to the valves already described, or straight through, which entails drilling the passages at an angle. With this type of valve it can be advantageous to fit a PTFE sleeve which makes the possibility of leaks rather less.

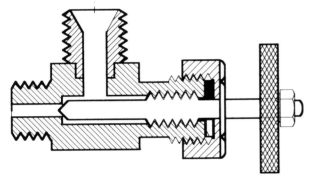

Unsafe type of Valve in which the Spindle can be completely
unwound from the Valve body

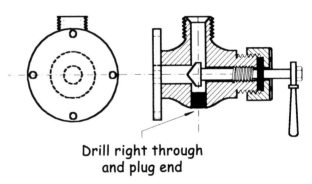

**Drill right through
and plug end**

Globe Valve suitable for Blower, By-Pass,
Injector Steam etc.

Globe Valves

Valves come in all shapes and sizes, a common type being a globe, which has a body like a globe or ball

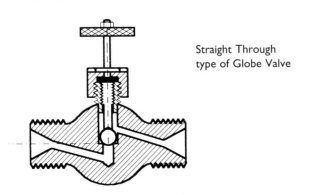

Straight Through
type of Globe Valve

Taper Plug Valves

So far we have dealt with valves, used for a variety of purposes, all of which are of the screw down type. There are occasions when it is desirable to have a means of quickly turning a supply of steam or water on and off, in which case the best type of valve to use is the taper plug. Making it calls for the manufacture of a taper reamer from silver steel and the photograph shows what this looks like. There is nothing difficult about making one; set the top slide over to the required angle and machine the taper, but care is necessary as the work must have a smooth finish if the valve is not to leak. File a flat to exactly half the diameter of the steel and harden and

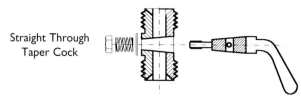

Straight Through
Taper Cock

temper to a dark straw colour, then hone the edges
with a fine stone to get them nice and sharp; this can
then be used to ream a number of pre-made bodies.
Without changing the setting of the top slide make

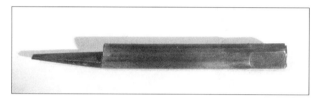

The taper reamer required for making taper plug valves.

up enough plugs for the valve bodies and a couple
of spares in case anything goes wrong with the
drilling, once the top slide setting has been

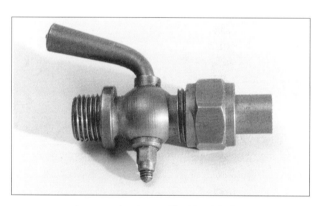

A taper cock valve machined in globe form.

destroyed it cannot be regained. The plug has to be
cross-drilled for the passage, which can either be
done by making a hardwood block with a suitable
taper and resting the plugs in that while working on
them, or alternatively a simple jig can be made from
a piece of brass or mild steel, using the reamer to
make the hole. This method is the most accurate but

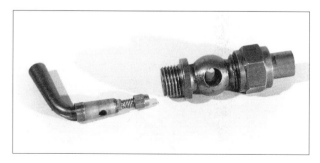

*The parts for the taper cock valve clearly showing all
necessary detail.*

there can sometimes be difficulty in removing the
plug, because burrs have been raised by the drill.
While this cannot be prevented completely, such
burrs can be kept to a minimum by passing the drill
through the work very slowly, using a light
pressure. Heavy pressure on a drill will always
increase the size of any burrs that are formed
because of the forcing action. The plug will need a
handle and this can either be made by bending it to
shape or by making a square and fitting a lever. If it
is to be made by bending, hold the plug in the
drilling jig referred to above and make sure the
material is well annealed, as there is nothing more
frustrating than finding the handle breaks off when
working on it.

Non-Return Valves

Non-return valves are
mostly fitted either to
the side of the boiler,
or to the backhead.
Their action has
already been referred
to, and it is usual
to use a ball as the

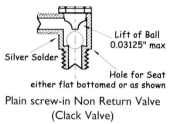

seating device, although in recent years designs
which use 'O' rings for seating have become popular.
When shaping the body, first try and find out what
shape the locomotive being modelled would have
had, as there were numerous types and it is nice to
get one that looks right. This apart, construction
follows the same general pattern of drilling and
tapping, plus drilling and squaring off a hole to
make a seat for the ball, this can be done with a "D"
Bit. This alone will not be completely effective and a
good seat for the ball is required. This can be made
by putting a ball of the same size on the hole and
using a piece of thin bar give it a smart tap with a
hammer; it must definitely be one tap only, any
more and the chances are there will be a double seat.
An alternative is to make an indent in a piece of steel
bar and to stick a ball to it with an epoxy resin. Use
this with a fine grinding paste, such as a brass cleaner,
or even toothpaste, to create the seat, rotating it
backwards and forwards on the hole.

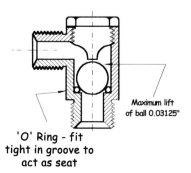

Non Return
Valve
using an 'O'
ring as a seat

A non-return valve; the additional screw plug allows the valve to be cleaned in the event of it becoming blocked.

Tool for seating ball valves.

A non-return valve made as a screw-in type, with false backplate to give the appearance that it bolts in place. Small bolt heads are fitted to the plate.

A non-return valve with a difference. Fitted to an early North American locomotive . Made by the late Eric Brown, it faithfully represents the valves used on that type of engine.

As a rule the top cap also acts as a stop for the ball when it lifts, although sometimes a tiny peg does the job. Either way the lift on the ball must not exceed 0.03125″, otherwise it will bounce about and not work efficiently. The ball should be of rustless material, at one stage that meant stainless steel or bronze, nowadays there are alternatives and Nitride in particular is proving popular; not being as hard as the metal ones, the balls sink themselves into the seating better. Another idea offering improved valve seating is to fit "O" rings - the ring must be a good fit to prevent it pulling out under pressure.

Steam Turrets

With various items such as injectors needing a supply of steam, to make individual valves is not

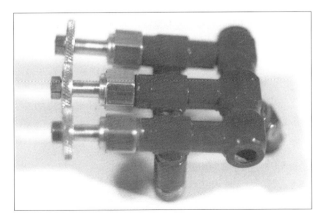

The three-valve steam turret, the hole at the end allows cleaning to take place and is plugged when in use.

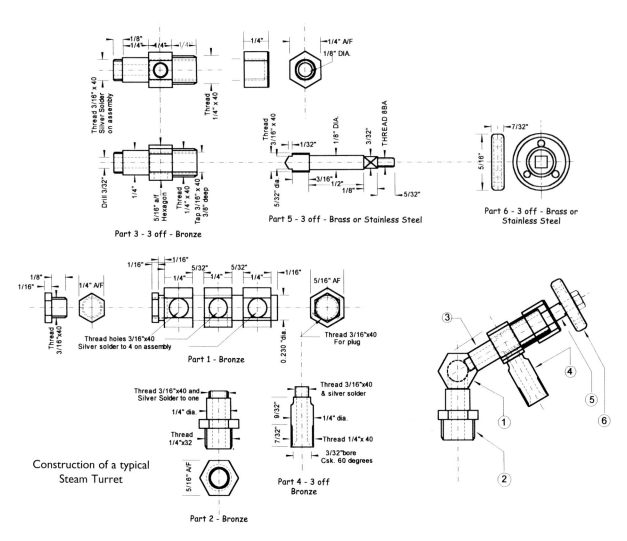

Part 3 - 3 off - Bronze

Part 5 - 3 off - Brass or Stainless Steel

Part 6 - 3 off - Brass or Stainless Steel

Part 1 - Bronze

Construction of a typical Steam Turret

Part 2 - Bronze

Part 4 - 3 off Bronze

such a good idea. The general way to tidy things up is to make a steam turret, sometimes referred to as a steam fountain. It is nothing more than a bar of metal with all the valves set out along it, which is situated somewhere high up on the boiler backhead. This is in line with full-size practice so any such turret must be kept as small and neat as possible, and the drawings above show one suitable for a five inch gauge model.

Water Gauges

A most important fitting is the water gauge, as it is essential to know how much water is in the boiler. On small-scale models it is satisfactory to have two on-off cocks, one high up and the other about level with the top of the firebox. Steam should come from

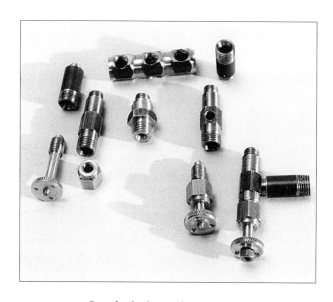

Parts for the three-outlet steam turret.

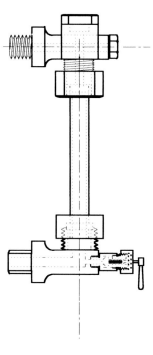

A simple Water Gauge

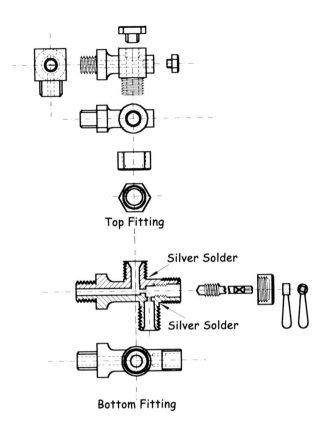

Top Fitting

Silver Solder

Silver Solder

Bottom Fitting

Parts for a simple Water Gauge

The parts for a simple three-cock water gauge.

very well and unlike the old fashioned rubber band do not perish. Gauges should be fitted with shields so that if a glass breaks some protection is offered while emergency action is taken. It calls for a metal framed fitting with some heat resisting clear substance fitted to it. Most plastics are unsuitable as they will not stand the heat, but Mica as at one time used in paraffin stoves is very good and is easy to work, the glass used for microscope slides is also quite good and gives a clearer view of the water level than Mica. The metal fitting consists of a tray, top and bottom, joined with pillars.

A three-cock water gauge with shield for a 5" gauge locomotive. Made by Tony Meek it is virtually scale-size while being fully functional

the top one if it is opened and water from the lower one; if steam comes out at the bottom, the water level is too low. When filling the boiler, the top one is opened and the boiler filled until water seeps from it.

With larger scale passenger hauling models a proper gauge is essential and it must have a blow down valve fitted to it, this is opened prior to taking a reading, to ensure that there is no trapped air giving a false level.

As a result of the Health and Safety Authorities taking an interest in our activities, many clubs now insist that models running on their tracks have the three cock type of gauge which has stop cocks at the upper and lower extremes of the gauge as well as a blowdown, the theory is that if the glass breaks the valves can be closed and prevent a leak of steam. Rules are rules, and must be obeyed, but from experience it can be said that if a glass does break, there is little chance of getting one's hand in to turn anything off until the steam has exhausted itself.

The main reason a glass will break is because it touches the nuts that support it. A seal is needed to prevent this happening and at one time rubber rings were used. Nowadays there are two good alternatives, PTFE tape and 'O' rings; both do the job

Pressure Gauges

When fitting a pressure gauge it should always be via a device known as a siphon which prevents damage to the gauge. It is only a piece of thin tube curved to a "U" shape, but in order to line up the gauge properly a banjo union will be needed. The drawing shows how this is done, a round fitting with a groove into which fits the siphon, is bolted to the boiler with a bolt that has a hole up the centre and is cross drilled to meet the groove. Making the parts calls for care to avoid leaks and it is best if some form of gasket can be fitted to make sure that everything really is steamtight. Very experienced model engineers sometimes make their own pressure gauges, but this is one item the author recommends the reader purchases, rather than tries to make.

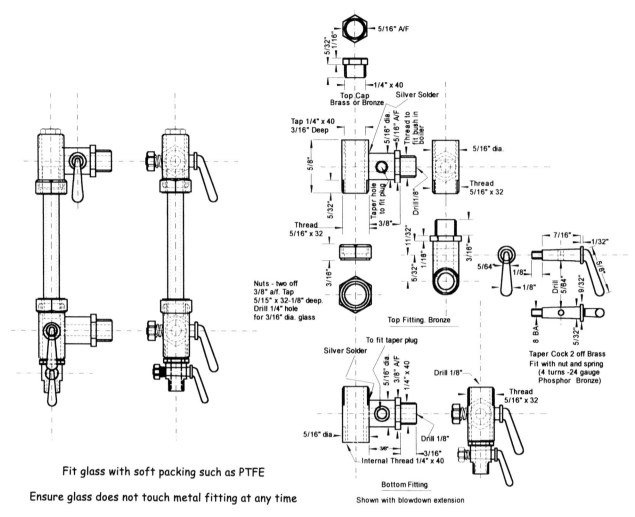

5/16" A/F

5/32"
1/16"

1/4" x 40

Top Cap
Brass or Bronze   Silver Solder

Tap 1/4" x 40   5/16" dia.
3/16" Deep   5/16" A/F   Thread to
                                fit push in
5/8"   5/16" dia.   boiler

                                         5/16" dia.

5/32"   Thread
                                         5/16" x 32
Taper hole
to fit plug   Drill1/8"
Thread   11/32"
5/16" x 32
                      5/32" 1/16"   3/16"
3/16"
                 5/64"   1/8"
Nuts - two off   7/16"   1/32"
3/8" a/f. Tap
5/15" x 32-1/8" deep.   Top Fitting. Bronze   5/8"
Drill 1/4" hole   Drill
for 3/16" dia. glass   5/84"   9/32"

                                     1/8"
Silver Solder   8 BA   5/32"
To fit taper plug
                                   Taper Cock 2 off Brass
                 5/16" dia.   Fit with nut and spring
                 3/8" A/F   (4 turns -24 gauge
                 1/4" x 40   Drill 1/8"   Phosphor Bronze)
                                    Thread
                                    5/16" x 32
5/16" dia
                      Drill 1/8"
              3/6"   3/16"
       Internal Thread 1/4" x 40

              Bottom Fitting
         Shown with blowdown extension

Fit glass with soft packing such as PTFE

Ensure glass does not touch metal fitting at any time

Taper Hole
To Suit Plug
5/16"   Thread
1/16"   1/4"   1/4" x 40
                9/32"   3/32"
                1/4" x 40   11/32"
1/4"
              5/16" A/F
Drill 3/32"
Csk. 60 degrees
                          10 BA 3/32"   1/8"
       Blowdown Section   5/64" dia.   1/8" dia
                                    Blowdown Taper Plug

A typical Three Cock Water Gauge

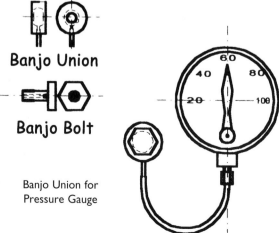

Banjo Union

Banjo Bolt

Banjo Union for
Pressure Gauge

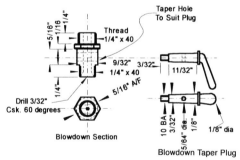

To Sum Up

There is no reason why the cab should not look neat and tidy and have a near scale if not actually a scale appearance. Study the layout of a full-sized cab and try and follow that and remember to keep all pipes as straight as possible, as nothing looks worse than pipes with kinks in them.

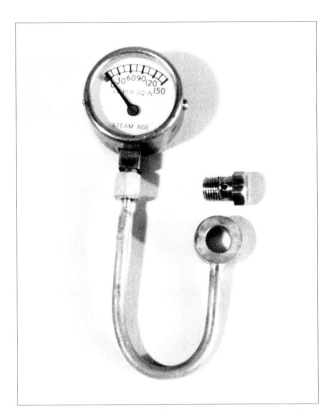

A pressure gauge and siphon, which protects the gauge from sudden surges of steam, which might otherwise cause damage.

A selection of neat scale-size fittings made by Tony Meek; all are functional.

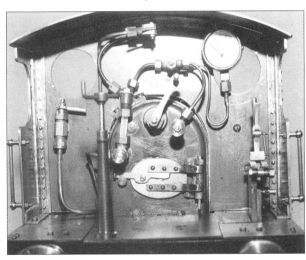

A basic cab layout on a "Tich" Locomotive. The fittings are not scale, but at the same time they are not obtrusively oversize.

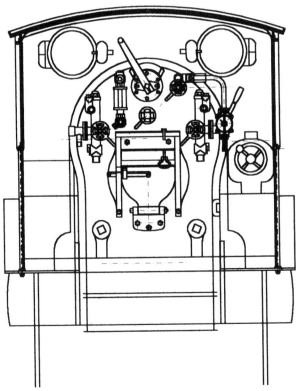

A drawing for a well laid out Cab

Design by Tony Meek

The cab of this 5" gauge German narrow gauge Mallet is definitely super-detail in every way.

Two very neat cab layouts, both are 5" gauge locomotives. The top is that of a GWR 2-6-2 tank to the 'Firefly' design, and bottom, the unusual, but practical, water gauge on Phil Hains' LBSC 'Terrier' 0-6-0 tank locomotive "Barcelona" should be noted.

Chapter 22: Platework

Whatever type of locomotive is being modelled, the final appearance is going to depend on two things, good platework and good finishing. Many of the working parts can be altered and adapted as we may wish, but unless the platework is good the model will never look right, as that is the part that shows. To ensure that it is a model to be admired, it is necessary that flat plates really are flat, and curved sections follow a true radius, with no kinks or bumps and with no unsightly file marks. It is also the part that is going to be painted, and it follows that it must be finished well enough to accept paint. This chapter is intended to offer hints and tips on how to get good platework that will provide a good foundation; painting and finishing will be discussed later.

Cutting sheet metal can be a bit difficult. Cutting shears, or tin snips as they are often called, have their own particular problems. Firstly they frequently cause the metal to distort and bend, often to a degree where it is difficult to get it back into shape. Secondly they often reach a point where, because of the shape of the cut, it is impossible to progress any further. They do have their uses in some instances where small items from very thin material are needed, but generally speaking when it comes to the plate-work of a locomotive it is as well to forget them. It is possible to purchase bench shears, consisting of a device that bolts to the bench with a movable blade, operated by a long lever. The static, supported part is large and firm, which stops some of the distortion that occurs with tin snips. Even so while fine for short cuts, it becomes very difficult when intricate shapes and lengthy cuts are required. They are extremely good where constant intermittent trimming of work is needed, for example if we had a three inch radius to cut from a square sheet; instead of trying to cut round the radius, use bench shears to keep trimming the corners until the edge of the metal is a series of very short flats close to the edge of the marked radius which can then be filed to the finished shape and size. The end result with this method can be very good indeed.

Nibblers

As long as our metal is no more than about 1mm or eighteen gauge in thickness, it may be practical to use a tool known as a nibbler. These can be obtained either as tools in their own right or as attachments to fit in a power drill, and although designed for the portable type of drill, they can be used with advantage in a bench drilling machine. The nibbler works by punching a series of holes that break into each other and while this may sound as though they will leave a rough edge, the holes are so finely spaced that the edge is quite smooth. The tools will cut straight lines or curves to quite a small radius and are very quick to use. In many ways the nibbler is the ideal tool for cutting sheet material but, of course, as usual there are a some snags. The first is the speed at which they will cut. Used in a portable electric drill the progress along the metal is fast enough to be almost self-destructive. It is, therefore, essential to secure the metal firmly before commencing work, and to hold the tool firmly, which is where the bench drill can be useful, because it is possible to use a slightly slower speed and so gain more control. The nibbler needs to be firmly secured on the machine by some form of bracket; this will leave two hands free for feeding the metal through the machine, which is a big help. Another snag to the nibbler is the noise it creates as each movement punches a hole in the metal. It sounds as though war has broken out and will definitely not be appreciated by the family or any near neighbours.

Hand Saws

For many years model engineers have used a good old fashioned hack-saw for cutting out sheet metal with every success. At one time it was possible to purchase special sheet metal saws that had a rigid back with a standard hack-saw blade bolted in line with it; the back enables a nice straight cut to be made through a sheet of metal without any restrictions on the amount of metal at the side, or the length of the cut. These saws are not generally available at normal tool suppliers, but it should be possible to order one through a specialist dealer. The ordinary hack-saw works quite well and for long cuts it is possible to turn the blade sideways, but there is limited room of about three inches at the side of the cut, which reduces its possibilities. A blade of either twenty-eight or thirty-two teeth per inch should always be used for thin sheet metal, never anything coarser.

For cutting curved sections with a hack-saw, a blade known amongst engineers as a sawing wire and sold under a number of proprietary names, is used. The blade or wire occupies the normal hack-saw blade position, sometimes clips are needed to hold it in place. It is round and can cut at any point on the circumference so that it can be used in any position and at any angle. It is most useful and blades can be obtained in various degrees of coarseness of teeth. Coping and piercing saws are also useful where it is necessary to cut radii, and special metal cutting blades are available for them. On a hack-saw the teeth of the blade should always project towards the front of the saw so they cut on the forward movement. With Coping and Piercing saws the blade is best used the other way round and allowed to cut on the backward movement, which stops the effect of it digging in, and also gives greater control of the cut. Do not expect too much from either type of saw, they are ideal for model making in the smaller gauges but have limited use on heavier section metal, even so they can and will cut intricate shapes when need be.

Power Saws

Band saws designed specifically for metal work are usually large and bulky, as well as being very expensive. In recent years small band saws have been produced for the use of DIY enthusiasts, bringing this useful type of machine within the scope of the average model engineer. They generally suffer from the problem of running rather fast for metal work but, if used carefully, can be an absolute boon, particularly as they are equally at home on straight or curved cuts. In general the blades supplied by the manufacturers of these machines, although sometimes described as suitable for metal, are not what is required for the type of work we are talking about. Special metal working blades can be obtained from good quality tool stockists, better still find the address of the nearest saw doctor and pay him or her a visit. The saw doctor can make suitable blades for the machine, often at a much lower cost than the commercial unsuitable item, and it is well worth getting to know the whereabouts of the local one.

Hand Held Jigsaws

Another item that is available for the DIY enthusiast is a jigsaw which, at first glance, would appear to be most unsuitable for our purposes. In fact with a little care there is not a great deal it will not do with sheet metal of around 1mm (18 gauge) and slightly thicker, but don't try and use it on thin stuff. To use a jigsaw, either the metal being cut or the saw itself need to be well supported. Clamp the metal down firmly on a pair of supports, getting the clamped area as close as is practical to the line of the cut. The saw must be held firmly and not forced in any way and, with a suitable blade, it will cut the metal very well. A number of enthusiasts seeing the advantage of the

jigsaw have taken things a stage further, and clamped the saw upside down to a small bench made from a suitable piece of metal or wood, with the blade protruding through a slot. A bar, which lays across the work, is clamped on the bench, to prevent it from trying to force its way upwards and the metal is manipulated by hand, an idea which is highly successful.

Scroll-Saws

Scroll-saws, fretsaws and commercial jigsaw machines work on the same principle as the above idea, but generally use much finer blades. A good quality machine, with a good quality blade, is capable of cutting thin material very quickly and efficiently.

Construction Details

Construction of general plate work, such as cabs, tanks for tank engines and tenders consists mainly of riveting or screwing plates to angles in order to obtain nice square corners. This is how it was done for many years in full-size practice and it was only later when welding came into general use that the practice was less frequently used. The position of rivets, screws etc. should be carefully marked out and the angle clamped in position so that both it and the sheet metal can be drilled as one. A good alternative to clamping, although not one to be used for water tanks or any other item that will hold liquid, is to stick the angle in place using a cyano-acrylic adhesive (*Super Glue*). This will hold it firm enough for drilling and filing, and means that there are no clamps to get in the way when trying to put the work on the drilling machine. Check that the angle that is used is square; frequently it is not and will need to be squared off before use. Always use the smallest size practical in order to get the best possible appearance. Although we generally think in terms of getting supplies of brass angle from model

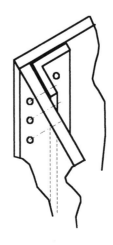

When possible to do so, joining with angle will give both strength and shape to corners

engineering suppliers or metal stockists, think also of the ordinary hobby shop which often has a wide choice when it comes to small brass angle section.

Some items may require the metal to be bent to an angle, all bends will have a radius as against the sharp edge of the joint manufactured by using angle. If possible it is best to use proper folding bars for any bending in order to get the best results. Bending Bars can be bought, alternatively they are comparatively easy and cheap to make. Unless building in a very large scale, the metal used will generally be no more that 18 gauge, or 1mm thick, and simple folding machines will deal easily enough with this. If such a machine is not available, no need to despair, as a couple of pieces of scrap angle iron will do quite well. If possible use something fairly heavy such as 2" x 2" x ¼", which can be screwed to the edge of a bench and left permanently in position. It is secured to the bench with countersunk screws and has a couple of tapped holes matching clearance holes in the other piece. Bolts tighten it on to the metal, which is pushed over by hand, using a wooden block to ensure as even a bend as possible - smaller angle can be used in the vice for the same purpose.

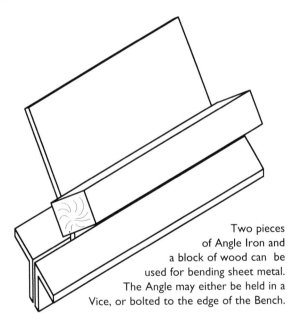

Two pieces
of Angle Iron and
a block of wood can be
used for bending sheet metal.
The Angle may either be held in a
Vice, or bolted to the edge of the Bench.

Do not try and knock the metal over without using a block as this definitely will result in damage to the finish.

An allowance must be made for the bend, and the correct figure for this is just under half the thickness of the metal being bent, assuming a true and sharp right angle bend. To get the sort of bend that will conform with the true figure will need a power press, and so it is as well to allow half the metal thickness, or even a little more, and to trim it off

afterwards if it happens to be too long. One thing that has to be considered is the ductability of the metal that is being used. In particular brass has a nasty habit of looking as though it is going to be all right and then splitting along the edge of the bend. Once it does this it is not possible to retrieve the situation, so it is best to try and bend a scrap of waste before starting on what will be the finished product. It is possible to anneal brass sheet, but it is difficult unless proper equipment is available. Using a blow-lamp to heat it leaves small areas softer than others which causes distortion. It needs to be heated all over in an oven which could be improvised, if one wished, from fire brick; if doing so care must be taken to ensure that the heat will be consistent over the whole area. Generally speaking mild steel does not suffer from this problem of splitting.

Generating Curves

The modeller making non-steam models is more likely to be involved making curved metal sections than the one who makes steam models. There are exceptions to all rules of course and if anyone wants to make one of the streamlined Pacifics that graced our railways a few decades ago, he or she will find plenty of curves are involved. Once again the proper tool for the job is the best way and a set of bending rolls cannot be beaten for generating curved sections. This does not mean that all is lost without them. The metal can be clamped in a vice with a round bar behind it, and rolled over the bar by hand, using a another bar of slightly smaller diameter. The idea requires a little patience but works quite well. No matter how the curve is made there are two dangers to look out for; firstly that of the metal springing out of radius as soon as it is released. If the metal used is

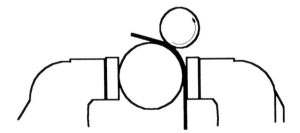

Using two round bars to create a curve on sheet metal

at all springy, allowance for the effect should be made by rolling it to a slightly smaller radius in the first place. It is usually better to ease off a radius rather than to try and make it tighter after it has already been made. Most curved section will need to be trimmed off as a final means of finishing.

Cab roofs as a rule need to have some means of removable section to allow the driver to get at the controls, this has to be done in such a way as not to impair the look of the roof. One suggestion is that guttering is a possible place to make a suitable joint, alternatively the edge of the roof itself. There were very few locomotives that did not have gutters of one sort or another, except those built with small roofs or little more than a shelf to protect the crew. With these there is often no necessity to have a removable section, as access is quite easy. It is largely a matter of how much room is needed, some people like a lot of space and remove the whole roof, others are content to just have a small section for access. Soldering narrow sections of material inside the proposed gap and just dropping the removable section on to these can make a simple slip-in plate. In the case of a tank engine it may be necessary to make part of the cab backplate removable in order to gain access and, again the position of this will vary according to the individual locomotive and the individual owner. Some people are content just to remove the cab roof or a section thereof, others like to take out the whole backplate and sometimes the bunker as well.

Boiler Cladding

Thin sheet metal is used to act as the outer lagging of the boiler, underneath being some suitable heat resistant material such as fibreglass matting or *Kaowool*. The metal has to be rolled into shape and this is where some problems do arise because of the difficulty of getting the ends rolled to the correct radius - as the end of the curve is reached, the metal tends to straighten out. The best idea is to cut the metal too large and to trim off the ends so that it will form a complete cylinder. There are several ways of fixing the cladding in position, one is to put it over the boiler and solder the seam, using the boiler bands purely for decorative purpose. It is a neat and effective system but does create problems if for any reason repairs are needed to the boiler. The alternative is to use the boiler bands to keep the lagging in position. This works very well, but the bands should not actually be used to draw the material into place; this can be done either with large Jubilee Clips or some home made clips, which are removed once the bands are holding. The cladding over the firebox can be difficult to deal with and may be best fixed with tiny screws to the inside of the locomotive frames, any boiler bands in the region being held in a similar fashion. Sheet metal, particularly brass, always tends to spring open after rolling or folding and particular attention must be paid to the edges, which can look very unsightly if they are sprung.

The cladding can be cut to size from a paper or thin card pattern and is best prepared, and if possible

fitted, before the boiler is assembled to the frames. Holes for safety valves, dome, non return valves, etc. should be cut very carefully, to avoid unsightly gaps round the edges.

Beading

Nearly all cabs and tenders will have a beading round some of the edges. This is to cover the ragged edges of the main material. In model form it is usual to make this from half round beading, which is soldered on, in full size the beading would be screwed in place and would more likely be a form of channel which would have been hammered and

A cab edge beaded with a specially rounded-off angle section which conforms to the prototype.
Other locomotives will have different types of beading.

screwed into position. Small channel is available from some model shops that sell small metal sections in brass or aluminium. It is only sold in short lengths and is difficult to bend to shape. Half round brass beading is fairly easy to work to shape and does not look out of place. Before shaping, it should be stretched by holding one end in a vice and pulling on the other end, which is gripped in a pair of pliers. This straightens the beading, and also tends to take the spring from it, making it easier to bend to any required shape. On larger scale models, whether standard or narrow gauge, it is possible to mill a slot in a length of brass strip and make a suitable channel section; pick a nice soft brass for the job, or cut strips from a sheet of gilding metal.

Tanks

Once again, angles and rivets, or screws are the usual form of construction. In full-size practice tanks and tenders would be fitted with internal baffle plates to prevent several tons of water swishing about and causing weight distribution problems. This is not necessary in the case of a model but often the line of these baffles would be shown up by the row of snap head rivets used to hold them in place. Dummy rivets can be used to simulate this effect. The tanks must, of course, be watertight, so it will be necessary to fill under and around the angle and rivets with either solder or an epoxy resin adhesive. The tops of the tanks must be removable for the purpose of maintenance which can be achieved either by screwing them in position, or using some form of clip. The latter is preferable as no matter how one tries to hide screw heads it is an almost impossible task.

Model locomotives frequently have hand pumps inside the water tanks, whether part of the locomotive or tender. This means a pipe must be taken from there to the boiler. It can be fitted to the tank by a simple nutted union, but it should be done in such a way as not to spoil the appearance. It will also be necessary to have a small extended opening through which the hand pump can be operated, here again care should be taken to make this in such a way as not to spoil the appearance of the model. One way to do so is to make it flush fitting on a recessed joint and use a fitting like a holder for fire irons or a tool box as a means of lifting it off.

There are examples of tanks having rounded edges, the very fine design by Martin Evans of "Rob Roy" being a typical example. The tops of the tanks can be bent to shape, but a neater way of doing this, which was demonstrated by Phil Hains, is to machine sections from a round bar, the diameter of which

will give the desired radius for the tank edges. This can then be soldered in place and left. The bar also provides an additional securing point for the tank ends as well as adding adhesive weight to the model.

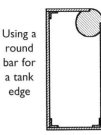

Using a round bar for a tank edge

Running Boards

Once again the use of angles to make up the boards is suggested. As a rule sections will have to be filed out to clear various parts of the chassis, and this is fairly straightforward. Where the footplate is curved narrow vees can be cut in the angle and joined again with soft solder to get the required shape, the surface is then filed to the desired shape and smoothed down, the whole taking on a nice smooth appearance. Splashers are made in a similar fashion but because of their shape it may be necessary to use angle in short sections rather than as a single length.

Steps

Except in the case of narrow gauge models all locomotives have steps which allow access to the cab and footplate as well as more often than not up to the smoke box end, tender too are fitted with steps,

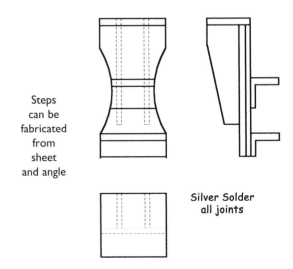

Steps can be fabricated from sheet and angle

Silver Solder all joints

in some case these reach to the top. The sides of steps are easily fabricated from sheet and angle section can be used for the actual step, although one edge will almost certainly have to be reduced in size.

Handrails

Handrails are best made from stainless steel to avoid the problem of rust, the handrail knobs that support them made from either from brass or nickel silver. These are cheap enough to buy and it is worth considering so doing, unless there is some particular shape required, or one feels that, if possible, everything on a model should be home made. The rail itself can be pushed through the holes and, to prevent it sliding out when the model is in use, just make a centre punch mark on the rail where it is pushed into the hole in the knob. When the rail is tapped home this will give sufficient grip to stay put. Soldering or using an adhesive will mean a more secure handrail but it is also very difficult to get off if repairs are needed at any time.

Making Knobs

To make handrail knobs a form tool is essential. The tool should be made in such a way that the threaded section of the handrail knob is outermost from the chuck and a curved parting tool used to cut the sections off. A small jig will be needed to drill the hole for the handrail; there is no need for this to be elaborate - like most engineering projects the simplest way will usually be the best.

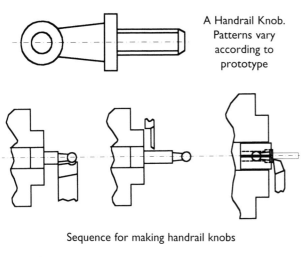

A Handrail Knob. Patterns vary according to prototype

Sequence for making handrail knobs

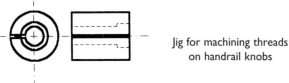

Jig for machining threads on handrail knobs

There is no doubt that making one's own means that exact conformity to the original shape is possible, whereas if they are purchased a standard type has to be used.

Attaching Tanks

The tanks of a tank locomotive need to be screwed to the running boards, and possibly also to the cab. Solder brass screws to the tanks and pass them through holes in the running board or cab, and

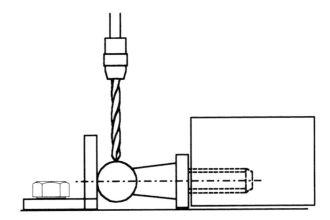

Set-up for drilling handrail knobs.
Screw knob into block and use a piece of angle for a stop

secure them with nuts. Trying to pass screws through holes in the tanks and running boards, and then putting a nut on will almost invariably mean leaks, not necessarily at first, but certainly after a period of running has moved the parts about. No matter how much packing is put under the screw heads it will not stop this happening.

Removing Marks and Scratches

It is essential to ensure the removal of all file marks and large scratches from the plate work; nothing looks worse than file marks along the edges of brass or steel sections. Draw filing is the best method of ensuring these are removed. Avoid removing solder, etc. from plate work with coarse emery cloth or paper, it will almost certainly cause scratches which are the very dickens to get out again. Blemishes should be removed with very fine waterproof abrasive paper, well soaked, followed by polishing with a good quality scouring pad such as *Scotch Bright*. It may even be worth considering the use of a soft rotating mop and a fine cutting compound for the final finish, but if so care must be taken, as excessive use of polishing mops can also remove wanted detail.

A good scratch-free finish will be essential for good paintwork, and the platework is the first thing that will be seen by anyone looking at a model. It is, therefore, well worth taking time and care over finishing.

Chapter 23: Tenders

Why can't an engine sit down? Because it has a tender behind.

Not all locomotives will need a tender and no doubt that is why many people prefer to build models of tank engines. A lot of work is involved in making a tender and sometimes it can be quite an irksome task when the locomotive itself has already been completed. As a result there is a school of thought that it is a good idea to start by making the tender, and then build the locomotive. It has already been said that there are many theories on the order in which the various parts of a model should be made, and the idea of the tender first is yet another. Have a look at what is involved in building one and the reader can then decide for him or her self at what stage the tender of a model should be constructed.

The Chassis

Basically tenders fall into two parts, the chassis and the superstructure, as against a locomotive where we have all sorts of other things, such as cylinders, boilers, etc. The chassis is quite straightforward and is built in a similar way to that of the locomotive, with plate frames, hornblocks and axleboxes into which the wheels are fitted. There are buffers at one end and at the other, where it joins the locomotive, rubbing blocks, which are very short buffers. Sometimes these are omitted, as in model form they generally serve no useful purpose. In full-size practice they are there to act as a cushion when the locomotive is backed up against the tender or sometimes when negotiating curves. Model rail tracks rarely have scale curves, usually they are of a much tighter radius than full-size practice which requires the tender to be set slightly further back from the locomotive footplate than in the real thing. By leaving off the rubbing plates it is possible to have a smaller gap than would otherwise be practical, thus enhancing the appearance of the model. Brackets are sometimes fitted to the top of the frames as a means of bolting on the superstructure, although in many instances chassis spacers are used for the purpose instead.

Hornblocks are fitted as they would be on the frames of a locomotive

and nearly always the leaf springs for the axle boxes will be fitted outside the frames. It is worth studying these in detail, as the shape of the spring arrangement on tenders varied considerably according to who built the locomotive and, although at first glance all types may seem similar, they most definitely are not. Most of the variation is in the shape taken by the spring hangers and it can be very distinctive. It is possible to use dummy springs made from castings with a concealed spiral spring running behind and this is a popular choice amongst model makers as leaf springing can be rather hard for a tender, the weight of which is comparatively light when compared to a locomotive. If full working springs are to be used, the details for making these can be found in the chapter dealing with the subject. The tenders on some 7¼" gauge models are used for the driver to ride on and if this is to be the case then much heavier springing will be required.

Stretchers

Frame stretchers for tenders are generally different to those on a locomotive. While the locomotive spacer will be placed so that the flat surface is vertical, on a tender it is more likely to be horizontal. Brakes are constructed in a similar fashion to those on a locomotive and invariably there is a hand brake arrangement.

Superstructure

The top part of the tender contains two main sections; a tank which holds the water, and a section which holds the fuel, generally coal. There are instances of oil burning locomotives, in which case

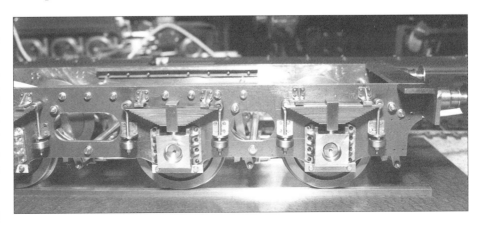

An excellent example of a tender chassis with working springs.
Note angle mounted inside to support superstructure.

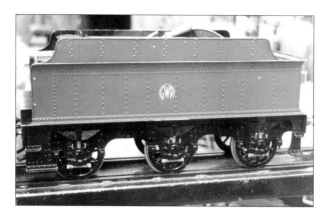

A model Great Western Railway tender, a different type of frame altogether. Note the careful attention that has been given to the rivet spacing in order to conform to the prototype. Many of the vertical rows of rivets in the lower half would have been for baffle plates to stop the water from swilling around when moving. These plates are not normally required in a model and the rivet detail is for appearance only.

Platework

Because of the need to carry water, the super-structure of tenders, except on very large models, is generally made from brass. Apart from not rusting it is also comparatively easy to solder. Most parts will be fabricated by using brass angle screwed or riveted to the sheet material. In the past it has been the practice to run soft solder into these joints to prevent leaks, recently more modern methods have been adopted and it is quite common for the joints to be sealed with an epoxy resin of the type used for fibreglass work.

To use the resin the joints are prepared for screwing together with all holes drilled and tapped where required. A layer of resin is run along the area which will form the joint and the angle screwed in place, tightening the screws hard so that they squeeze into the resin. The surplus that is squeezed out is wiped away with a cloth soaked in very hot water or scraped off just before it is fully set. The result is a strong, watertight joint and the process is much easier than trying to run soft solder into the gaps.

that section will also be a tank. In particular models built for the garden gauges are likely to require a tank for fuel and it may be desirable to disguise this to give it the appearance of a coal hopper. In full-size practice a tender might sometimes also have well tanks, to increase the water capacity. These are tanks, connected to the main one by pipes and which drop below the superstructure into the chassis. It is unlikely any model would ever have the need to carry such an extra water supply unless it was being entered for efficiency trials, but those interested in making exact scale models may wish to fit them.

Making up the angles calls for some careful cutting in order to get close fitting joints so that maximum strength can be obtained, and care must be taken to remove all the burrs from holes which are drilled or tapped to ensure that good flush joints are made.

Not only is it necessary to carefully fit and file the

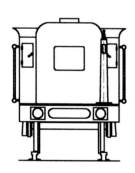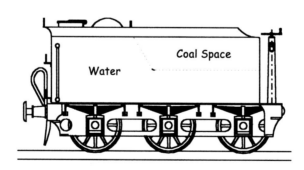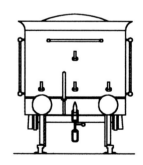

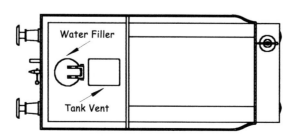

General Arrangement of a typical tender.
Outlines will vary according to railway or country, but all types basically function in the same fashion

angles to shape, it is also essential to make sure that the angle itself is absolutely square, which is not often the case when angle, whether iron or brass is purchased, as is mentioned in the chapter on frames. It is, therefore, as well just to put the angle in a four-jaw chuck, or on the milling machine, and machine one face in order to get it right. This will also help to remove any uneven parts of the surface and make it easier to seal to a watertight joint.

Rivets

Whether or not rivets should be countersunk or left proud so that the round or snap head is showing will depend on the prototype or, in the

A model of a tender for the London Midland and Scottish railway. Yet another type of frame, and an entirely different pattern from the Great Western one. The rear steps were fairly typical as were the lamp brackets. The dome in front of the water filler is for the scoop and the pipes either side of it are air vents to prevent air pressure building up when the tender is filled with water.

case of a free-lance model, on the whim of the constructor. Many designers used countersunk rivets, believing that round headed ones showed sloppy work as well as being unsightly. Particularly keen on hiding rivets was the late Sir Nigel Gresley who absolutely despised seeing them. On the *Great Western Railway* and the *London Midland and Scottish* they were left proud, and engines and tenders became quite distinctive with the various patterns that were formed. Careful attention to rivet detail has been paid on all the tenders, photographs of which appear in this chapter.

If the rivets are to be countersunk it is best to use a small drill to make the recess rather than the more normal countersink bit. Invariably when a countersink bit is used and the rivet filed flush a small indented ring is left, something which seems to happen less if a small drill is used and allowed to go just beyond the countersink stage. Either way it is advisable to put some form of filler in the hole before final finishing takes place and to smooth over that to get a good flat finish.

Drilling

In particular if snap head rivets are used, it is essential to get all the holes accurately lined up and properly spaced. If a milling machine is available this can be used to co-ordinate them, if not clamp a

piece of bar to the table of the drilling machine and use it as a straight edge to run the sheet of metal against, so that all the holes will then be accurately in line. A simple jig can be made to take care of evenly spaced holes but if unevenly spaced ones are called for, they will have to be carefully marked out. Some parts of the tender may call for bending the metal, either to an angle or a radius as described in the previous chapter.

Suitable Metals

Brass and gilding metal are at a disadvantage when it comes to painting, as well as being very expensive. Some people, therefore, might like to use steel for the platework. It is not advisable to be tempted into the use of galvanised sheet as after a period the galvanising tends to start to peel off, leaving an even more vulnerable area than if non-galvanised material had been used. One of the softer leaded steels is probably the best type to use and, if assembled using the epoxy resin method, it is possible to give this a couple of coats of paint before assembly. Don't, of course, put the paint on anywhere that the resin will go, and try and leave as little resin surplus to be wiped off as possible. Use brass angle for assembly and you will have gone some way to obviating the rust problem. If at all possible give a couple more coats of paint after assembly, although on some types of tender this may not be practical, so all internal painting will have to be done prior to assembling parts. It may be possible to apply paint along the seams after assembly by using a spray and injecting the paint through the water filler hole.

Although very expensive Nickel Silver is another ideal material, it solders particularly well and will form shapes nicely, although it is a little springy. It will accept paint readily without the need of a self-etching primer, and is non-rusting.

Accessories

As well as making the actual platework of the tender, quite a few other parts will be needed. The water filler is a typical example and, as usual, the form this will take will vary according to the design of the locomotive. Basically though it will consist of a piece of round tube fitted in a hole in the top plate of the tender, usually by soldering; a hinged lid prevents dirt from getting in and water from

splashing out. The actual filler is quite straight-forward to make as it is simply a piece of tube machined to fit in a hole, but the lid with its hinges can be a little tricky. The disc for the lid is machined to a step to fit inside the filler and hinged, usually with two hinges that have extended arms. One of the best materials to make the hinges from is brass angle. It can be cut out to form the hinge parts after drilling through for a pin. The actual drilling operation can be a little difficult as we are probably looking at a pin of very tiny diameter. This is where the use of angle helps; the ends can be machined square in a four-jaw chuck and this helps them sit square when positioned for drilling. People with small lathes can get even greater accuracy by drilling them in the lathe at the same time as the ends are squared. Having drilled one short length of angle it can, if done accurately, be used as a jig to drill others. Cutting out the sections can be done either on a milling machine or by filing.

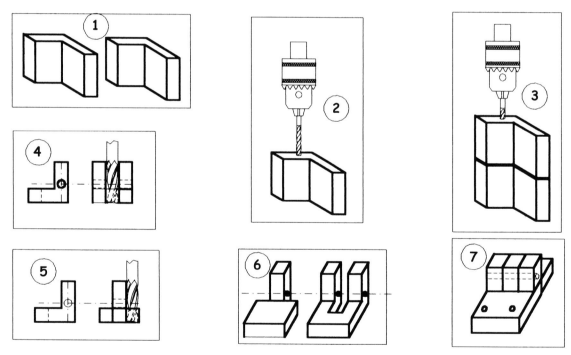

Stages in making small hinges from angle

1 Cut two pieces of small angle to the same size
2 Drill through first piece
3 Soft solder pieces together and pass drill through second piece
4 Mill or file slot centrally through one piece
5 Mill ends off other piece to form a 'T'
6 There should now be two pieces as shown
7 Join pieces back to back and pass pin through holes, drill for
   fixing screws and then round off edges as required

An alternative method of making hinges and one favoured by many people is to drill small diameter brass in the lathe and solder it to pieces of sheet material. It is then cut out and assembled in a similar way to the angle mentioned above.

On top of the filler will be some type of clasp for securing it and, generally speaking, this can be filed out of brass to a reasonably accurate replica of the original shape.

Water Scoops

Most locomotives would have had a water scoop on the tender in order to take water from troughs between the rails whilst moving. Operation of the scoop required the fireman who worked it to have excellent judgement to get the scoop lowered via a hand wheel at exactly the right time as the locomotive ran over the trough. The speed of the locomotive had to be reasonably fast to force sufficient water up

water was inevitable. In theory such happenings were supposed to be prevented by the crew but in fact it was virtually impossible to avoid. Even so the driver could get into trouble if there was a complaint. Fortunately these things happened in the days when people did not instantly seek financial redress through the courts and so, usually, the driver got little more than a dressing down following a complaint from a passenger. It was not unknown for a driver who had got out of bed the wrong side or was feeling in the mood for a joke, to ensure that a few people got a soaking.

But we have digressed. In general water scoops are of no use whatever on models. It has been known for a club to fit water troughs in the track and for drivers of models to try and collect water on the run. Usually most will splash down their trousers and so fitting troughs is very rare. On the tender top plate would be a domed pipe, this ensured that the water that was drawn up the scoop would rise above the

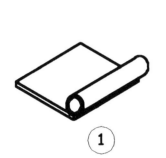 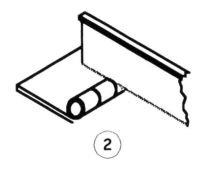 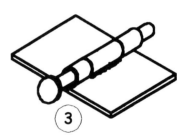

Stages in fabricating a hinge

1 Silver solder tube to edge of plate
2 Saw tube into three parts using a very fine toothed saw
3 Pass pin through tube and soft solder second plate into position
4 Finish by drilling fixing holes

and into the tender. It called for excellent teamwork by the crew. Bad judgement on the part of either could create problems, such as damage to the scoop if lowered too early or lifted too late, insufficient water through at too low a speed and excessive water flowing out the side of the scoop. For anyone who has not seen a locomotive picking up water in this way, or been in a train when it is happening, an experience has been missed. Water would spray up the side and be carried by the air flow along a considerable length of the train. If the unlucky passenger had his or her window open as the train reached the troughs, a shower of none too clean

level of that in the tender water tanks and then drop down on to it, rather than trying to force it in against the weight of water already carried. This pipe was more often than not covered with a plate, giving it the appearance of a hump from the Loch Ness Monster. The actual scoop would be visible in between the tender frames and the handle for operation would be somewhere on the tender footplate. It is doubtful if anyone is going to look for the scoop and so there is little need to include it in the model. The hand wheel can be used for other purposes or left as a dummy, one use that readily springs to mind is to operate the by-pass valve for water returning from the locomotive pump to the tender. Alternatively it could be used as the water valve for an injector.

Finishing Touches

Finishing the platework on a tender is little different to finishing the platework for a locomotive and the necessary information can be found on the chapter dealing with the subject. There are a few other refinements we are likely to find on a tender. One obvious thing to look for is the coal rails. Some companies built these as standard, in other cases they were added to increase the coal carrying capacity. As usual a study of the original or a photograph is worthwhile. Some coal rails were flat, others were half round and some were even angle, the stanchions that held them in position could also be either flat or angular. It is usually worthwhile screwing the coal rail stanchions to the tender, although more often than not in full-size practice they would be riveted. There is always the danger they might get bent on a working model and it is better, therefore, to make them removable. Some modellers make them a push-on fit which allows them to be taken off for safe-keeping.

The Tender Fittings

Finally there are various functional fittings needed for the tender. If the locomotive is fitted with an injector, the water valve should be situated on the tender. In full-size practice these took various forms, frequently a hand wheel on the front bulkhead being used, it might be very short with virtually no stem showing at all. Another type of valve consisted of a stanchion with a single lever attached to it, looking rather like a truncated brake stanchion, the lever was adjusted for the required quantity of water. There might be a water gauge on the front bulkhead as well, giving the crew some indication of the quantity of water in the tender. Whilst not impossible these are difficult to replicate in small models and it may be as well to make a dummy version, if authenticity of appearance is being sought. After all, it is only a case of opening the filler to see how much there is, where as in full-size it meant the fireman clambering across the top of the tender to do so. Toolboxes were often a feature on tenders and their addition can improve the looks of a model, but not all tenders had tool boxes. Some instead had a form of recess in the front bulkhead into which tools, sandwiches, etc. were slipped for storage; as usual research of the prototype will be required to see how these were fitted.

Hand Pumps

The actual construction of hand pumps is described in the chapter on pumps in general but it must be remembered that if a hand pump is fitted it will be necessary to have some means of access to it for maintenance. It will also often be necessary to remove a section in order to actually use the pump, as it is unlikely that the filler hole will be large enough for the purpose. Often the top plate is made a push fit and this gives plenty of room to get at things if need be. A pipe will be needed from the hand pump to a non-return valve on the boiler which means a flexible connection between tender and engine. When in use, particularly if the locomotive is in steam, the connection will be under pressure and some form of screwed fitting is desirable. The

Tool boxes needed to be locked and many modellers faithfully follow full sized practice and fit them. Some have recessed locks, other are padlocked. This is an excellent example of a working lock made by Peter Robinson, although not for a locomotive it would be suitable for use on one. It is compared with a 5 pence piece.

late LBSC used to recommend the use of a cycle pump connector and it was an idea that worked quite well. Modern facilities mean that we can now keep that to pump up cycle tyres, as there are a variety of commercial pressure hose fittings available if we do not wish to make one. They are not that difficult to make, ordinary nut connections as used on other fittings will do and a special nipple made out of flexible tube can go over. A couple of ridges are put on the nipple and a small brass clip fitted over the tube between the ridges.

This will prevent it coming off under pressure but to make sure use one of the modern liquid pipe sealers between the nipple and pipe before tightening the clip. The best tube to use for the purpose is the type purchased in a model shop for fuel lines on model aircraft and made of Neoprene. This withstands high temperatures which is useful should the clack valve on the locomotive boiler fail and hot water leak back towards the water tank.

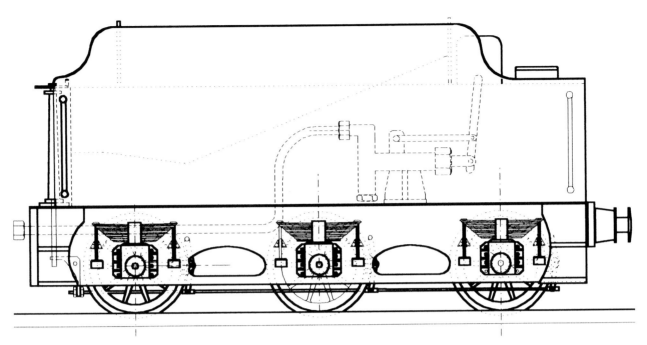

Typical layout of a hand pump fitted in the water space of a tender.
A handle extension has to be made to make pumping easier.

One final point when using a tender is the damage that is done to paintwork when shovelling coal on the fire. One way to avoid this is to carry the coal in a box on top of the tender, but this looks a bit odd. Another idea is to make a little removable metal section to fit in the coal space over the top of the permanent one. This can, if one wishes, have felt or something similar stuck on the bottom so that the paintwork is completely protected. It is not difficult to do and is well worth while.

*From an earlier age, a London North Western Railway Tender, showing fine detail. A lot of attention has been paid to the tool boxes.
A protective cover for the coal section can just be distinguished.*

An "intercontinental" locomotive

Yoichi Niizaki from Tokyo, Japan, is a fine model engineer (and designer - see the photograph at the bottom of page 7); he is also a frequent visitor to clubs in Europe.

Rapidly becoming frustrated that he could only drive other people's engines, and show photographs of his own work during these visits, he decided to make a locomotive that would be small enough, and light enough, to fall within his luggage allowance on transcontinental flights.

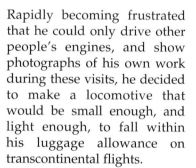

The result is this 5" gauge i.c. engine powered industrial shunting engine, shown during a visit to Britain. As can be seen this is as neat under the bonnet as it is in external appearance.

Is this the very first model locomotive specifically designed to operate on more than one continent?

Chapter 24: Non-Steam Locomotives
Alternative Power Sources

Steam locomotives have a fascination all their own, a distinctive sound and a distinctive smell with an air of mystery about them. Youngsters of today, unless their parents take them to a preserved railway, have no knowledge of them, only ever having seen Diesel or Electric Trains, if indeed they have seen a train at all. Many have never seen coal either. Sometimes when giving rides to the public on miniature trains it is quite noticeable that many of the youngsters prefer to ride behind a non steam model, with which they are more familiar. It is not surprising therefore that recent years have seen an increasing

also they are difficult to model, because they are trains and not locomotives. Even so it has been done and quite effectively too. There are diesel and electrically propelled locomotives that many people would consider quite attractive. A wide variety of types have been produced in full-size, some with quite distinct outlines which are of sufficient interest to attract the attention of the preservationists. This particularly applies to narrow gauge engines supplied to individual firms, where shapes were very varied and many quite quaint. Such prototypes could well be worth while modelling.

Although not actually a locomotive this very fine example of a tram from Toyohashi City built by Saturo Hiroto is both appealing and a fine example of craftsmanship.

Possibly the only design ever published of an internal combustion engine designed specifically to drive a model locomotive. It is "Wallaby" by the late Edgar Westbury.

interest in models of non-steam locomotives. For those whose interest is in running models rather than building, there are other advantages too. Electric models are mostly battery driven. Take out the battery or batteries and the model becomes very light to handle, when compared with a steam engine. Non-steam models are quicker to start up. There is no need to light a fire and boil the water in the boiler. Simply switch on and away you go. They are also much cleaner to operate, with none of the mess which we get from coal which means a big saving in time when preparing for a run, and when putting the model away afterwards.

Some might feel that such models do not have the character of steam engines and when we consider the modern multiple units that may well be true;

Power Units

The big difference between steam and non-steam models is generally in the power units. Although there have been some examples of models designed and built, complete with a near scale power plant, this is rare.

Mostly builders will incorporate a commercial motor. Sometimes this will be an internal combustion engine, possibly taken from a lawn mower or something similar. More likely it will be an electric motor, or motors; even models of Diesel Locomotives are more often than not fitted with electric motors. Because of this power units will vary considerably, depending on what the builder can obtain, and his or her ingenuity.

Fitting an i/c engine to power electric traction motors in a model is very difficult but can be done, as shown by this photograph of the works in a model "Deltic" Locomotive.

Full-Size Practice

In full-size practice, locomotives would generally be driven by a Diesel Engine linked to some other motive power. These would be either hydraulic or electric motors, the main engine acting as a power source and the other used for traction. On very small shunting engines a plain diesel or possibly petrol engine might be used as the prime mover working through some form of clutch and gears, probably a fluid flywheel. In the case of electric engines, they

A chassis for a small petrol-electric locomotive built in Japan gives some idea of how to fit the components in.
The model was built by Mr T. Inoue.

are obviously equipped with electric traction motors and pick up power from an outside source, either overhead cables or a third rail, neither of which are practical sources of power in model form.

Converting to Model Form

There have been examples of models made similarly to full-size diesel locomotives, involving fitting an internal combustion engine to drive a generator, which in turn supplies electricity to one or more electric traction motors. Quite often the generator supplies power to charge a battery and the motors are in turn driven from that. Unfortunately it is not easy to make small sized generators that will produce enough power for the model to haul passengers and this seems to have been the main stumbling block. It is far easier to use a ready-made power plant and make the outline as per the prototype.

Petrol Engines

With small Diesel Engines almost non-existent, petrol motors are generally pressed into service. They can come from all sorts of machines and many motors with around a 30cc capacity can be obtained. Generally they are designed for hedge trimmers, chain saws etc., with slightly larger ones used on lawn mowers.

When using such a motor it is also necessary to install a fuel tank, a silencer and some form of transmission; a gear box is not necessary for this sort of work but a clutch is, and can be quite easily made in the workshop. In motor cars a plate clutch is used which is permanently engaged unless the clutch pedal is dipped in order to change gear. This is not a suitable arrangement for a model locomotive. The plate clutch needs to be a comparatively large component if it is to be effective and finding room for it is difficult. Also we want the opposite operation, a clutch that is generally disengaged, and only engaged when necessary, and which, as a safety precaution, must be physically held on when the model is running. On a car the gearbox has a neutral position, which neutralises the engaged clutch; without a gear box there is no neutral position consequently, unless the vehicle is moving, the clutch must be disengaged. This rules out the use of a commercial component, unless one is prepared to carry put extensive modifications.

The Cone Clutch

Possibly the easiest way to solve the problem is to make a cone clutch. It is basically a very short length of tube with a disc that fits in it. Both of these are tapered and so as the disc slides in it mates with the tube and grips, the motor is engaged and away we go. The drawing explains how it operates - of course it is also necessary to connect the motor via the clutch to the wheels. An alternative to the cone is something known as a dog clutch, which can be made in a variety of ways, either some pegs that mate with holes in a second plate or a half-circular section on each side which will engage with each other. If pegs are used they need to be a fairly loose fit to make engaging and disengaging the clutch easy and also to avoid the possibility of them binding in the holes while they are engaged.

Final Drive

Whether an internal combustion engine or an electric motor is used, it will revolve far faster than required for a model locomotive which means that the final drive must be geared down to decrease the speed. By far the easiest arrangements are either a chain, such as we have on a cycle, or a toothed belt

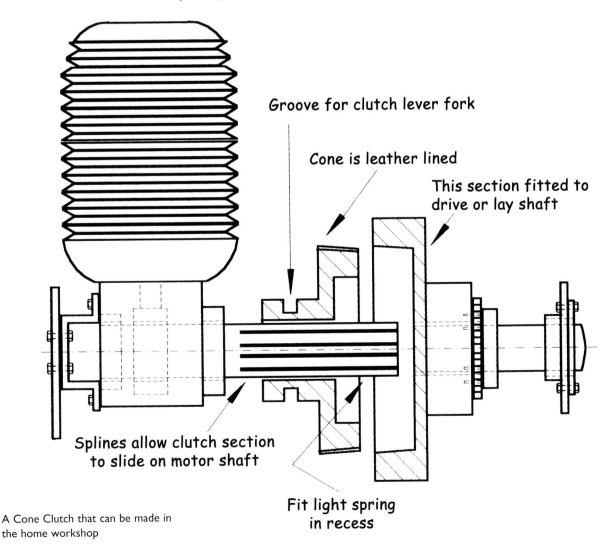

Groove for clutch lever fork

Cone is leather lined

This section fitted to drive or lay shaft

Splines allow clutch section to slide on motor shaft

Fit light spring in recess

A Cone Clutch that can be made in the home workshop

as used on electric lawn mowers or for timing belts on motor cars. The lawn mower version is the easiest to obtain as well as being considerably cheaper, although there may be some problem obtaining pulleys of a size suitable for getting the required ratio. Many of the commercial items are quite large and finding one small enough to fit on the locomotive axle, yet of a smaller diameter than the driving wheels, could be difficult. In the case of the cycle chain very small chain wheels can be obtained, or made and the problem does not arise. The chain drive is noisier than the pulley but is unlikely to be heard above the noise of the motor anyway. It is possible to purchase drive chains in a variety of sizes, or pitches as they are known. This will allow the builder to use a small and neat final drive system.

Ordinary vee belts have been used as a means of driving models, sometimes with success and it may be worthwhile experimenting with these. Again large pulleys would be required and some form of tensioning device. This could be a small pulley running on a shaft in a curved slot, allowing it to be positioned as required.

The easiest model in which to use a petrol engine is the shunting type locomotive that has a fixed wheelbase. Using them on a bogie locomotive creates its own problems as, ideally, each bogie should be powered and swing individually. The size of the petrol engine makes this difficult except in the larger gauges and there is also the problem of getting two clutches to operate at the same time. It can be taken care of with cable operation, and careful adjustment of the connecting cables. This would be easier to do if the two clutches were to be normally engaged and a lever used to release them, but this is not a practice to be encouraged on a model where safety is of paramount importance; there is always the danger of the model running away if for some reason the clutch could not be disengaged.

Electric Traction

The most popular form of power by far for the non-steam model is the electric motor. It is flexible to use, requires no clutch and is very controllable. Depending on the type of model more than one motor can be used and controlled from the same panel. As the power to drive the motor will almost certainly be a battery, the system will have to operate on direct current. Many direct current motors, if rotated will generate electricity and so can be used as a generator, from that follows the fact that the reverse is true. If we can get a D/C dynamo and put current in to it, it will revolve in the same way as an electric motor. Before the days of alternators in

motor cars, they used dynamos or generators, which yield a ready supply of hefty motors. One snag is that they have to operate on a higher voltage than they generate. Old *Ford* and *Volkswagen* cars had six-volt systems and the generators worked well on a twelve-volt battery. The more modern type, although even those are now superseded of course, generated twelve volts, needing twenty-four to drive them successfully as a motor; this means two car batteries which in turn adds to both weight and bulk. Car dynamos are certainly very rugged, they are still obtainable from car scrap dealers and if cost is a priority are well worthwhile considering.

There are numerous low voltage motors available which will suit our purpose very well. Lawn mowers and other garden equipment can offer a supply of heavy-duty low voltage electric motors as well as petrol engines. Car scrap yards also have many small twelve-volt motors which are used to drive car heater fans and wind windows up and down. Invalid carriages are propelled by powerful little electric motors which are arguably the motors best suited for locomotive construction. They are quite capable of driving a model locomotive and hauling several passengers. Purchased new they can be fairly expensive but a look in the local "Yellow Pages" will usually show details of one or more firms who renovate electric invalid carriages and from whom used motors in good condition can often be obtained at reasonable prices. In case some readers feel that these motors will lack power, it is necessary to think about the difference in the way they will be used. Lower gear ratios will be used on a locomotive and it will have smooth wheels running on smooth rail, decreasing the friction involved by something like eighty percent; this is also the reason why small motors such as those used on car heater fans will work quite well.

Drives

When making a rigid wheelbase model such as a shunting engine, a single motor will generally be used and can be connected to the wheels via a cycle type chain, or a toothed belt. In order to transfer the direction of rotation a gear will be needed and this can take either the form of bevel gears, or a worm and wheel. The latter does tend to absorb more power than a bevel gear but a greater reduction of speed can be obtained in a small space.

Gears

Gears can be obtained to suit whichever type of motor is chosen and a cheap and very effective bevel gear can be obtained from an old wheel and brace

Suitable bevel gears for a locomotive, giving a nice reduction, can be obtained by stripping down a hand drill.

A six wheel power bogie driving on two axles, built for a British prototype locomotive. Note that a bogie constructed for this purpose has only a central pivot and no side thrust. Axles are sprung via the coil springs resting on girders.

hand drill, which give quite sufficient reduction and are usually very robust. Whether bevel or worm is used, the wheel has to be fitted to a lay shaft and the drive then taken to the axle. As we are at present talking about shunting type locomotives, the wheels will be connected with rods which will transfer the drive to all wheels. If coupling rods are not used, chains or toothed belts can be used instead to couple the axles together and increase the traction.

Because a lay shaft with chains or belts is in use, the motor can be mounted rigidly on the chassis. Any movement of the axles on the springing will be taken up by the chain or belt. There is not a great deal of movement on the springs and the arrangement is easily able to cope with it.

Multiple Motors

Where a bogie-type locomotive is being modelled a different situation arises; ideally each bogie should have at least one drive motor, in order to get the best from the model and if possible it is preferable to

have a motor drive each axle. To install and use a motor on each axle means a different type of layout is called for. Whereas on the fixed wheel model a vertically mounted motor was quite suitable, in this case the ideal thing is to mount the motors horizontally, between the bogie frames. This does not mean that a single motor mounted vertically will not do, but a neater job can be obtained with them horizontally mounted. Unfortunately almost certainly this will severely limit the ability to build models for gauges much smaller than 5", purely because of the difficulty of getting motors of suitable power that can be mounted in this way.

Bogie Drives

The next problem is how to mount the motors and connect them to the drive; a small chain or belt drive is technically possible but space will severely limit the amount of reduction that this can give. Whereas a worm wheel can reduce the speed of the motor by twenty or even twenty-five to one, a chain or belt drive in this case is unlikely to give more than a maximum of about three to one.

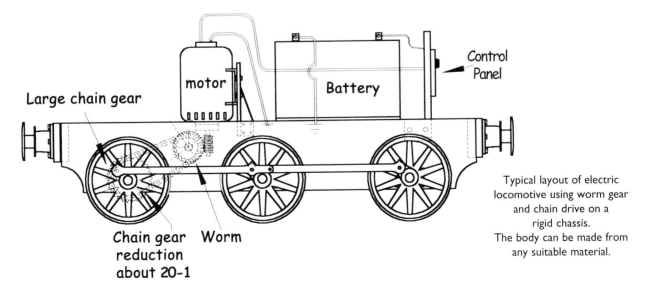

Large chain gear

motor

Battery

Control Panel

Chain gear reduction about 20-1

Worm

Typical layout of electric locomotive using worm gear and chain drive on a rigid chassis.
The body can be made from any suitable material.

A very neat example of a power bogie using two motors, built by Tateo Nakano.

Flexible Motor Mountings

Assuming we have found a suitable gear ratio, and have fitted the gears to the motor and axle, we are now confronted with where and how to mount the motor. If it is mounted directly to the bogie frame and the axle lifts on its suspension, the gears will lock up and the locomotive will not work, so it is essential that the motor must lift with the axle. This means mounting the motor on a bracket fitted to a plate which is directly connected to the axle boxes. A slot in the frames can be used as a guide for the assembly if necessary, although generally the axle box will, in itself, provide sufficient support for the purpose.

Control

Most small D/C electric motors are designed for on-off working. If the lawn mower, or car window switch are turned on, they start and finish at a constant speed with no variation at all. To run a locomotive it is necessary to be able to control the speed at which motors will run. Possibly a heater blower motor may operate at two or three different speeds, and it might just be possible to use the speed controller in a model, but it is far from an ideal situation as a full range of speeds or power from zero to maximum is really needed.

If the voltage sent to the armature of the motor is cut down, via the brushes, the motor will run at a slower speed. Assuming the use of a car battery as the power source, it is necessary to reduce the voltage travelling from that to the armature. A series resistance between it and the battery will work, although it will also absorb a great deal of current, which is generally disposed of in the form of heat.

A simple way to reduce the voltage would be to put a number of twelve-volt light bulbs in the circuit, with a switching arrangement so that each could be switched on as required. The more bulbs in use the slower the motor will go. Quite a few bulbs would

be needed and they would take a lot of space, so some other form of resistance is preferable. Electric fire elements cut into short lengths will do, but will also get hot. It is possible to obtain suitable wire to create a resistance, without a massive build up of heat and it is worth making enquiries at an electrical contractor. Supposing it is necessary to use something like the electric fire element, one way of reducing the heat build up is to put two or three lengths in parallel. It will also decrease the resistance, so the lengths of wire will need to be longer, but it is possible to get the required result in this way, and the arrangement can be used with a stud controller, which will give a series of steps in the supply of electricity, starting with a high resistance and reducing it until full power is reached. It is a system that was used on trams and worked well, and has been used with success on model locomotives.

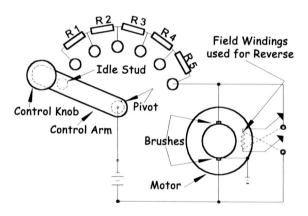

Simple stud & resistor controller

Field Windings

The field windings of the motor can, within certain limits, also be used to control its speed. If the voltage going to the windings is reduced the motor will slow down. As usual, there are advantages and disadvantages to the idea. The main advantage is that reducing voltage to the armature also reduces power; this is not so obvious when it is reduced at the field windings, the amount of reduction possible being very limited.

Reversing

The field windings can be used to reverse the motor. A simple change over switch reversing the direction of the flow of current will cause it to rotate in the opposite direction. This should always be done when the motor is stopped and never whilst it is running. When using any of the forms of resistance suggested above, it is advisable to fit a solenoid in

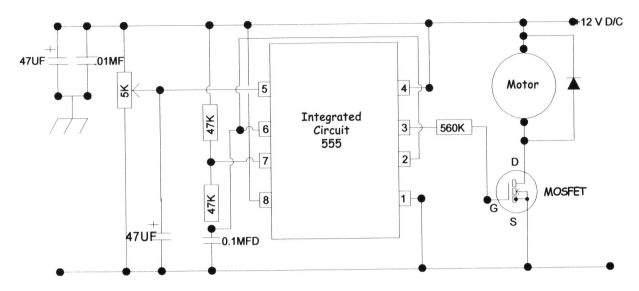

Electronic control system

the circuit as then the wire needed to supply the current to the motor can be a great deal thinner than it will need to be with the motor wired direct to an on-off switch.

Electronic Circuits

The modern way to control motors is to use an electronic circuit board. There are lots of ideas on how simple or complicated these should be and many versions have been produced, some using just a single transistor and others incorporating a large quantity of equipment. Making a controller is not for those without some knowledge of electronics and it is advisable to either purchase one or get someone who knows something of the subject to make it.

We must always have in mind that an electrically powered model locomotive, when starting from scratch, will require a large amount of current and the controller must be capable of dealing with this. Surge and heavy-duty transistors or other devices are needed, some modern controllers use integrated circuits which are really a number of transistors incorporated into one tiny module; they frequently also use Metal Oxide Semi Conductors or MOSFET for short. The integrated circuit boards are basically very high speed switching circuits, the MOSFET is a form of voltage controlled variable resistor. The use of these can save space and allow the controller to be made smaller than would otherwise be possible. It will also provide much smoother operation than a stud box and resistors. Care must be taken to ensure that all components are capable of handling the currents involved, which will depend entirely on the type of motor being used. In particular car dynamos, when used as motors, absorb a very heavy current

when starting, this also means that when driving such a model, the motor should be set running before engaging the clutch. Starting with the clutch engaged will create an enormous current surge which will require very heavy wiring in order to cope with the heat generated.

Mounting The Panel

Arrangements must be made to house the control panel so that the model can be driven, and care should be taken to ensure it is secure. An ammeter should be included amongst the instruments so that a check can be kept on current consumption. A system that has been used with great success is to have this connected to the model by a length of flexible wire. The driver sits at the rear of the train and controls things from there; whilst there is obviously no advantage in this method of driving, it

This is a very fine model of a British Railways 08 Class Shunting Locomotive built by Rudy Michetchlager. Everything, including the body, was built from stock material, only the electric motor being purchased. Since this model was constructed parts have become available for such a model, including complete fibreglass body shells.

can provide a great thrill for a youngster to be able to sit next to the locomotive on his or her journey round the track, possibly operating dummy controls that have no effect on the running of the locomotive. It is a very nice idea, and would be great fun for the children, but how a Health and Safety Inspector would view such an arrangement may be open to doubt. It could be that it would be considered the driver did not have sufficient control in the case of an accident.

The Body

Assuming the chassis, whether rigid or bogie, has been successfully completed, the next task is to make a suitable body. Many materials have been used for this, and it is possible to obtain complete moulded bodies for various prototypes. For home production, metal, wood, or plastic can be used, as can a combination of all three. For a really durable body, thin mild steel sheet is an ideal material, it is easy to bend and can be joined by a variety of methods. Brass is less suitable, apart from the high cost it can be difficult to bend to shape and is not the easiest material to paint. Aluminium also forms shapes quite well. At one time it was not popular as, owing to the difficulty in joining sections, rivets and screws had to be relied on. The use of up to date welding methods means that parts can now also be welded together giving, in some cases, improved appearance as well as greater strength.

Wood can be formed to shape and is quite durable. Thin plywood as used in the construction of model boats can be used for curved sections, with heavier strip hardwood used as a frame. Where strength is of importance, sections can be fabricated by gluing layers of wood together and such things as louvres can be made from metal, using the same methods as one would for a metal body, and then using one of the modern adhesives to mount them. For intricate detail it is worth considering moulding small parts, using flexible rubber moulds, a technique that is also useful when a number of duplicates of an item are needed.

A wooden body should be well sanded and given at least two coats of sanding sealer before applying a primer and any subsequent coats of paint. If aluminium or brass has been used, a coat of self-etching primer is advisable before attempting to apply paint. With an electrically driven model little is needed in the way of maintenance, other than to ensure that moving parts are lubricated, and to keep a check on the wire for possible fraying of insulation. An internal combustion driven model will need regular maintenance and, in particular, it is necessary to ensure that the fuel/air mixture is maintained at the correct ratio. For those whose main interest is in running, a non-steam locomotive has much to commend it as a working model that is not only easy to build and run, but is comparatively maintenance free and should give years of pleasure.

When the late Edgar Westbury designed his "Wallaby" engine illustrated on Page 161, he also designed the locomotive it was to fit - a 3½" gauge 0-6-0 shunter based on a prototype built for the LMS Railway before World War II. Having built one in 3½" gauge, Phil Hains then built this model in 5" gauge.

Chapter 25: Finishing
Paintwork & those extra touches

Accessories

There is a great deal more to finishing a model than just a good coat of paint. Although, in fact, many fine models are spoiled by the paint, there are often other areas that let the finished object down. The necessary finishing touches include things like correctly placed hand rails, lamp irons and such things as racks for holding firing tools, tool boxes, etc. The builder can go to all sort of lengths to get such things right and we see many ingenious solutions to tricky problems.

Hand rails have been dealt with at some length in a preceding chapter and there is little to add except that care should be taken to keep the holders or knobs in line, and to ensure that any intentional bends in the rail have contours in keeping with the full sized prototype. Generally the knobs are fitted with nuts to the boiler lagging and screwed into plate work, this is easy enough, but keep the threads short and use very thin specially made nuts, otherwise ugly bulges appear on the cladding which are not always immediately visible, but become apparent after the model has been in use for a while. Holes in the lagging for whatever purpose should be punched rather than drilled as no matter how careful one is, a drill never leaves a round hole in thin material. Hand rails and handrail knobs were only ever polished in exceptional circumstances, yet we see many models displaying quite inappropriate polished hand rails, etc. An example of where this might be seen in full size was if a locomotive was to be exhibited at an event, or if it was to haul the Royal Train. The latter at one time meant that quite a lot of special treatment would be given to an engine that was generally set aside especially for the duty. On the *Great Eastern Railway*, and later the *LNER*, the Royal Locomotive always had the cab roof painted white or cream and it also received many other embellishments.

Lamp irons can be fabricated from mild steel and are generally fitted with very small rivets to the super-structure. Different railway companies fitted them in different places so check for the correct position. Lamps can be fabricated from thin brass, but tin plate is possibly better, and is easily obtainable by cutting up old food tins. As well as bending easily to shape it also takes solder well. Other items likely to be seen on a locomotive are racks for holding fire irons, which are usually on the top of a tender or tank depending on the type of locomotive. These can be made of mild steel and screwed in position. Toolboxes were also quite a feature on many locomotives and some types such as the old *LNER*, ex *Great Eastern* " F " classes were distinguishable by them. Once again tin plate is an ideal material and small brass angle makes good hinges if they are to open. Failing that they can be made as dummies. Some model engineers go a step further and fit tiny padlocks all of which enhance the appearance of the model.

Painting

So often we see models that have poor, or downright bad, paint work and yet, with modern facilities, this need not be so. The days of enamel paints of indifferent quality are long over and, whilst some people still prefer a brush finish, modern paint, if used as per the manufacturers instructions, can give a first class finish. It must be agreed that the instructions are not always as comprehensive as they might be and in, particular, tend to be lacking in one important aspect; some paints need to be applied very thinly, while others benefit from fairly thick coats. The only way to be sure is to try the paint on some scrap metal before using it on the model. For those who find it impossible to get along with hand painting, there are tiny spray guns and air brushes available that are easy to use, and give a really professional looking finish. Many paints are suitable for spraying as well as brushing and, for anyone who wants to spray a model but not invest in spraying equipment, there are plenty of spray cans that can be used. Although

A small spray gun which can be operated either from a compressor or a can of compressed air, and is an ideal size for painting a model locomotive.

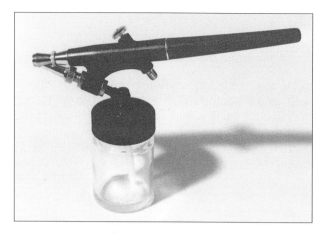

A comparatively cheap air brush, which is capable of painting the larger areas, as well as very small sections on a model.

these are sold mainly, but not always, as matching colours for motor cars rather than in railway liveries, there are so many of them that quite frequently a decent match to the required colour can be found. It is also possible to purchase rechargeable spray cans which are used with ordinary enamel type paints, as well as air canisters with which to power air brushes. The choice is wide and it is a case of simply picking the method that suits oneself. These days the choice of paint is also very wide with numerous modern synthetic types to be bought, amongst these are the acrylic paints which are very good and give an excellent finish

Preparation

The finished quality of any paint work will depend on the preparation of the surfaces to be painted, which need to be clean, smooth and matt. A start should be made by filling any uneven parts, small dents, etc. with a good metal filler in the case of a steam locomotive, or a wood filler if a wooden body is being been used on a non-steam model. For metal there are various proprietary fillers available from car accessory shops. There are numerous of the two-part variety consisting of a filler and hardener,

An airbrush designed for very fine work. It is not really suitable for painting the main areas of a larger model but is particularly useful for small areas, with the ability to cope with very fine lines. Using it for such work requires a very steady hand.

which have to be mixed up. For tiny blemishes it is possible to get a form of putty, this requires no mixing, and yet will set very hard. Some of these single substance types are designed to be used over the priming paint, so make sure which form it is before using it.

The model should be rubbed over with either a very fine emery cloth or wire wool to obtain a good matt finish and all burrs must be removed; make sure there are no file marks along any edges that might be showing. Once satisfied with the finish, wash the surface down with some White Spirit or Turpentine and then go over the whole thing with a Pre-Paint Cloth. These are also known as "After Sand Cloths" or by professional car sprayers as "Tacky Cloths", again these can be obtained from car accessory shops or, sometimes, from places dealing with painting and decorating material. For anyone who has never seen one, they are like a piece of fine muslin, impregnated with a sticky material which picks up all dust, dirt and metal particles from the model as they are stroked over it.

If the parts to be painted are steel, an ordinary priming coat will be satisfactory. If they are brass, a good self-etching primer should be applied and allowed plenty of time to thoroughly dry. It is no good hurrying any part of the painting process; it must be allowed to take its time in order to ensure that any coats of paint are not just dry, but thoroughly hard before going any further. Whilst it might feel dry after a few hours, to become really hard it must either be baked or given a great deal of time. Small models can benefit from a few hours at a low heat in the domestic oven, but this is hardly possible with a large-scale model, although there is no reason why removable parts of the model, such as the cab should not receive the treatment.

With the primer hardened, the ideal thing is to use a base coat of some sort that has a colour similar to the final one, but just slightly lighter and a flat finish. Once more let it harden completely before applying the topcoat or coats. All the various coats should be applied thinly, unless the paint being used is designed for laying on thick coats. When using any sort of spraying device, it is definitely a case of thin coats only, using as many as is thought necessary to get the required result. Prior to spraying, mask off any areas that are to be left as bare metal, or they will be of a different colour. Masking tape cut to size and shape is easy to use. It can be shaped with a sharp modelling knife while stuck to a piece of glass and then transferred to the model; larger areas can be covered with brown paper or something similar held round the edges with masking tape.

Once again it must be emphasised that paint to be brushed should be done in accordance with the manufacturers instructions. Some require brushing well in, others must not be over brushed. In some instances it is necessary to paint in two or more directions, and with others it is strictly one way only. Some brush-on paints require that thick coats are used, and do not work well if attempts are made to use thin ones, directions are usually given on the tins. Take care to use a paint which is compatible with the undercoat or primer, using the wrong one can cause the carefully laid on primer to lift. For example, if an enamel undercoat is used a cellulose topcoat is most definitely taboo, it will act like a paint stripper to the enamel, no matter how long the latter has been allowed to dry and harden. Strangely the reverse does not apply, and enamel or acrylic paint can be applied over cellulose that has been allowed to dry with no ill effects.

Lining

Once the paint is really dry the model is ready for lining out and there are many opinions on how it should be done. One thing that is certain is that the job should not be started too soon, unless one is skilled enough to use a fine brush for the lining. Paint remains soft for a long time, often as long as a few weeks, and trying to use any form of lining pen on soft paint will inevitably cause scratches in the soft surface. Special lining pens can be bought and are highly effective, they even come with a couple of guides to allow the pen to follow certain contours. They use enamel paint straight from the tin, giving nice bold colours, which is another advantage. Another useful tool is a bow pen, although these days they are not all that common. At one time they were very popular with draughtsmen and have the advantage that the width of the line is adjustable.

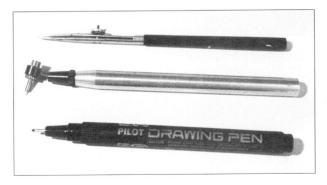

Three appliances for lining out work. At the top is the draughtsman's bow pen. It is comparatively easy to use and will do lines of different thickness. In the middle is a special lining pen capable of using paint straight from the tin. It comes with special guides for various operations. At the bottom is a standard drawing pen used with either ink, or ink cartridges. They are available in a variety of widths, and ink can be obtained in all colours.

They too can be used with paint direct from the tin. Yet another school of thought is to use modern draughtsman's pens, which need coloured ink. This is water based and is easily wiped off with a damp rag if an error is made, while paint needs a solvent such as Turpentine. The water-based inks do not give such a bold colour as paint and need to be varnished over to preserve them. They can be very effective and are comparatively easy to use. In general varnish is not a good medium to use on a boiler barrel as most varieties will discolour with heat; if lines and transfers are varnished therefore, the medium must only be applied in the immediate area.

Guides

Unless a person has a very steady hand, some sort of guide is essential when lining out a model and it should, wherever possible, be secured rather than hand held. A plasticine-based medium is useful for this and a variety of suitable ones are available, sold under various names by stationers. A couple of tiny pieces between template and model is all that is needed to give the necessary support, the fact that it lifts the template proud of the surface is an advantage. The actual templates can be cut from plastic sheet, old credit cards being ideal for small items. Long straight lines can often be done with a plastic ruler, which sometimes may have to be narrowed by splitting lengthways. Whatever form the template takes, the edge being used as a guide must be proud of the models, otherwise capillary action is likely to cause the lining medium to run under it.

Where possible it is best to line out sections of the model before final assembly. For example it is easier to line a cab on its own, rather than when it is all part of the superstructure. Many parts lend themselves to this way of working and this also assists if it is planned to use the domestic oven to harden the lining in the same way as the paint. Boiler bands are difficult to deal with once they are in place but if laid flat are very easy to line. Either way, special guides should be made to run along the edge of the bands at the required distance from the centre. These are supplied with the special lining tools but otherwise can be fabricated from brass.

Transfers

With the model successfully lined there will be some lettering to do and it is doubtful if many people will have the skill to do this successfully by hand, so it will be necessary to use transfers. There is quite a range available from model engineering suppliers but if the ones wanted cannot be obtained all is not lost. A search through the Yellow Pages should reveal details of firms prepared to make them and prices are quite reasonable. All that is needed is a picture of an original. For example if it is a coat of arms, get hold of a coloured photograph of it, take it to somewhere that can do photocopying in colour and get copies made to the size required, trot along to the transfer maker and he or she will do the rest. Likewise if it is special lettering, the required style is almost certain to be available on a computer, copies can be made to the right size and usually printed in the right colours, and again we are in business. It is not always possible to get the colour exactly right on a computer, as few will produce the colour of gold, in that case it might be necessary to resort to a local art studio to do the work. It must be said that life gets more difficult where lettering is lined round the edges with a different colour, but only marginally so as two copies can be overlaid to produce the required result. It is even possible to use a photograph by removing the backing paper. Photographic paper is coated to make it light sensitive and with care this coating, which contains the finished image, can be separated with a sharp modelling knife. With a little ingenuity there is nothing in this line that cannot be achieved.

Types of Transfers

If it is proposed to purchase the transfers there is a wide choice, as many different types are available. At one time they were highly complicated affairs which had to have a special backing removed, they were then covered in Gold Size and applied, with a top paper being removed when things were dry. It was great fun as quite frequently half the letter came away with the paper, and after despairingly trying to get the rest of it in line, it was usually back to square one. Improvements in the way transfers are made means that this type can now be applied with varnish and will usually adhere to the surface with little difficulty. A more modern development is the waterslide transfer, which is soaked and applied and the backing peeled off when dry. The letters are fixed to a very thin clear plastic sheet, which is not obvious and remains in place. For safety they need to be varnished, as over a period of time with hard wear they are likely to fall away. Rub on letters will no doubt be familiar to all readers and they can be used if the right size and shape can be found. The manufacturers make a very wide range of them and they are best purchased from a shop supplying artists and draughting materials, who should be able to order them if they are not in stock. Because the range is so vast it is not practical for a single shop to be able to stock the full range and pattern books can be browsed in order to find the right ones.

The home computer comes in useful for those wanting to make their own design of transfer, either to prepare the artwork for professional transfer makers, or to provide suitable lettering or designs which can be cut out and applied as appropriate.

Nameplates

Many locomotives had nameplates and most had other cast plates, such as those depicting the maker, or perhaps the depot where the locomotive was stabled. There are specialist suppliers of such plates who will make up any not normally stocked and, in addition, some cast nameplates are available. It is quite easy to make ones own. Take a piece of brass of suitable size and rub it over with fine emery cloth to get a clean, matt surface. Apply letters in the form of rub on transfers to make up any writing and mark the edges with a waterproof laundry pen. From a supplier of electronic components get a bottle of etching fluid, which is sold for etching printed circuit boards. Put sufficient in a plastic tray to cover the brass plate and leave it to soak for twenty-four hours. After that time the area around the letters and edge will have been etched away, leaving them standing proud. If it needs to be deeper put it in a fresh solution for another twenty-four hours and so on. Finally trim the edges and the plate is complete.

There are many other refinements that can be added to the model and most can be made easily enough with a little thought. Lamps certainly enhance a model and they can be fabricated from brass or tin plate. The lens can be made from plastic and if it is thought that it should light up, then a little LCD bulb will do it. It will be necessary to supply a battery and if the lamps are large enough, the sort used for a watch will do. If not it will be necessary to fit a battery under the running board and take a wire to the lamp, leaving the other side of the circuit to travel to earth via the frames. The wire can be run through the lamp iron. The only difficulty with that

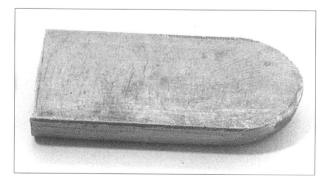

To make a shovel, whether a small one for show or a larger one for use, start by making a former and then use it to form thin mild steel sheet to shape.

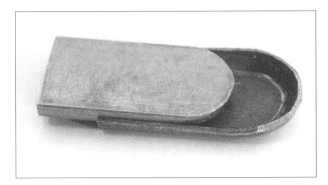

Showing how the shovel begins to take shape.

The shovel body has been shaped and will be trimmed with a file, using the former to get it to the correct size.

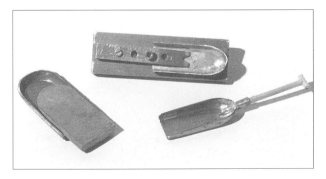

Various stages in the making of a shovel, and a finished one fitted with a wooden handle. If the shovel is to be used for firing a steel handle should be used. The special clamp was used to hold it when drilling for the rivets.

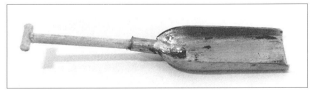

A finished shovel.

idea is that it is not then all that practical to take the lamps on and off. A word of warning - most LEDs require a small resistance between them and the battery; check to see whether this is so before wiring up.

Fire Irons

Fire-irons, rakes, shovels, prickers, etc. were all part of the scene and generally would be visible. In addition to miniature ones for show, slightly larger ones are needed to actually fire the locomotive. Prickers should be bent from stainless steel rod, rather than mild steel, which quickly burns away. Shovels will generally be of mild steel as they are not subject to the same amount of heat. A former should be made and the blade beaten round it, a metal shaft should be fixed to it with rivets if it is to be used to fire the locomotive. If it is there for appearances, a wooden shaft can be used in line with full sized practice.

All these little bits and pieces make a difference to the finished model and while things such as lamps are not actually required, they are worth making. Most locomotives had some clutter such as oilcans around, and it is quite possible to make all these from our old friend - tin plate.

The finish on this customised model of a "Sweet Pea" is quite plain, without any lining, and yet is very good. Attention has been paid to the paintwork and all pipework, handrails etc. kept very neat.

A very good example of finishing a model, this 3½" gauge "Rob Roy" has nice neat lining, a dummy whistle, maker's plates and lamps, giving it an authentic air.

"Mabel" to a 3½" gauge design by LBSC, built in 1972 by Maurice Foord of Vancouver and photographed in 1997, having seen a great deal of service. The finish, over which a great deal of trouble was taken, remains superb. The potential longevity of well made models is illustrated by the 5" gauge 0-4-2 in the background, which was built during the 1930s.

Chapter 26: Running
Operating & Maintaining a Locomotive

With the locomotive finally built, it is time to try it out and see what it will do. In the case of a non-steam locomotive there is not a great deal to do, which is the advantage such models have. Simply oil all the moving parts, check the battery in the case of an electric locomotive, or the fuel tank if internal combustion, switch on and away it will go. At the end of a run, a good clean down, then put the battery on charge and tuck the model safely away until next time.

By comparison life is more complex if it is a steam driven model, but that is all part of the fun. Start by checking that the tanks or tender have an adequate supply of water in them and that the water level in the boiler is right. When the boiler starts to heat up the water will expand, so the level should be slightly lower than it will be when running. If the boiler is too full it will not only take an excessive time to raise steam, but will also prime when the regulator is opened. Priming is the act of water flowing through the regulator, and out through the chimney via the cylinders. There are other reasons for priming but they need not concern us at the moment.

With the water level right, the fire can be lit, this is done with either small pieces of wood or lumps of charcoal soaked in a combustible material such as paraffin, **but never petrol**. Left to itself there will not be sufficient draught to draw the fire and so a fan is used in the chimney, and this remains in operation until the pressure gauge reads about twenty pounds per square inch, at which point the blower valve on the locomotive can be opened and left in tandem with the mechanical blower until another ten or so pounds per square inch are on the gauge. The mechanical blower can then be removed and the locomotive blower left to raise steam to the required pressure. There should be no need to open it wide, doing so will draw the fire too quickly and create a hole in the centre of it, as well as drawing ash into the tubes; experience will tell the right position which varies from locomotive to locomotive.

While steam is being raised check the level of the oil in the lubricator and give it a twist by hand to inject a small amount into the steam pipe. Allow steam to rise to a point where the safety valves lift, and check to ensure they are working correctly, open the drain cocks and just crack open the regulator to warm the cylinders. After this put the locomotive in full forward gear, the regulator can be opened and the locomotive allowed to run. Once it has got going

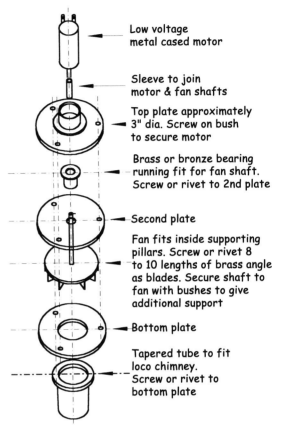

Low voltage metal cased motor

Sleeve to join motor & fan shafts

Top plate approximately 3" dia. Screw on bush to secure motor

Brass or bronze bearing running fit for fan shaft. Screw or rivet to 2nd plate

Second plate

Fan fits inside supporting pillars. Screw or rivet 8 to 10 lengths of brass angle as blades. Secure shaft to fan with bushes to give additional support

Bottom plate

Tapered tube to fit loco chimney. Screw or rivet to bottom plate

Assemble unit using studding, nuts & spacers

An easily made Blower Fan for starting the fire

close the drain cocks. As regular running commences it should be possible to move the reverser nearer to the centre point, which will use the expansion property of the steam more efficiently. In full-sized practice many drivers would leave the regulator at a set point and drive the locomotive entirely on the reverser, although the regulator was necessary when stopping or starting. On most model tracks there is not sufficient run to allow much manipulation of the reverser, and many modellers drive with the locomotive in full gear, using the regulator as the means of control. Unfortunately there will never be sufficient length of track to drive as one would a full sized locomotive, the operation of which was a highly skilled occupation, particularly when running at high speeds over long distances.

But back to the model, if the locomotive slips when starting, don't open the regulator wider in an attempt to make it move, as nothing much will be achieved. Use the regulator sparingly, allowing the steam to expand and create additional pressure,

A "Rob Roy" being prepared for a run. The fan is inserted in the chimney and connected to a battery, the fire started with charcoal soaked in paraffin.

"Will it or won't it light"? The panic stricken moment whilst the driver waits to see if the fire is really alight, and if it will stay that way

Note interested observers in these two photographs; the author advise that, if possible, first runs should be made when the track is not open to the public, with just one or, at the most two, experienced drivers as advisors. This can be less stressful, and you don't have to worry about other trains.

rather than flooding the cylinders with steam that passes through before the opportunity for it to expand has occurred. If there is trouble in starting ensure that the drain cocks are fully opening, sometimes the cylinders will just lock up and the engine will not move at all. Usually this is because the regulator has been opened wide, before the drain cocks have done their work, or perhaps they have not even been opened at all.

Once the locomotive is running, turn the blower off, as pressure should now be maintained by the efforts of the blast pipe, with no other assistance. If pressure is lost, the first check must be to ensure that the smokebox door is fully closed and, if after checking this pressure is still going down, it will be necessary, when things cool off, to check the front end to ensure it is air tight. If further tests do not solve the problem, check to see that the blast nozzle is in line with the centre of the chimney orifice and, if there is still no luck, try reducing the size of it - as a temporary measure put a small collar on it.

As well as keeping an eye on the boiler pressure, the water gauge must also be watched. Careful adjustment

of the balance between boiler feed and by-pass will generally allow a setting to be reached that can be more or less left alone, unless there is a change in operations, such as an extra load to haul. If an injector is fitted the water should be turned on first and allowed to run from the overflow for a second or so, then turn on the steam; water will still be running from the overflow, so adjust the water valve until it stops. It is possible to tell if an injector is working properly as it literally sings when it is; it is a sound that can be described in no other way and one soon gets used to it. While running the locomotive on test, also watch the situation as regards cylinder lubrication. Too much oil will not harm the locomotive but it will not do a lot for the driver's shirt. The optimum is to see a tiny ring of oil around the edge of the chimney, while none escapes with the exhaust. Generally lubricators cannot be adjusted while running, and final adjustments will have to be made over a period of time.

Priming has been mentioned in relation to an over full boiler, but there are also other causes. Opening the regulator wide too quickly is a common one. One that is less well known is a change in the type of water used. If a boiler is normally run on hard water a change to soft, particularly if it is distilled, will cause priming that can only be stopped by changing the water supply. The only way to avoid this is to keep the boiler clean. Not only does priming soak the driver and bystanders with water that is generally quite dirty, but also, far worse, it can quickly empty a boiler. Once it starts to come out there is a siphoning effect and unless the regulator is closed very smartly a small boiler will completely empty itself, with the obvious dangers associated with such a thing.

When running is completed, open the fire hole door and, when pressure has dropped to about 20 psi, release the ash pan and grate and allow the boiler pressure to drop slowly, this should happen if regulator and blower are closed. When it reaches about 5 psi open the blow-down valve, steam will gush out and take many of the impurities and foreign bodies that find their way into the boiler with it. Leave the valve open until all water has gone. Do not be tempted to open the valve when the pressure is any higher as the sudden release of pressure may cause boiler plates to buckle. Clean out the smokebox and sweep the flue tubes, a small vacuum cleaner helps with the smokebox. Finally clean the paintwork using a clean rag soaked in a light machine oil.

Copper boilers are best left empty when the locomotive is not in use, steel boilers should be filled to the top removing every possible particle of air. It is air that causes oxidisation or rust, and eliminating this will preserve the boiler. If the locomotive has cast iron cylinders they should be given a coating of oil; a few turns of the lubricator and then pushing the locomotive backwards and forwards will do the trick. To make a good job of it, some model engineers fit a small nipple on the main steam pipe, and pump in a separator oil such as Ensis which actually forms a barrier between water and the cylinder walls. **Do not use one of the proprietary sprays such as WD40 as these all contain solvents that attack cast iron.**

Before finally putting the locomotive away, it is a good idea in hard water areas to open all screw down valves, including the regulator, to prevent them furring up. Deposits in hard water can cause a great many problems and, if the model is being put away for a long period, it is worth putting a mild solution of a descaler in it; a couple of table-spoons of vinegar in a boiler full of water can work wonders. When the time comes to steam the model again, reduce the water to the required level and then raise steam with the vinegar still in. It will work its way into small areas and keep things clean. Mind you it smells a bit like a fish and chip shop when you do it. Don't repeat the mistake made by a driver who shall remain nameless; intending to fill the boiler with vinegar and put the locomotive away for the winter, Soy Sauce was accidentally used instead. At the *Model Engineer Exhibition*, held in those days at Seymour Hall in London, a shortage of motive power caused the engine to be pressed into service earlier than anticipated. It was not until the water started to heat and a smell like a Chinese restaurant started to prevail around the hall that it was realised what had happened. It was too late to do anything about it and for the next couple of days visitors did not know whether they were eating out or visiting an exhibition.

The Joys of Steam! A young steam fan waiting hopeful that he might get a ride as steam is raised at the Albuquerque track in the U.S.A.

Len Mills of York checks to ensure that all is well, before setting off with his lovely 5" gauge model of "Dolgoch" of the Talyllyn Railway.

The brothers Brown take their father Eric's superb 4-4-0 American locomotive,
many parts of which are seen in various chapters of this book, for a spin at Peterborough.

Chapter 27: The Workshop

To build a locomotive it follows that one must have a workshop of one sort or another, the size and construction of which will depend entirely on individual circumstances. It is probably everyone's dream to have a large, fully equipped place in which to work and some are fortunate enough to be able to fulfil this dream, others have to make do with lesser facilities. Having to do this does not mean the model or models produced need be in any way inferior to those made by our more fortunate colleagues and, in fact, more often than not just the opposite is true, many of the finest models are

A neatly laid out workshop, even though space is very limited. Every possible space is pressed into use, while at the same time tools are mainly kept adjacent to the area where they will be used. Wall charts are hung on the walls to provide easy reference.

made with the absolute minimum of facilities as, in the end, it all comes down to the amount of care the builder is willing to give to the construction.

The Premises

Polls have shown that model engineers work mainly in two places, a wooden shed in the garden or a garage; the latter may or may not be shared with a car and or other domestic items, while, in nearly every, case the wooden shed appears to be exclusive to the model maker. There are, of course, those who have workshops within the home, either in a basement, loft or even a special room that is set aside but these are very much in the minority. How to set up and insulate a workshop is a subject that can and, in a number of instances does, fill a whole book and so it is not within the remit of this volume to discuss that, instead we will go into the equipment that might or might not be needed and suggestions on ways to lay things out.

Rust Prevention

However a few pointers may be of interest, for example, unless a room in the house is being used, the workshop should be well insulated by fitting a lining, and insulation between the inner and the outer walls and roof. If a building is not insulated it will both rapidly loose heat in the winter, and become overbearingly hot in summer. The loss of heat in winter creates two different problems, firstly the building become prohibitively expensive to keep warm and, secondly, the rapid loss of heat will create condensation that in turn will cause tools and equipment to rust. It is possible to keep everything sprayed with a solvent that will stop rust forming, but this can be an irksome task and all too often one forgets to do it, with disastrous results. Keeping tools in cupboards that are closed when the workshop is not in use is also an aid to the prevention of rust, and covering machinery with a soft cover also helps. Make sure that the cover does not in any way become damp or the purpose will be defeated.

Storage

It is a good idea where tools with taper shanks or, indeed, straight shanks are concerned to set shelves at an angle and keep the tools in position by passing the shanks through holes. This not only ensures that the tools are easily located but also that dirt and swarf slides from the shelf instead of laying on it. Screws, hooks or other means of preventing the tools from sliding off can be used for tools that cannot be located into holes. Where tools are kept in drawers it is as well if the drawers are made as slim as possible, deep drawers are generally a waste of space and invariably seem to be untidy, making it difficult to find things.

Tools that are used for cutting of any sort, or indeed any tool that has a sharp edge, should not be stored together in tins or boxes; in no time at all they will lose their edge. Drills, taps, etc. can be stored in wooden blocks or commercially made storage plates, and for lathe tools and similar items it is easy enough to make a special storage box.

A particularly fine example of making the maximum use of space, small tins that are clearly labelled hold screws, etc. collets are to hand in specially made racks and drawings are kept comparatively clean by storing them under some drawers.

Hand Tools

There is far less reliance nowadays on the use of hand tools than there was not so many years ago, when the only machine likely to be found in a home workshop was an ancient and probably much renovated lathe. A combination of a more affluent society and cheap imports from the far east have made machinery more readily available and the result is that many operations once carried out with hand tools are now done by machine. This does not mean that we can dispense with hand tools, which are still just as essential as they always were. Unfortunately their correct use is rapidly becoming a dying art.

Quality

Never buy cheap hand tools - in the long run it will pay to purchase a quality item. We see many market stalls with a variety of tools on display and while some might well be of a suitable quality, many are most certainly not. That bargain pack of hack saw blades, where ten or more can be purchased for the price of a single blade of good quality, turns out not to be such a good buy when the teeth of the blade strip off as the first couple of strokes are made, and what good is a set of needle files that, when used, will not remove any metal? Likewise many tools sold in DIY shops are meant for just that – DIY not

engineering – and more often than not such tools are best avoided. Good tool stockists catering for professional engineers can easily be located by reference to the Yellow Pages and are invariably quite happy to deal with a non-professional; the range of tools available is extensive and the quality high. Alternatively deal with a specialist model engineering supplier, again the quality will be good although the range that is available will be more limited.

Saws

A good hacksaw will be essential to any workshop as, even if power tools are available, they are not always convenient to use. In addition to a normal hacksaw, one of the Junior Saws is also a good investment, they are very useful for small work when the more normal sized tool becomes a little clumsy. For very delicate work there are various types of special saws that can be used, including the coping saw that has a very fine flexible blade and is particularly useful for cutting radii in thin sheet metal.

The type of saw will be a matter for individual choice but the blades used in it will have to depend on the work that is being carried out. As well as a variation in the number of teeth, that we will deal with shortly, blades are also generally available in three forms, carbon steel, high-speed steel and bi-metal. Although at one time they were the most popular, carbon steel blades are now rarely used, the teeth tend to wear away fairly quickly, which probably accounts for their loss of popularity, although as they are considerably cheaper than the other two types it is doubtful if, in the end, they work out any more expensive. They do have the advantage of flexibility and this means that someone not skilled in the art of hacksawing is less likely to break them than they are the other types. The correct way to saw is to use the full length of the blade, without applying too much pressure, and to work slowly, between ninety and a hundred and twenty strokes per minute is recommended, keep the saw at ninety degrees to the work and no matter what type of blade is used there should be no breakages. When sawing mild steel, a drop of cutting fluid can help and, in the case of any copper alloy or aluminium, a tiny drop of white spirit will do the same job.

As well as the three grades of metal, hacksaw blades are also classed by the number of teeth per inch and, for most purposes, these are 18 - 24 and 32. Two factors are used to decide the number of teeth required, the hardness of the material and how thick it is, the general rule is the thicker the metal the coarser the blade, and the harder the metal the coarser the blade. That sounds rather contradictory so let us look at it this way, a piece of mild steel an inch thick would be best cut with a blade of 18 teeth per inch. The same size piece of metal, but brass instead of steel would need a blade with 24 teeth. Likewise on a piece half that thickness one would expect to use a 24 tooth blade on steel while almost certainly a 32 tooth blade would cope with brass. If we come to sheet metal then, whether steel or brass, the finer toothed blade should be used. One soon learns by experience what blade suits which material.

For metal working there is only one grade of blade for the junior hacksaw, but then we would not expect to use one when cutting large pieces of metal and so a coarser blade is not necessary, much the same applies to piercing saws, although a wide range of blades are available for use with them, most are meant for use on wood, and only a couple of grades intended for use with metal.

Power Saws

The ultimate luxury is to own a power saw and there is a wide variety available that basically fall into three types: The reciprocating saw that works in the same fashion as a hack saw, the dual purpose band saw that can do duty for cutting lengths of metal from bars and has some limited capacity as a band saw, and the band saw itself. The true band saw has a narrow blade and is useful for cutting thin metal

and has the advantage that it can be used to generate curves. These come in two versions, two or three wheeled, the three wheels type allows a greater length of metal to be moved under the throat but it is not as reliable as a two wheel type. Most band saws sold for DIY purposes are not suitable for our purposes as they are too fast for successful metal cutting; a speed of no greater than eight to nine hundred revolutions per minute is desirable and speeds appreciably higher than this will do little more than rapidly wear out the blade.

A two wheeled band saw by EMCO that is ideal for cutting thin metal, particularly when intricate shapes are required. An abrasive disc is mounted on the side, allowing metal to be cleaned up after shaping.

It is possible to use a DIY type of jig saw, fitted with a suitable blade for metal cutting. This will cut curves, and has the advantage that it is possible to cut internal radii with it, something that is not usually practical with a band saw.

Files

Files are available in a whole range of shapes and sizes, and it is up to the individual to decide from this huge range the size, shape and cut required for the job in hand. In general readers will find three grades of teeth, fine, middle cut and bastard but really top quality files are available in a much wider range, the degree of coarseness being indicated by the number. Files can be kept in racks that allow them to be stored in an upright position and, as with all cutting tools, must never be allowed to rub together in drawers. Something that always seems rather strange is the fact that both hacksaw blades and files that have been used to cut steel will not cut brass very well, they tend to skid across the material. As brass is the softer of the two, it would seem more logical if it were the other way about. Because of this it is wise to keep separated the blades or files that have been used on steel, so they do not get used on brass, as damage to the material can result. A touch of paint is the easiest method of identification.

Drills - Taps & Dies

There are many ways to store these small but important tools, but it worth giving some thought as to how many we really need. Most workshops have some, at least, that will probably never be used, and it is hardly worth while going out and buying a complete set of drills when in fact only a few will ever be used. A good idea is to decide on what threads are likely to be used and then to buy two taps, (a taper and a plug) as well as tapping and clearance sized drills, plus a die. Instead of keeping all the workshop drills together make little wooden blocks and on each store a tapping and clearance sized drill, the two taps and a die. The drills and taps can be kept in holes drilled in the wood and the die retained by hanging it on a small nail on the edge of the block. There is now no need to ever refer to tables for the size of drills required for tapping holes, they are all to hand and ready for use.

Marking Out Tools

Marking out tools must always be treated with great care, if they get damaged it is possible that the damage may lead to lack of accuracy when they are used. They are best kept in a special box or drawer and care taken that they are put away immediately after use. The points of scribers, dividers and odd leg calipers should never be sharpened on a grindstone, they are far too delicate for that and, in no time at all, they will become soft and it will be necessary to re-harden and temper them. The best way to sharpen them is to use a piece of emery, or similar abrasive paper laid flat on the bench, and to rub the points lengthways on that, at the same time slowly rotating them. On the other hand centre punches can be re-ground by using the grindstone, they should be held on the rest at the required angle and the point rotated as the stone revolves.

The Workbench

All too often the workbench has to be something of a compromise, either an existing structure pressed

into use or constructed from materials that just happen to be on hand. This is a fact of life but it is also a great pity as the workbench is where all the work is to be done and so it follows that ideally it should be tailored towards the needs of the individual; particularly where the height and width is concerned. A very wide bench usually ends up with a great deal of clutter at the back of it, pieces of metal that might come in handy at a later date can get pushed to the back, and before we know where we are, there is a whole pile of bits and pieces along the back. Unless there is some reason to make it otherwise, about eighteen inches or four hundred millimetres deep is sufficient to work on and at the same time, because of the width, there is no room to store that rubbish that might be handy sometime in the next twenty or thirty years, but in fact never is. It is also advisable to either have a small lip at the back of the bench or to fit it very tight to a wall, in order to prevent screws, small tools etc. from falling behind it.

Height

For comfort it is essential that the bench be of a suitable height for the person that will be using it. We all have different needs of course, but a good guide is to ensure that the jaws of the bench vice are about level with the operators elbow. This gives the ideal position for sawing and filing operations, as well as a good height for the top during fitting operations. The material from which the bench is built is again a matter of personal choice, although quite frequently it could be Hobson's choice. Many people like benches to be of steel construction and to even have a steel top, others like wood or one of the proprietary manufactured boards. Whatever material is used the top must be as solid and possible, and this will frequently involve the use of several layers of material.

When building a model locomotive in the larger scales it is frequently not practical to make it on the bench and in that case a suitable stand should be made. As locomotives, particularly the larger ones, can be very heavy it might be desirable to put the stand on wheels and so allow the model to be easily moved when required. In that case thought should be given to providing some form of brake to the wheels so that it can be prevented from running away. The brakes do not have to be very complicated and some form of pad that will press on either the wheel or the floor immediately adjacent to the stand will do. Many people make a stand that has a rise and fall action and some even allow the model to be rotated in order that work can be carried out on the underside. If considering making a stand with these facilities, it is advisable that both the lifting and rotating actions are controlled by mechanical means rather than by physical strength. A hydraulic car jack makes an ideal means of lifting and lowering a model, and a hefty worm and wheel can be used for rotation.

Lighting

We all realise how important good lighting is, but it is not always easy to achieve the desired result. There are three types of lighting that can be used, tungsten, fluorescent and halogen; whichever is chosen it is essential that sufficient lamps are supplied to ensure a well-lit workshop. Tungsten is the standard lighting we use at home and is very efficient. It does have a fault in as much as, in addition to providing illumination it also gives off a great deal of heat and, while during the winter that can be very welcome, in the summer it can become overbearing. Fluorescent lighting is very efficient indeed and it is also economical to use; in this case the disadvantage is the fact that the lights have a distinct flicker that some people find very annoying, and some even quite hypnotic. With fluorescent

lighting a choice of colours is available and while these are all basically white some, such as warm white, are not the best suited to our purposes. The type to select is known as daylight; the light released has less red and yellow and is, as the name implies, more the true colour of daylight, making it far easier to work with. Halogen lighting usually works on low voltages and so a transformer is needed; these are neither expensive nor bulky, and some are even built into the light fittings. It is a good economical form of lighting and, although slightly more expensive to begin with, the cost is soon recovered. The light generated is a clear white and suited to the workshop.

Where possible all work areas and machines should be fitted with small individual lamps that will shine directly on the work and these should always be of a low voltage because of the danger involved when using full mains voltages in these conditions. It is here that the halogen bulb has an advantage, with the low wattage but high intensity light. It goes without saying that all electrical circuits in the workshop should be properly installed and under no circumstances should loose live wires ever be left trailing across the floor.

MACHINERY

The Lathe

The machinery installed in the workshop will depend on the space available, how much cash is available to buy it and what ones individual needs might be. By far the most important machine of all is the lathe and for many, many years people built excellent model locomotives with that as the only motorised tool available. However, even that must be tailored to our individual need; for example if one intends to concentrate purely on building Gauge '0' or Gauge '1' models there is little point in buying a large lathe with about a ten inch centre height. It would probably do the job but working with it would be very difficult and, as well as wasting space in the workshop, it would also waste much valuable time. Likewise, if one's intention is to build 7¼" gauge models a miniature lathe would not be the best buy, although there are people with sufficient ingenuity to manage it. For building locomotives in 3½" and 5" gauges, a lathe of around 3½" centre height is ideal and will also be quite suitable for small 7¼" gauge models. For larger work in that gauge it would be better to use a lathe with a 5" centre height. From 2½" gauge downward one of the small models with a centre height of around 1½" will

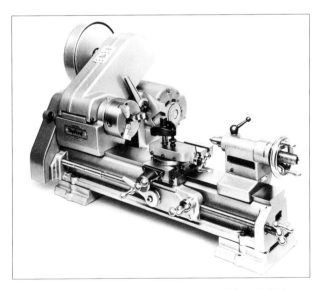

A Myford lathe, one of the most popular makes, it is available in a range of specifications and with a wide range of accessories.

usually suffice but again the 3½" lathe can be used quite successfully to build those also, making that size of lathe easily the most versatile.

To decide on the best type of lathe to buy, visit one of the many model engineering or machinery exhibitions that are held around the country. A vast range of models will invariably be on display, and frequently one is able to see them in operation, or

*For those working on small gauge models a lathe such as this one
by Cowell is ideal. It is capable of coping with exactly the same range
of operations as the larger Myford, but takes considerably less space
in the workshop.*

even have a hands on experience. Even if it is intended to buy a used model such a visit will give an idea of what to look for on the used machine market.

Drilling Machines

A drilling machine is desirable and can either be floor standing or bench mounted. A bench mounted type has the advantage of allowing for storage space below it but the cost of this is some loss of height between the drilling table and chuck, when the table is at its lowest point. Few people will find the need for this extra height and if the worst comes to the worst it is usually possible to swing the head of the machine round on its column, and mount the work that is to be drilled on some form of improvised sub table. For most workshops therefore the bench-mounted machine is an advantage. Always make sure the machine has at least six rotational speeds and more if possible. The variation in drilling speed between a drill of say a ¹⁄₁₆" (1.5mm) diameter and a ½" (1 2mm) is very wide, and it is always wise to get to as near the correct drilling speed as possible.

MILLING MACHINES

Horizontal Machines

Horizontal milling machines have only limited use in the home workshop, and although small used machines can be purchased at reasonable prices, the cutters are expensive and frequently unsuitable for the type of work involved in making model locomotives.

Vertical Machines

Vertical milling machines are better suited to our purpose and, with the advent of cheap imports from the Far East, they are now to be found in a very large percentage of workshops. As with all machines it will be a matter of selecting the one that fits best into ones budget, as well as the space that is available for it. Quality will as always depend largely on price, but even the cheaper ones are usually, if properly used, quite adequate for our purposes.

Universal Machines

The true universal milling machine will have an interchangeable head that allows it to be used in a horizontal or vertical mode, thus giving the best of both worlds. However there are some machines described as "universal" where there is only one head that has the ability to rotate from the horizontal to the vertical position. In the case of a very heavily built and usually quite large machine this can be a quite satisfactory arrangement; in the case of a lighter model there will invariably be some lack of rigidity in the construction that can cause some problems unless extreme care is taken. Possibly the biggest advantage of the universal machine will be that it is possible to machine at an angle with the work bolted firmly to the table or held in a solid machine vice, whereas this type of work, when carried out on other types of machines, requires the actual work to be set at an angle. As well as an inevitable loss of rigidity when this is done, it is also difficult to get the precision that might be required.

Milling Attachments

There are many attachments available that allow the lathe to be used for milling, the most basic of which is a vertical slide to which work is bolted and the milling cutter then held in the lathe mandrel. The slide can be raised and lowered and sometimes also set at an angle, thus allowing milling operations to be carried out. The travel of the slide is obviously limited but, nevertheless, for many milling operations required when building a model locomotive, the system is adequate.

More recent developments include various types of milling attachments that allow work to be bolted to the lathe cross slide, so giving a larger amount of travel than generally available with a vertical slide. There are two common types, one is powered from the lathe mandrel, using a device that moves the rotation from horizontal to vertical; the other comes with its own motor, and this type often has facilities

A useful milling machine, such as might be purchased second-hand. It differs from the modern, lighter models where the head lowers to adjust the height as in this case the bed is raised and lowered to meet the head. The result of this arrangement is a particularly rigid machine. Note the table has a dividing head bolted to it and this too was a second-hand purchase

A vertical slide in use, the cutter is held in the lathe chuck and the combined movement of the vertical slide and the lathe cross slide give all the versatility of a small milling machine.

for setting it at an angle. Both of these attachments are particularly useful when space is at a premium, but as any attachment of a good quality will be heavily built, it will be quite heavy to move on and off the lathe. This has resulted in a number of lathes having been constructed that have a milling head permanently in place and once again this can be an ideal solution where space is limited, even though such machines are restricted on the size of work they will accept.

Safety

It is impossible to over stress the need for safe practices in a workshop; floors should be kept clear of clutter and machines should be fitted with suitable shields. Take care that electrical circuits are maintained in good order and, if gas containers are used, do not keep them in the workshop, valves can and do leak sometimes with disastrous results.

Keep a fire extinguisher available and never use water to put out a fire. Keep some basic first aid equipment to hand to be used in case of emergency.

Always wear boots or heavy shoes when working and ensure that loose clothing cannot get caught in rotating machinery. Use protective glasses when working on operations that can result in the discharge of swarf or dust.

Last but most certainly not least, ensure there is a means of rapid communication between the workshop and somewhere or somebody that can assist should an accident happen.

A workshop is not a dangerous place when used properly, but carelessness can result in accidents.

A quart in a pint pot, a small workshop in an old outbuilding. Because of the lack of room, a milling attachment of the self-powered type is fitted to the lathe and also does duty as a drilling machine. Note the compact storage of strip metal by putting it in drainpipes, screwed to the wall.

Catch 'em young!

Left: Judging by his expression, sitting on the tender of Erik Kammeyer's 7¼" gauge Union Pacific 0-6-0 switcher may just be the defining point of this young man's life - or is there an ice cream van to the left of the photographer?

Right: As the shadows lengthen, a proud father introduces his daughter to the delights of his steam locomotive on the *Nienoord Spoorwegen* at Leek in Holland. Did he succeed, or was setting off with the safety valves lifting straight into the young lady's face not such a good idea?

Chapter 28: Some Random Thoughts.

What Size?

Traditionally, and model engineering is very traditional, 2½" and 3½" gauges have been regarded as the ideal gauges for the beginner. Historically this was dictated by the fact these were the common gauges at one time, and because the beginner was quite likely to be a skilled man, but on a low wage. Also these were, and are, the cheapest gauges in which passenger hauling is possible.

In the 21st century things have changed, and whilst 3½" gauge is still common on Club tracks, 5" is more common, and 7¼" not unusual. Additionally the beginner is much less likely to be a skilled man, and more likely to have a higher income, all of which means that the larger gauges can be considered by the beginner.

My personal opinion is that 3½" gauge is by far the best for the beginner. The parts are small enough to

Possible Beginner's Locomotives

Without implying any particular recommendation, three recognised and successful beginner's steam locomotives are illustrated here.

Top left is an example of the Gauge 1 "Project" design which, because of its size, is especially suited to those whose budget or equipment are limited. Whilst not a passenger hauling locomotive, the builder of a 'Project' undertakes all the machining and manufacturing processes involved in building a larger gauge locomotive. A construction manual, including drawings, is available.

Top right is Kozo Hiraoka's 3½" gauge American Pennsy A3 switcher. Designed to be built without castings, an extremely good construction manual

is available for this attractive design.

Finally, no less than five examples of the American beginner's locomotive par-excellence are shown in the bottom photograph. This is Bill Morewood's 3½" gauge 1870s 2-4-0 tender locomotive, "Raritan", based on a Baldwin prototype. A construction manual, including drawings, is available.

Probably the most popular British beginner's locomotive at present is Martin Evan's "Rob Roy", illustrated on page 174. No construction manual is currently available for this design, or for the same designer's 5" gauge beginner's locomotive "Simplex", an 0-6-0 tank locomotive.

handle without any unusual set-ups being needed, as can be the case with even a small 5" gauge model. They are large enough not to be too fiddly, very few designs call for for anything under 6BA in threads and, apart from things like injector cones, there are not any really small parts involved. There are a good number of beginner's locomotive designs, and castings, available in this gauge which the beginner should certainly consider.

There are also a growing number of beginner's locomotive designs in 5" gauge and, if finance, machinery and physical ability permit, the beginner can also consider these. A difference of 1½" in gauge may not sound much, but it does give more room for correcting errors, fitting the awkward bits with 12" = 1' fingers and running well. But there is also a considerable difference in weight, which has to be taken into account.

Following this reasoning through, then 7¼" should be even better for the beginner and, indeed some of the freelance narrow gauge designs in this gauge are essentially very simple to make. However, whilst the benefits of increasing gauge go up exponentially, so do the negatives; in this size you are likely to need bigger machinery, the cost is greater and the weight of the finished article is going to be considerable.

The beginner should remember that the model engineering trade survives, not on the casting sets it sells which end up as complete models, but on those that don't, and end up as rusting scrap under the bench. So whilst the reader is advised not to start with a "Flying Scotsman" or a "Big Boy" in any gauge, at the end of the day he or she must make their own choice, make one part for it, then another,

Jan Kieboom demonstrates his wheelbarrow arrangement for moving 5" gauge locomotives. This very practical idea consists of a tubular cradle in which the locomotive is secured, and removable wheel and handles. The ramp is a piece of channel.

and another, and so on, until one day they look at a glistening complete locomotive and think, with pride, "I built that".

Model Engineering Societies

If the reader has not already joined a model engineering society, the author strongly suggest they do so. Not only will membership of such a society result in meeting similar minded people socially, it will also give access to help and advice, as well as somewhere to run the engine once it is built, and in Britain at least, to officially test the boiler, if it is a steam model. Very few parts of the British Isles do not have such a Society within reach, and they will also be found in western Europe, notably the Netherlands, Germany, Switzerland, Belgium, France and Spain, with at least one in Italy and Denmark. Further afield there are many clubs in Australia, New Zealand, Canada, the U.S.A. and Japan, although distances between them will be greater in at least Australia and the U.S.A. Most magazines contain details of Club meetings.

Magazines

Magazines are an invaluable source of information, hints and tips, and advertisements from suppliers of model engineering items. The major professionally produced English language magazines are:

U.K:

Model Engineer
Model Engineer's Workshop
Engineering in Miniature

All the above are available through newsagents.

U.S.A.:

Live Steam *
Home Shop Machinist *
Machinist's Workshop *

These are available by subscription only, but non-American readers can purchase sample copies of them from the publishers of this book.

Another magazine, this time produced by a Society, but to a highly professional standard, is:

Australian Model Engineer *

Again samples of this magazine can be purchased from the publishers of this book.

In the same category, but Dutch language, are:

Onder Stoom
Modelbouwer

It should be noted that *Model Engineer's Workshop, Home Shop Machinist* and *Machinist's Workshop* deal almost exclusively with tool building and use, whilst the others cover all aspects of model engineering, including construction series.

Books

A very large number of books are available on all aspects of model engineering, engineering practice and skills, which can be invaluable in helping the beginner to acquire the skills needed to build their locomotive successfully. The main sources of these are:

U-K:

Camden Miniature Steam Services
TEE Publishing

U.S.A.:

Lindsay Publications. Inc *
Village Press. Inc *

An alternative way of raising steam to the blower shown on page 175 is to adapt a pipe to fit the chimney and then insert a second smaller tube into that so that its end is pointing vertically up the centre line of the outer tube. Here a blower is forcing air up the tube, but this method is especially suitable if compressed air is available on your steaming bay. In terms of efficiency there is little to choose between the two methods, but this one does have the advantage of lifting paraffin and coal fumes clear of the area, reducing coughing and watery eyes.

Australia:

Plough Book Sales

Readers would be well advised to obtain these firms' Booklists, which are free. Non-American readers should note that *Lindsay Publications* do not export, but the bulk of their books are available from the other suppliers. Addresses will be found in magazine advertisements.

Videos

Videos can be excellent teaching aids, but to date no professional videos have been produced for the model engineer. However Joe Rice, recently retired editor of the American magazine *Live Steam,* has produced a series of what can be described as semi-professional videos, featuring Rudy Kouhoupt, the veteran American writer on model engineering matters. To date these cover the use of lathes, milling machines and shapers and grinding tools, with more to come. NTSC versions for America and Japan may be obtained from *New Life Video Productions* in America, and PAL versions are available from the publishers of this book.

Two Cautions

If building your own locomotive from an established design, you should be aware that, sadly, the drawings for some designs are not 100% accurate. Talking to builders of the same model (one of the many benefits of joining a Club) may reveal some of these inaccuracies, but you should always cross-check dimensions on the drawings, and against work you have done so far.

Lastly - take your time. Rushing in your enthusiasm will almost certainly result in errors and actually lose time. Spend time thinking about how you are going to set pieces up in the lathe, milling machine or drill and especially take time to make sure you mark out from the correct datum points.

Accidents may lose you blood, boiler making will cause you to sweat, and mistakes will cause tears, but all should be avoidable if you plan what you are going to do carefully, and prepare accordingly.

One of the great pleasures of model engineering is the cerebral activity associated with it, one of the reasons many model engineers keep going to a considerable age.

* Available from the publisher of this book.

A final selection of models

This 3½" gauge Pacific represents one of André Chapelon's re-builds of older locomotives, when the power output and efficiency were increased very considerably.

In the mid 70s the Antony Vapeur Club inaugurated its first track, near Paris, an event which was attended by the author and a number of other British model engineers. Also in attendance that day was the great French locomotive designer André Chapelon; the time spent talking to this exceptional, but very modest, gentleman is one of the author's abiding memories. Chapelon is see above centre talking to Phil Hains to the left, whilst Pierre Bender is on the right.

Built to 1/8th scale for 7¼" gauge, Rob van Dort's battery powered model of a German built shunting locomotive can be run on 5" gauge railways by the simple expedient of moving the wheels in on the axles. In this photograph it is on 5" gauge track.

Continuing the French theme, here John Stewart of the Ottawa Valley Live Steamers in Canada prepares his 3½" gauge SNCF 141R for a run with his daughter's help.

This 1' scale, 3½" gauge model of a New Zealand Government Railway KB class 4-8-4 looks just the job for serious hauling.

Rudy Memin of France specialises in unusual machines; this 5" gauge, gas fired locomotive, with 4 oscillating cylinders is amongst the more conventional that he has built.

Neville Levin's 5" gauge model of a Victorian Railways J class 2-8-0 with matching rolling stock.
Note the footrests on the tender needed for ground level running.

Tom Oversluizen, a Dutchman who moved to the U.S.A., built this neat 7¼" gauge model of a Dutch steam tram locomotive in America, and then brought it to run in Holland when he paid a visit to the country of his birth.

Yvon Genty from France constructed this 7¼" Mallet compound "Mar.y" which is an accurate model of one of the very first articulated Mallets, built to 600 mm gauge by Decauville.

Bert Perryman from Brighton was a very skilled model builder and, having served his apprenticeship at the Brighton works of the old LB & SC Railway, it was not surprising that he chose to model the locomotives of that railway. His last model, which ran as well as it looked, was this lovely 5" gauge model of No. 200, one of the 'Gladstone' class of express passenger locomotives.

Vagn Hansen's 7¼" gauge model of the first locomotive in California - the "C.P. Huntington" is steamed for a night run.

On the steaming bays at the Pennsylvania Live Steamers track in the U.S.A. is this lovely 3½" gauge model of a 3' gauge 2-6-6 'Mason Bogie'. Like to a 'Single Fairlie', the engine unit and pony truck of these engines articulated. A model of one of the Pennsylvania Railroad's legendary K4 Pacifics can be seen on the 4¾" gauge ground level track in the background.

The basic Zimmermann 5" gauge tank locomotive was austere looking, but the addition of some super-detailing could result in a very attractive engine, such as the one shown above.

Narrow Gauge prototypes running on 7¼" gauge are about one third full size, as this French "Decauville" shows.

Manfred Knupfer organised the Öhringen Meeting in 1973; five years before that he had completed his first 3½" gauge locomotive, this Prussian 0-8-0 goods locomotive.

Many Australian 5" gauge tracks are ground level and narrow gauge prototypes are popular as a result. Ray Bannerman and Ross Bishop double-head with two Fowler 0-6-0 tank locomotives, as used on sugar cane lines in Queensland.

As mentioned earlier, the 'Project' in Gauge 1 is a very good first locomotive for the beginner with limited resources. One of the beauties of this design is that it can be adapted to cover a wide range of inside cylinder locomotives. The model shown on page 187 has been made as a Southern railway Q class 'Austerity' 0-6-0 but the design is actually based on the LMS 4F 0-6-0 tender freight locomotive. Whilst not quite finished, this super-detailed example of the model as designed, built by Rudi Mitelschlager, is worthy of note.

John Brotherton readies Mike Comben's 5" gauge 2-6-0 Tralee & Dingle tank loco for a run. Based on an Irish 3' gauge prototype, this model is actually a cleverly modified "Butch" 0-6-0 standard gauge tank locomotive design.

'IMLEC' - the International Model Locomotive Efficiency Competition started by Martin Evans, first lived up to the 'International' part of its title in 1973 when Jean Villette, on a visit to England, was persuaded to drive Phil Hains' 5" gauge experimental locomotive "Weirdy" in that year's event. On a strange locomotive Jean did well to complete his run and, from memory, came sixth or seventh.

This 3½" gauge 4-6-0 is a model of a Swedish Railways design, fifteen of which were purchased new in 1945 & 1946 by the Dutch State Railways to ease their post-war motive power situation.

Another locomotive on the Vancouver Island Model Engineers track, this time a 5" gauge Canadian Pacific 2-8-4.

This 5" gauge model of a Swiss metre gauge prototype used on the Rhaetischbahn, is on the track of the Centre d'Estudis-Modelisme Vapor in Barcelona.

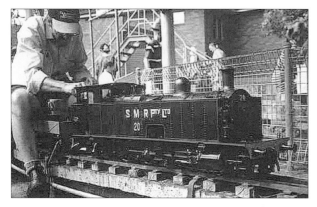

Seen on the 5" gauge track of the Sydney SMEE is this chunky Maitland RL10 class tank locomotive.

An international mixture. This 5" gauge model of a British GWR 2-6-2 tank locomotive, to the 'Firefly' design, has been paired by its Dutch builder with a Dutch beer wagon he also built.

Ron Barrett drives his 7½" gauge model of a British Railways "Drewry" shunter off a splendid bridge at the track of the Vancouver Island Model Engineers in Canada.

No. 3 "Dickie" on the 7¼" gauge Beer Heights Light Railway in Devon is a freelance, narrow gauge outline, 0-4-2 tender locomotive.

Despite the rolling stock in the background this is 5" gauge in Australia. The beautiful model, made by Len Whalley, is of an Australian CLP diesel.

Danish steam locomotives were distinctive, with the national colours around the chimneys and domed smokebox doors, features evident on this 5" gauge model of a 'J' class 0-4-2 locomotive, running on the København Club's track.

LBSC's "Maid of Kent" design is popular in 5" gauge; here Rudi Memin's son drives a nice example whilst visiting the U.K.

John Wakefield rolls along the 7¼" tracks of the Lake Macquarie Live Steam Locomotive Society on his model of a 3'6" gauge South Africa class 22 2-10-4; superpower in miniature!

This is very nice scratch-built Gauge 1 model of a 3900 class 4-6-0 of the Nederlands Spoorwegen has a considerable amount of fine detail, despite the smaller scale.

This 5" gauge 'Glaskasten' German 0-4-0 tank locomotive is an unusual, and easily portable, model.

This 7¼" gauge Queensland Government Railways PB15 class 4-6-0 is the work of Lloyd Dannenberg from Brisbane.

15" gauge is generally regarded as outside the range of model engineer sizes, but locomotives have been built by amateurs for this gauge, including one of "Flying Scotsman". More modest, but still large and heavy, is this 0-4-0 American switcher seen on the turntable of the Evesham Vale Light Railway.

This attractive 5" gauge DH73 Australian diesel belongs to Don Hinchcliffe of the Queensland SMEE.

The author and his 5" gauge "Simplex" 0-6-0 tank, steaming ever onwards.

Scale Tables

The tables on the following four pages were kindly prepared by Dr Mark Phillips and are an easy reference for scaling figures in the most popular passenger hauling gauges, including narrow gauge prototypes. They are in Imperial measurements but, of course, conversions to metric can quickly be made with the use of a calculator.

The numbers on the left hand side are whole numbers and beside them is the fractional figure when scaled.

The line across the top shows fractions in 1/8″ and immediately below are the figures when scaled.

To take an easy example look at the table for 1 inch = 1 foot and go to the number 12 on the left hand side the figure, the scale figure not surprisingly is 1″. Suppose one foot and five eighths of an inch is needed move along to the figure on the same line but under 5/8″ and we have the scale size for a component that is one foot and five eighth of an inch long.

To obtain fractions of less than those shown on the top line i.e. 1/16″ inch simply divide the difference between the two fractions.

Suppose therefore we wanted one foot and nine sixteenths of an inch we take the number for one foot and a half inch which is 1.042″ and using only the fraction (0.042″) subtract that from the fraction for one foot and five eighths of an inch (0.052″) and the answer is 0.010″. Halve that and take the answer from the higher figure and the answer is 0.0425″, replace the inch that was temporarily removed and we have the figure for one foot and nine sixteenths of an inch.

Appendices

SCALE FACTORS FOR A SCALE OF 3/4 INCHES = 1 FOOT

	1/8	1/4	3/8	1/2	5/8	3/4	7/8
0		0.008	0.016	0.023	0.031	0.039	0.047	0.055
1	0.063	0.070	0.078	0.086	0.094	0.102	0.109	0.117
2	0.125	0.133	0.141	0.148	0.156	0.164	0.172	0.180
3	0.188	0.195	0.203	0.211	0.219	0.227	0.234	0.242
4	0.250	0.258	0.266	0.273	0.281	0.289	0.297	0.305
5	0.313	0.320	0.328	0.336	0.344	0.352	0.359	0.367
6	0.375	0.383	0.391	0.398	0.406	0.414	0.422	0.430
7	0.438	0.445	0.453	0.461	0.469	0.477	0.484	0.492
8	0.500	0.508	0.516	0.523	0.531	0.539	0.547	0.555
9	0.563	0.570	0.578	0.586	0.594	0.602	0.609	0.617
10	0.625	0.633	0.641	0.648	0.656	0.664	0.672	0.680
11	0.688	0.695	0.703	0.711	0.719	0.727	0.734	0.742
12	0.750	0.758	0.766	0.773	0.781	0.789	0.797	0.805
13	0.813	0.820	0.828	0.836	0.844	0.852	0.859	0.867
14	0.875	0.883	0.891	0.898	0.906	0.914	0.922	0.930
15	0.938	0.945	0.953	0.961	0.969	0.977	0.984	0.992
16	1.000	1.008	1.016	1.023	1.031	1.039	1.047	1.055
17	1.063	1.070	1.078	1.086	1.094	1.102	1.109	1.117
18	1.125	1.133	1.141	1.148	1.156	1.164	1.172	1.180
19	1.188	1.195	1.203	1.211	1.219	1.227	1.234	1.242
20	1.250	1.258	1.266	1.273	1.281	1.289	1.297	1.305
21	1.313	1.320	1.328	1.336	1.344	1.352	1.359	1.367
22	1.375	1.383	1.391	1.398	1.406	1.414	1.422	1.430
23	1.438	1.445	1.453	1.461	1.469	1.477	1.484	1.492
24	1.500	1.508	1.516	1.523	1.531	1.539	1.547	1.555
25	1.563	1.570	1.578	1.586	1.594	1.602	1.609	1.617
26	1.625	1.633	1.641	1.648	1.656	1.664	1.672	1.680
27	1.688	1.695	1.703	1.711	1.719	1.727	1.734	1.742
28	1.750	1.758	1.766	1.773	1.781	1.789	1.797	1.805
29	1.813	1.820	1.828	1.836	1.844	1.852	1.859	1.867
30	1.875	1.883	1.891	1.898	1.906	1.914	1.922	1.930
31	1.938	1.945	1.953	1.961	1.969	1.977	1.984	1.992
32	2.000	2.008	2.016	2.023	2.031	2.039	2.047	2.055
33	2.063	2.070	2.078	2.086	2.094	2.102	2.109	2.117
34	2.125	2.133	2.141	2.148	2.156	2.164	2.172	2.180
35	2.188	2.195	2.203	2.211	2.219	2.227	2.234	2.242
36	2.250	2.258	2.266	2.273	2.281	2.289	2.297	2.305
37	2.313	2.320	2.328	2.336	2.344	2.352	2.359	2.367
38	2.375	2.383	2.391	2.398	2.406	2.414	2.422	2.430
39	2.438	2.445	2.453	2.461	2.469	2.477	2.484	2.492
40	2.500	2.508	2.516	2.523	2.531	2.539	2.547	2.555
41	2.563	2.570	2.578	2.586	2.594	2.602	2.609	2.617
42	2.625	2.633	2.641	2.648	2.656	2.664	2.672	2.680
43	2.688	2.695	2.703	2.711	2.719	2.727	2.734	2.742
44	2.750	2.758	2.766	2.773	2.781	2.789	2.797	2.805
45	2.813	2.820	2.828	2.836	2.844	2.852	2.859	2.867
46	2.875	2.883	2.891	2.898	2.906	2.914	2.922	2.930
47	2.938	2.945	2.953	2.961	2.969	2.977	2.984	2.992
48	3.000	3.008	3.016	3.023	3.031	3.039	3.047	3.055
49	3.063	3.070	3.078	3.086	3.094	3.102	3.109	3.117
50	3.125	3.133	3.141	3.148	3.156	3.164	3.172	3.180

SCALE FACTORS FOR A SCALE OF 1 INCH = 1 FOOT

		1/8	1/4	3/8	1/2	5/8	3/4	7/8
0		0.010	0.021	0.031	0.042	0.052	0.063	0.073
1	0.083	0.094	0.104	0.115	0.125	0.135	0.146	0.156
2	0.167	0.177	0.188	0.198	0.208	0.219	0.229	0.240
3	0.250	0.260	0.271	0.281	0.292	0.302	0.313	0.323
4	0.333	0.344	0.354	0.365	0.375	0.385	0.396	0.406
5	0.417	0.427	0.438	0.448	0.458	0.469	0.479	0.490
6	0.500	0.510	0.521	0.531	0.542	0.552	0.563	0.573
7	0.583	0.594	0.604	0.615	0.625	0.635	0.646	0.656
8	0.667	0.677	0.688	0.698	0.708	0.719	0.729	0.740
9	0.750	0.760	0.771	0.781	0.792	0.802	0.813	0.823
10	0.833	0.844	0.854	0.865	0.875	0.885	0.896	0.906
11	0.917	0.927	0.938	0.948	0.958	0.969	0.979	0.990
12	1.000	1.010	1.021	1.031	1.042	1.052	1.063	1.073
13	1.083	1.094	1.104	1.115	1.125	1.135	1.146	1.156
14	1.167	1.177	1.188	1.198	1.208	1.219	1.229	1.240
15	1.250	1.260	1.271	1.281	1.292	1.302	1.313	1.323
16	1.333	1.344	1.354	1.365	1.375	1.385	1.396	1.406
17	1.417	1.427	1.438	1.448	1.458	1.469	1.479	1.490
18	1.500	1.510	1.521	1.531	1.542	1.552	1.563	1.573
19	1.583	1.594	1.604	1.615	1.625	1.635	1.646	1.656
20	1.667	1.677	1.688	1.698	1.708	1.719	1.729	1.740
21	1.750	1.760	1.771	1.781	1.792	1.802	1.813	1.823
22	1.833	1.844	1.854	1.865	1.875	1.885	1.896	1.906
23	1.917	1.927	1.938	1.948	1.958	1.969	1.979	1.990
24	2.000	2.010	2.021	2.031	2.042	2.052	2.063	2.073
25	2.083	2.094	2.104	2.115	2.125	2.135	2.146	2.156
26	2.167	2.177	2.188	2.198	2.208	2.219	2.229	2.240
27	2.250	2.260	2.271	2.281	2.292	2.302	2.313	2.323
28	2.333	2.344	2.354	2.365	2.375	2.385	2.396	2.406
29	2.417	2.427	2.438	2.448	2.458	2.469	2.479	2.490
30	2.500	2.510	2.521	2.531	2.542	2.552	2.563	2.573
31	2.583	2.594	2.604	2.615	2.625	2.635	2.646	2.656
32	2.667	2.677	2.688	2.698	2.708	2.719	2.729	2.740
33	2.750	2.760	2.771	2.781	2.792	2.802	2.813	2.823
34	2.833	2.844	2.854	2.865	2.875	2.885	2.896	2.906
35	2.917	2.927	2.938	2.948	2.958	2.969	2.979	2.990
36	3.000	3.010	3.021	3.031	3.042	3.052	3.063	3.073
37	3.083	3.094	3.104	3.115	3.125	3.135	3.146	3.156
38	3.167	3.177	3.188	3.198	3.208	3.219	3.229	3.240
39	3.250	3.260	3.271	3.281	3.292	3.302	3.313	3.323
40	3.333	3.344	3.354	3.365	3.375	3.385	3.396	3.406
41	3.417	3.427	3.438	3.448	3.458	3.469	3.479	3.490
42	3.500	3.510	3.521	3.531	3.542	3.552	3.563	3.573
43	3.583	3.594	3.604	3.615	3.625	3.635	3.646	3.656
44	3.667	3.677	3.688	3.698	3.708	3.719	3.729	3.740
45	3.750	3.760	3.771	3.781	3.792	3.802	3.813	3.823
46	3.833	3.844	3.854	3.865	3.875	3.885	3.896	3.906
47	3.917	3.927	3.938	3.948	3.958	3.969	3.979	3.990
48	4.000	4.010	4.021	4.031	4.042	4.052	4.063	4.073
49	4.083	4.094	4.104	4.115	4.125	4.135	4.146	4.156
50	4.167	4.177	4.188	4.198	4.208	4.219	4.229	4.240

SCALE FACTORS FOR A SCALE OF 1 1/16 INCHES = 1 FOOT

		1/8	1/4	3/8	1/2	5/8	3/4	7/8
0			0.011	0.022	0.033	0.044	0.055	0.066	0.077
1		0.089	0.100	0.111	0.122	0.133	0.144	0.155	0.166
2		0.177	0.188	0.199	0.210	0.221	0.232	0.243	0.255
3		0.266	0.277	0.288	0.299	0.310	0.321	0.332	0.343
4		0.354	0.365	0.376	0.387	0.398	0.410	0.421	0.432
5		0.443	0.454	0.465	0.476	0.487	0.498	0.509	0.520
6		0.531	0.542	0.553	0.564	0.576	0.587	0.598	0.609
7		0.620	0.631	0.642	0.653	0.664	0.675	0.686	0.697
8		0.708	0.719	0.730	0.742	0.753	0.764	0.775	0.786
9		0.797	0.808	0.819	0.830	0.841	0.852	0.863	0.874
10		0.885	0.896	0.908	0.919	0.930	0.941	0.952	0.963
11		0.974	0.985	0.996	1.007	1.018	1.029	1.040	1.051
12		1.063	1.074	1.085	1.096	1.107	1.118	1.129	1.140
13		1.151	1.162	1.173	1.184	1.195	1.206	1.217	1.229
14		1.240	1.251	1.262	1.273	1.284	1.295	1.306	1.317
15		1.328	1.339	1.350	1.361	1.372	1.383	1.395	1.406
16		1.417	1.428	1.439	1.450	1.461	1.472	1.483	1.494
17		1.505	1.516	1.527	1.538	1.549	1.561	1.572	1.583
18		1.594	1.605	1.616	1.627	1.638	1.649	1.660	1.671
19		1.682	1.693	1.704	1.715	1.727	1.738	1.749	1.760
20		1.771	1.782	1.793	1.804	1.815	1.826	1.837	1.848
21		1.859	1.870	1.882	1.893	1.904	1.915	1.926	1.937
22		1.948	1.959	1.970	1.981	1.992	2.003	2.014	2.025
23		2.036	2.048	2.059	2.070	2.081	2.092	2.103	2.114
24		2.125	2.136	2.147	2.158	2.169	2.180	2.191	2.202
25		2.214	2.225	2.236	2.247	2.258	2.269	2.280	2.291
26		2.302	2.313	2.324	2.335	2.346	2.357	2.368	2.380
27		2.391	2.402	2.413	2.424	2.435	2.446	2.457	2.468
28		2.479	2.490	2.501	2.512	2.523	2.535	2.546	2.557
29		2.568	2.579	2.590	2.601	2.612	2.623	2.634	2.645
30		2.656	2.667	2.678	2.689	2.701	2.712	2.723	2.734
31		2.745	2.756	2.767	2.778	2.789	2.800	2.811	2.822
32		2.833	2.844	2.855	2.867	2.878	2.889	2.900	2.911
33		2.922	2.933	2.944	2.955	2.966	2.977	2.988	2.999
34		3.010	3.021	3.033	3.044	3.055	3.066	3.077	3.088
35		3.099	3.110	3.121	3.132	3.143	3.154	3.165	3.176
36		3.188	3.199	3.210	3.221	3.232	3.243	3.254	3.265
37		3.276	3.287	3.298	3.309	3.320	3.331	3.342	3.354
38		3.365	3.376	3.387	3.398	3.409	3.420	3.431	3.442
39		3.453	3.464	3.475	3.486	3.497	3.508	3.520	3.531
40		3.542	3.553	3.564	3.575	3.586	3.597	3.608	3.619
41		3.630	3.641	3.652	3.663	3.674	3.686	3.697	3.708
42		3.719	3.730	3.741	3.752	3.763	3.774	3.785	3.796
43		3.807	3.818	3.829	3.840	3.852	3.863	3.874	3.885
44		3.896	3.907	3.918	3.929	3.940	3.951	3.962	3.973
45		3.984	3.995	4.007	4.018	4.029	4.040	4.051	4.062
46		4.073	4.084	4.095	4.106	4.117	4.128	4.139	4.150
47		4.161	4.173	4.184	4.195	4.206	4.217	4.228	4.239
48		4.250	4.261	4.272	4.283	4.294	4.305	4.316	4.327
49		4.339	4.350	4.361	4.372	4.383	4.394	4.405	4.416
50		4.427	4.438	4.449	4.460	4.471	4.482	4.493	4.505

Model and Miniature Locomotive Construction

SCALE FACTORS FOR A SCALE OF 1 1/2 INCHES = 1 FOOT

	1/8	1/4	3/8	1/2	5/8	3/4	7/8
0		0.016	0.031	0.047	0.063	0.078	0.094	0.109
1	0.125	0.141	0.156	0.172	0.188	0.203	0.219	0.234
2	0.250	0.266	0.281	0.297	0.313	0.328	0.344	0.359
3	0.375	0.391	0.406	0.422	0.438	0.453	0.469	0.484
4	0.500	0.516	0.531	0.547	0.563	0.578	0.594	0.609
5	0.625	0.641	0.656	0.672	0.688	0.703	0.719	0.734
6	0.750	0.766	0.781	0.797	0.813	0.828	0.844	0.859
7	0.875	0.891	0.906	0.922	0.938	0.953	0.969	0.984
8	1.000	1.016	1.031	1.047	1.063	1.078	1.094	1.109
9	1.125	1.141	1.156	1.172	1.188	1.203	1.219	1.234
10	1.250	1.266	1.281	1.297	1.313	1.328	1.344	1.359
11	1.375	1.391	1.406	1.422	1.438	1.453	1.469	1.484
12	1.500	1.516	1.531	1.547	1.563	1.578	1.594	1.609
13	1.625	1.641	1.656	1.672	1.688	1.703	1.719	1.734
14	1.750	1.766	1.781	1.797	1.813	1.828	1.844	1.859
15	1.875	1.891	1.906	1.922	1.938	1.953	1.969	1.984
16	2.000	2.016	2.031	2.047	2.063	2.078	2.094	2.109
17	2.125	2.141	2.156	2.172	2.188	2.203	2.219	2.234
18	2.250	2.266	2.281	2.297	2.313	2.328	2.344	2.359
19	2.375	2.391	2.406	2.422	2.438	2.453	2.469	2.484
20	2.500	2.516	2.531	2.547	2.563	2.578	2.594	2.609
21	2.625	2.641	2.656	2.672	2.688	2.703	2.719	2.734
22	2.750	2.766	2.781	2.797	2.813	2.828	2.844	2.859
23	2.875	2.891	2.906	2.922	2.938	2.953	2.969	2.984
24	3.000	3.016	3.031	3.047	3.063	3.078	3.094	3.109
25	3.125	3.141	3.156	3.172	3.188	3.203	3.219	3.234
26	3.250	3.266	3.281	3.297	3.313	3.328	3.344	3.359
27	3.375	3.391	3.406	3.422	3.438	3.453	3.469	3.484
28	3.500	3.516	3.531	3.547	3.563	3.578	3.594	3.609
29	3.625	3.641	3.656	3.672	3.688	3.703	3.719	3.734
30	3.750	3.766	3.781	3.797	3.813	3.828	3.844	3.859
31	3.875	3.891	3.906	3.922	3.938	3.953	3.969	3.984
32	4.000	4.016	4.031	4.047	4.063	4.078	4.094	4.109
33	4.125	4.141	4.156	4.172	4.188	4.203	4.219	4.234
34	4.250	4.266	4.281	4.297	4.313	4.328	4.344	4.359
35	4.375	4.391	4.406	4.422	4.438	4.453	4.469	4.484
36	4.500	4.516	4.531	4.547	4.563	4.578	4.594	4.609
37	4.625	4.641	4.656	4.672	4.688	4.703	4.719	4.734
38	4.750	4.766	4.781	4.797	4.813	4.828	4.844	4.859
39	4.875	4.891	4.906	4.922	4.938	4.953	4.969	4.984
40	5.000	5.016	5.031	5.047	5.063	5.078	5.094	5.109
41	5.125	5.141	5.156	5.172	5.188	5.203	5.219	5.234
42	5.250	5.266	5.281	5.297	5.313	5.328	5.344	5.359
43	5.375	5.391	5.406	5.422	5.438	5.453	5.469	5.484
44	5.500	5.516	5.531	5.547	5.563	5.578	5.594	5.609
45	5.625	5.641	5.656	5.672	5.688	5.703	5.719	5.734
46	5.750	5.766	5.781	5.797	5.813	5.828	5.844	5.859
47	5.875	5.891	5.906	5.922	5.938	5.953	5.969	5.984
48	6.000	6.016	6.031	6.047	6.063	6.078	6.094	6.109
49	6.125	6.141	6.156	6.172	6.188	6.203	6.219	6.234
50	6.250	6.266	6.281	6.297	6.313	6.328	6.344	6.359

MODEL ENGINEER (ME) THREADS
TAPPING AND CLEARANCE DRILLS

Size	40 TPI		32 TPI		26 TPI		Clearance	
	100%- 80%		100%- 80%		100% - 80%		100% 102%	
1/8"	2.4	2.6					3.2	3.3
5/32"	3.2	3.4	3.0	3.2			4.0	4.1
3/16"	4.0	4.2	3.8	4.0			4.8	4.9
7/32"	4.8	5.0	4.6	4.8			5.6	5.7
1/4"	5.6	5.8	5.4	5.6	5.2	5.4	6.4	6.5
9/32"	6.4	6.5	6.2	6.4	5.9	6.2	7.2	7.3
5/16"	7.2	7.3	7.0	7.3	6.7	7.0	8.0	8.2
3/8"	8.8	8.9	8.6	8.8	8.3	8.6	9.6	9.8
7.16"	10.4	10.5	10.2	10.4	9.9	10.2	11.2	11.4
1/2"	11.9	12.1	11.7	11.9	11.5	11.8	12.8	13.0

These threads were devised specially for model engineering puposes.Where pipe fittings etc. are concerned 100% engagement is desirable. Drill sizes are given in metric. Imperial drills of the nominal thread diameter can also be used for clearance purposes. 26 TPI threads are also known as brass threads.

UNIFIED COARSE (UNF)

Size	TPI	Tapping Drill	Clearance Drill
1	64	1.5	2.0
2	56	1.8	2.3
3	48	2.1	2.7
4	40	2.3	3.0
5	40	2.6	3.3
6	32	2.8	3.6
8	32	3.5	4.3
10	24	3.9	5.0
12	24	4.5	5.6
1/4"	20	5.2	6.5
5/16"	18	6.6	8.1
3/8"	16	8.0	9.7
7/16"	14	9.4	11.3
1/2"	13	10.8	13.0

The Unified Thread form is American and will mainly be of interest to readers in that country. The smaller sizes are of particular interest and very useful for model engineering puposes. Drill sizes are in metric.

UNIFIED FINE (UNF)

Size	TPI	Tapping Drill	Clearance Drill
0	80	1.2	1.7
1	72	1.6	2.0
2	64	1.9	2.4
3	56	2.1	2.7
4	48	2.4	3.0
5	44	2.7	3.5
6	40	2.9	3.7
8	36	3.5	4.4
10	32	4.1	5.0
12	28	4.6	5.6
1/4"	28	5.5	6.5
3/8"	24	8.5	9.7
7/16"	20	9.9	11.3
1/2"	20	11.4	13.0

BRITISH STANDARD WHITWORTH (BSW)

Size	Threads Per Inch	Tapping Drill MM	Clearance Drill MM
1/16"	60	1.4	1.7
3/32"	48	2.1	2..5
1/8"	40	2.6	3..3
3/16"	24	3.9	4.8
1/4"	20	5.10	6.40
5/16"	18	6.50	8.00
3/8"	16	7.90	9.60
7/16"	14	9.30	11.20
1/2"	12	10.50	12.70
9/16"	12	12.10	14.50
5/8"	11	13.50	16.00
11/16"	11	15.00	17.50
3/4"	10	16.25	19.25
7/8"	9	19.25	22.25
1"	8	22.00	25.50

Although generally considered to be obsolete, many older model locomotive designs specify these threads. People working in Imperial units may find them essential. Drill sizes are metric.

BRITISH STANDARD FINE (BSF)

Size	Threads Per Inch	Tapping Drill	Clearance Drill
----	----	----	----
----	----	----	----
1/8"	48	2.9	3.3
3/16"	32	4.0	4.8
1/4"	26	5.30	6.40
9/32"	26	6.10	7.20
5/16"	22	6.80	8.00
3/8"	20	8.30	9.60
7/16"	18	9.70	11.20
1/2"	16	11.10	12.70
5/8"	14	14.00	16.00
11/16"	14	15.50	17.50
3/4"	12	16.75	19.25
7/8"	11	19.75	22.25
1"	10	22.75	25.50

BRITISH ASSOCIATION THREADS (BA)

Size (Number)	Outside Dia. Ins.	Outside Dia. mm	Threads Per Inch	Tapping Drill mm	Clearance Drill mm
0	0.2362	6.0	25.38	5.10	6.00
1	0.1850	5.3	28.25	4.50	5.40
2	0.1850	4.7	31.35	4.00	4.80
3	0.1614	4.1	34.84	3.45	4.20
4	0.1417	3.6	38.46	3.00	3.70
5	0.1260	3.2	43.10	2.65	3.30
6	0.1102	2.8	47.85	2.30	2.85
7	0.0984	2.5	52.91	2.05	2.55
8	0.0866	2.2	59.17	1.80	2.25
9	0.0748	1.9	64.94	1.55	1.95
10	0.0669	1.7	72.46	1.40	1.80
11	0.0591	1.5	81.97	1.20	1.50
12	0.0511	1.3	90.91	1.05	1.30
13	0.0470	1.2	102.04	0.90	1.20
14	0.0390	1.0	109.89	0.72	1.00
15	0.0350	0.9	120.48	0.65	0.65
16	0.0310	0.8	133.33	0.56	0.80

The British Association, or BA series of threads is popular with model makers because of the wide range of great versatility. Originally based on the metric system, in the smaller sizes the fine threads in particular can be used to obtain a scale appearance. There are twenty five sets in all, but the small sizes are rarely used, which also applies to many of the odd numbers. Of these the most commonly used are five and seven which closely relate to Imperial measurements. It is likely that taps and dies, as well as nuts and bolts in this series will be available for many years to come. Metric drill sizes are shown.

CENTRE DRILLS

Combined drills and countersinks. Sizes generally considered likely to be used by model engineers shown.
These are also sometimes referred to as Slocombe Drills

Number	Body Dia.	Drill Dia.
BS1	1/8"	3/64"
BS2	3/16"	1/16"
BS3	1/4"	3/32"
BS4	5/16"	1/8"
BS5	7/16"	3/16"
BS6	5/8"	1/4"

Imperial sizes on the left.

Metric sizes on the right.

Body Dia.	Drill Dia.
3.15mm	1mm
4.0mm	1.6mm
5.0mm	2.0mm
6.3mm	2.5mm
8.0mm	3.15mm
10.0mm	6.2mm

SHEET METAL SIZES

Metric	Decimal
6mm	0.2362
5mm	0.1969
4mm	0.1575
3mm	0.1181
2.5mm	0.0984
2.0mm	0.0787
1.0mm	0.0384
0.9mm	0.0354
0.8mm	0.0315
0.7mm	0.0276
0.6mm	0.0236
0.5mm	0.0200

Sheet metal and Wire are sold according to their thickness.
Sheet is now always metric.
Most older plans will specify either imperial or S.W.G. sizes.
This table should offer help in deciding the thickness required.
Only common sizes are shown, but there are fortytwo sizes.
Wire is still commonly sold by gauge.

S.W.G.	Decimal
4	0.2320
6	0.1920
8	0.1600
10	0.1280
12	0.1040
13	0.0920
16	0.0640
18	0.0480
20	0.0360
22	0.0280
24	0.0220
26	0.0180
28	0.0148
30	0.0124

PIPE CONE SIZES

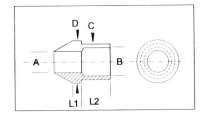

Pipe Size	Dia. A	Dia. B	Dia. C	Dia. D	Length L1	Length L2
1/16	3/64	1/16	3/32	1/8	1/32	3/32
3/32	1/16	3/32	1/8	5/32	1/32	7/64
1/8	3/32	1/8	5/32	3/16	1/32	1/8
5/32	1/8	5/32	3/16	7/32	1/32	7/32
3/16	5/32	3/16	7/32	1/4	1/32	7/32
1/4	7/32	1/4	19/64	0.335	3/64	7/32
5/16	1/4	5/16	13/32	27/64	1/16	1/4
3/8	5/16	3/8	27/64	29/64	1/16	1/4

UNION NUTS USED WITH CONES

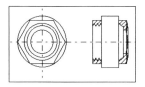

Pipe Size	Thread Size	Thread Length	Nut A/F
1/16	6BA	9/64	6BA
3/32	5/32x40	5/32	7/32
1/8	7/32x40	5/32	7/32
5/32	1/4x40	11/64	1/4
3/16	9/32x40	3/16	11/32
7/32	5/16x32	7/32	3/8
1/4	3/8x32	1/4	7/16

NIPPLES OR OLIVES

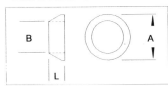

Pipe Size	Dia. A	Dia. B	Length L
1/16	0.25	1/16	1/32
3/32	0.150	3/32	1/32
1/8	0.180	1/8	1/32
5/32	0.205	5/32	1/32
3/16	0.235	3/16	3/64
7/32	0.275	7/32	3/64
1/4	0.3	1/4	1/16

UNION NUTS USED WITH NIPPLES

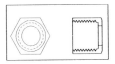

Pipe Size	Thread Size	Thread Length	Nut A/F
1/16	1/8x40	9/64	5/32
3/32	5/32x40	5/32	7/32
1/8	7/32x40	5/32	7/32
5/32	1/4x40	11/64	1/4
3/16	9/32x40	3/16	11/32
7/32	5/16x32	7/32	3/8
1/4	3/8x32	1/4	7/16

NOTE: Nipples are suitable for smaller diameter pipe. For large diameter pipe, which requires greater support, cones should be used. The usual angle of the nipple or cone ends is thirty degrees, and fittings must have the same angle. Nuts may be made of brass, but the nipples or cones must be made from bronze.

This freelance 3½"Pacific was built in 1933 to a design by Ernest Twining which appeared in 'Model Engineer', by an Englishman living in Holland. Built with a rivetted and soft-soldered boiler, the builder only ran the engine on compressed air. The model was presented to the Dutch Live Steam Group by the builder's widow and it has been successfully steamed following the fitting of a pump and a grate assembly.

BRITISH STANDARD NUMBER AND LETTER DRILLS.

The old system of numbered and lettered drills is now virtually obsolete. Many old drawings will still refer to drills in this way and this chart enables accurate conversions to be made.

Gauge	mm	Imp	Gauge	mm	Imp	Gauge	mm	Imp	Letter	mm	Imp
80	0.343	0.0135	55	1.321	0.0520	28	3.569	0.1045	A	5.944	0.2340
79	0.368	0.0145	54	1.397	0.0550	27	3.658	0.1440	B	6.045	0.2380
78	0.406	0.0160	53	1.511	0.0595	26	3.734	0.1470	C	6.147	0.2420
77	0.457	0.0180	52	1.613	0.0635	25	3.797	0.1495	D	6.248	0.2460
76	0.508	0.0200	51	1.702	0.0670	24	3.861	0.1520	E	6.350	0.2500
75	0.533	0.0210	50	1.778	0.0700	23	3.912	0.1540	F	6.528	0.2570
74	0.572	0.0225	49	1.854	0.0730	22	3.988	0.1570	G	6.629	0.2610
73	0.610	0.0240	48	1.930	0.0760	21	4.039	0.1590	H	6.756	0.2660
72	0.635	0.0250	47	1.994	0.0785	20	4.089	0.1610	I	6.909	0.2720
71	0.660	0.0260	46	2.057	0.0810	19	4.216	0.1660	J	7.036	0.2770
70	0.711	0.0280	45	2.083	0.0820	18	4.305	0.1695	K	7.137	0.2810
69	0.742	0.0292	44	2.184	0.0860	17	4.394	0.1730	L	7.366	0.2900
68	0.787	0.0310	43	2.261	0.0890	16	4.496	0.1770	M	7.493	0.2950
67	0.813	0.0320	42	2.375	0.0935	15	4.572	0.1800	N	7.671	0.3020
66	0.838	0.0330	41	2.438	0.0960	14	4.623	0.1820	O	8.026	0.3160
65	0.889	0.0350	40	2.489	0.0980	13	4.700	0.1850	P	8.204	0.3230
66	0.838	0.0330	39	2.527	0.0995	12	4.800	0.1890	Q	8.433	0.3320
65	0.889	0.0350	38	2.578	0.1015	11	4.851	0.1910	R	8.611	0.3390
64	0.914	0.0360	37	2.642	0.1040	10	4.915	0.1935	S	8.839	0.3480
63	0.940	0.0370	36	2.705	0.1065	9	4.978	0.1960	T	9.093	0.3580
62	0.965	0.0380	35	2.794	0.1100	8	5.055	0.1990	U	9.347	0.3680
61	0.991	0.0390	34	2.189	0.1110	7	5.105	0.2010	V	9.576	0.3770
60	1.016	0.0400	33	2.870	0.1130	6	5.182	0.2040	W	9.804	0.3860
59	1.041	0.0410	32	2.946	0.1160	5	5.220	0.2055	X	10.084	0.3970
58	1.067	0.0420	31	3.048	0.1200	4	5.309	0.2090	Y	10.262	0.4040
57	1.092	0.0430	30	3.264	0.1285	3	5.410	0.2310	Z	10.490	0.4130
56	1.181	0.0465	29	3.454	0.1360	2	5.613	0.2210	*	*****	*****
**	****	*****	**	*****	*****	1	5.791	0.2280	*	*****	*****